DECISION MATHEMATICS

The Spode
Group

DECISION
MATHEMATICS

Editors:

JOHN BERRY, DAVID BURGHES and IAN HUNTLEY

Published by
Oxford International Assessment Services Limited and

ELLIS HORWOOD
NEW YORK   LONDON   TORONTO   SYDNEY   TOKYO   SINGAPORE

First published in 1986
and Reprinted in 1990 by
**OXFORD INTERNATIONAL
ASSESSMENT SERVICES LIMITED**
Ewert Place, Summertown, Oxford
and
ELLIS HORWOOD LIMITED
Market Cross House, Cooper Street,
Chichester, West Sussex, PO19 1EB, England
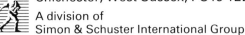
A division of
Simon & Schuster International Group

Printed and bound in Great Britain
by Hartnolls, Bodmin

British Library Cataloguing in Publication Data

Decision mathematics. — ('A' level mathematics)
1. Decision-making — Mathematical models
I. Berry, John, *1947*– . II. Burghes, D. N.
III. Huntley, Ian. IV. Spode Group. V. Series.
153.8'3'0724   HD30.23
ISBN 0–13–200973–0

Library of Congress Cataloging-in-Publication Data available

*The views expressed and conclusions drawn and
recommendations made are entirely those of the Authors
for which the Editors, the Publishers and the copyright
owners disclaim any responsibility.*

Contents

6　Contents

8   Contents

Acknowledgements

This text has been written at weekend meetings of the Spode Group, and we would like to thank the Schools Curriculum Development Committee for financial support for the Group. We would also like to thank the University of Oxford Delegacy of Local Examinations, who have encouraged us to write this text to fit in with their proposed new A-level Mathematics option in Decision Mathematics. We would particularly like to thank Susan Timperley and Simon French for their helpful suggestions and guidance throughout the preparation of this text, and Doug White whose enthusiasm motivated us to start this Decision Maths project.

We would like to acknowledge Tony Beames for his assistance and helpful comments in writing Chapter 14 and to John Laing Construction Ltd for permission to use their teaching materials on Critical Path Analysis and Cascade programming techniques.

We are very grateful to Edward Arnold for permission to use a number of exercises taken from 'Basic Linear Programming' by B. Bunday. We are also indebted to our support team, Sally Williams, Ann Tylisczuk, Mariette Grantham and particularly Margaret Roddick for their hard work in turning our handwritten manuscripts into a real typescript, and to Sue de Pomerai and Pete Warlow of Guernsey Grammar School for their assistance in error amendment at such short notice.

Preface

Over the past four decades we have seen rapid advances in the development of suitable techniques for solving decision making problems. Alongside these rapid mathematical advances, we have also seen a revolution in computing power. We can now buy powerful computers at relatively cheap prices across the counter in many retail shops—all firms and businesses, however small, can have access to their own computing power. This has proved to be another incentive for mathematicians to develop efficient techniques for solving decision making problems.

The first chapter of this text introduces the concept of an algorithm by considering and applying some of the many **sorting** techniques that have been developed.

The second chapter considers the important problem of **packing**, which is relevant to many industries and commercial organisations. A number of approaches are developed to solving packing problems, and the efficiency of various algorithms is discussed.

The third chapter is devoted to **linear programming**, which is probably the best known and applied technique in Decision Mathematics. It was originally developed during the Second World War to help optimise convoy sizes across the Atlantic, and has since been applied to almost every conceivable branch of planning and management. In this text, we will only deal with the simplest problems, developing the well-known simplex algorithm for solving the basic problem. There are numerous texts (see 'Further Reading' at the end of this text) which extend the basic theory.

The fourth chapter in this text is on **game theory**, which is an attempt to model how we behave in a competitive situation. It was first put forward by Von Neumann and Morgenstern in their text *Theory of Games and Economic Behaviour* in 1946. Although it cannot directly be used to predict the future, it does give an understanding of the forces at work in our competitive society.

The fifth chapter deals with **planar graphs**. The main problem discussed here is that of deciding if a graph can be redrawn without crossovers. This is of particular relevance to the efficient design of silicon chips, where crossovers need insulating and consequently should be avoided if at all possible.

The sixth chapter looks at three important problems concerning **networks**. These are

(i)   the minimum connector problem,
(ii)   the travelling salesman problem.
(iii)   the route inspection problem.

All these problems have important applications for many commercial organisations, but the techniques for solution are very varied. There is a very straightforward algorithm for problem (i), but not for problem (ii), and (iii) can normally be readily solved.

Chapters 7 and 8 are devoted to developing the theory of **recurrence relations** (often referred to as 'difference equations'), both first and second order. Recurrence relations are now playing a vital role in modelling non-physical phenomena, similar to that of differential equations in the physical world. Indeed the theory in some parts resembles that of differential equations but it does have important differences. We show in the text how the theory can be applied to problems in biology and economics.

The next chapter deals with the topic dynamic programming, explaining clearly the concept and showing how it can be used in practical problem solving.

The tenth chapter of this text deals with the important topic of **network flow**, illustrating clearly the maximum flow/minimum cut theories and developing the algorithm to solve such problems.

The next two chapters deal with the related topics of **assignment** and **transportation**, both of which have obvious applications in today's commercial world.

In Chapter 13 the theory of **coding** is dealt with. A number of particular codes are referred to, including the Huffman code which is used in computing.

This is followed by an introduction to **critical path analysis**, which is now used for the planning of many major projects, such as the space programmes or the construction of new shopping centres. The technique is explained clearly, and we have made use of material made available by John Laing and Sons.

Finally we look at some of the more general problems associated with **algorithms**, and in particular we show how the order of an algorithm is defined and determined.

Throughout the text we have used examples to illustrate the techniques. We have also set exercises at the end of each section, and miscellaneous exercises at the end of each chapter. Answers to all these exercises are given at the end of the text. Full solutions, though, can be obtained from the *solution manual* available direct from the Spode Group (School of Education, St. Luke's, Heartree Road, Exeter, Devon, EX1 2LU).

We have also produced an accompanying suite of programmes on disc, available for the BBC Microcomputer, which interactively explain the algorithms whilst also providing a useful package to solve problems which require these techniques for solution. Full details of this software are available from the publisher.

1

Sorting

1.1 INTRODUCTION

Very often we need to sort a list of things into order, either size order or alphabetical order, for example. An everyday example of this is the Football League table given below, where the 22 teams are given in alphabetical order. We would like to sort the table by points, to find out which team won and which 3 teams are due for relegation. The teams earn 3 points for a win, 1 point for a draw and 0 for a loss.

Team	P	W	D	L	F	A	Points
Arsenal	42	19	9	14	61	49	66
Aston Villa	42	15	11	16	60	60	56
Chelsea	42	18	12	12	63	48	66
Coventry	42	15	5	22	47	64	50
Everton	42	28	6	8	88	43	90
Ipswich	42	13	11	18	46	57	50
Leicester	42	15	6	21	65	73	51
Liverpool	42	22	11	9	68	35	77
Luton	42	15	9	18	57	61	54
Man. Utd	42	22	10	9	77	47	76
Newcastle	42	13	13	16	55	70	52
Norwich	42	13	10	19	46	64	49
Nott'm For.	42	19	7	16	56	48	64
QPR	42	13	11	18	53	72	50
Sheff. Wed.	42	17	14	11	58	45	65
Southampton	42	19	11	12	56	47	68
Stoke	42	3	8	31	24	91	17
Sunderland	42	10	10	22	40	62	40
Tottenham	42	23	8	11	78	51	77
Watford	42	14	13	15	82	72	55
WBA	42	16	7	19	58	62	55
West Ham	42	13	12	17	51	68	51

This is a bit daunting as the first example, so we look at the results of the 1985 Five Nations Rugby Union Championship. Here the teams have been awarded

2 points for a win and 1 point for a draw. The teams are written in alphabetical order below.

Team	P	W	D	L	Points
England	4	1	1	2	3
France	4	2	2	0	6
Ireland	4	3	1	0	7
Scotland	4	0	0	4	0
Wales	4	2	0	2	4

Sorting 5 numbers like this into descending order is fairly easy, since most people can keep 5 numbers in their memory for a short while. We quickly get the sorted list given below.

Team	Points
Ireland	7
France	6
Wales	4
England	3
Scotland	0

Exercise 1.1 Go back to the Football League example, and try to sort the 22 teams into descending order.* When you have done it, you should have a completed version of the table below.

Team	Points	Position	Team
Arsenal	66	1	Everton
Aston Villa	56	2	Liverpool
Chelsea	66	3	Tottenham
Coventry	50	4	Man. Utd
Everton	90	5	Southampton
Ipswich	50	6	Chelsea
Leicester	51	7	Arsenal
Liverpool	77	8	Sheff Wed.
Luton	54	9	Nottm. For.
Man. Utd	76	10	Aston Villa
Newcastle	52	11	Watford
Norwich	49	12	WBA
Nott'm For.	64	13	Luton
QPR	50	14	Newcastle
. . .	. .	.	. . .
. . .	. .	.	. . .
. . .	. .	.	. . .
West Ham	51	22	Stoke

The important thing to note here is that *sorting is a job best done by computer*; just imagine trying to sort the 16 000 runners in the London Marathon into alphabetical order, or compile your local telephone directory!

---

*   The order of teams with equal points is determined by highest goal difference, i.e. goals scored for (F) minus goals scored against (A).

1.2 HOW TO DO THE SORT

You probably noticed when you were sorting the 22 football teams how important
it was to be systematic; once you had decided how to do it, you had to be careful
to repeat the process exactly so that you did not make any errors. The name for
such a systemic process, which, if followed properly, will give the required answer
is an **algorithm**. This chapter looks at some of the algorithms used in sorting,
and the various advantages and disadvantages of each method.
     The 22 football teams is rather a large example to keep using, so we will take
just 10 numbers and try to sort them into ascending order.

49	48	75	28	2	28	66	76	20	58

The obvious way to do this is to:

        pick out the number which will eventually be first

        record it

        pick out the number which will eventually be second

        record it

and so on.

We will soon want to introduce some notation to help record what is going
on at each pass, but for the moment we will just put things in boxes:

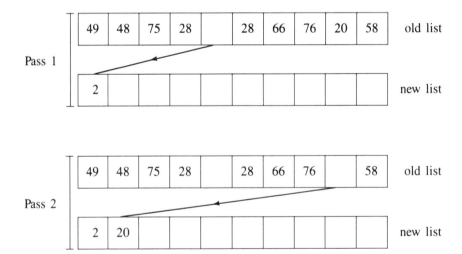

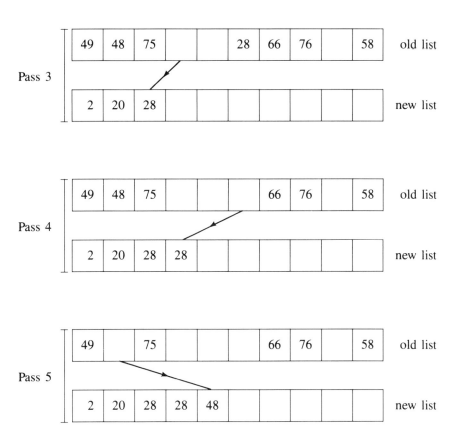

and so on, until we arrive at

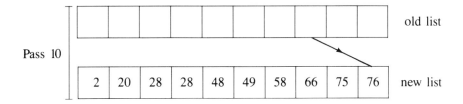

This is probably the most obvious way of proceeding, and is actually called the **minimum in pass** method.

Recording the sort in boxes, however, is cheating somewhat since it hides a large part of the process, that is how we identify the minimum number in the old list at any time. The way that most people do this, and certainly the way that computers would do it, is to do a lot of comparisons:

take first number in list

compare with second number

pick smallest

┌ compare with next number

↑ pick smallest
└─────────────◄──────┘
end

To explain this better, we will introduce some notation in the next section.

Exercise 2.1 Use the minimum in pass method, as above, to sort the Football League example.

1.3 NOTATION

Our original list was:

49	48	75	28	2	28	66	76	20	58

Let us call this old list $A(i)$, where i goes from 1 to N and $N = 10$ in this example. So

$A(1) = 49$

$A(2) = 48$

$A(3) = 75$

and so on.

Our new list we will call $B(i)$, where i again goes from 1 to N. The minimum in pass method can now be written out as:

look for the smallest number in $A(i)$

put into $B(1)$

delete from $A(i)$

┌ look for smallest $A(i)$ remaining

│ put into next box in $B(i)$

└ delete from $A(i)$

end

The method we have here is beginning to look like something which could be put onto a computer. We can, however, make a small change and make it considerably easier to program. Instead of using two lists A and B, we can merely use one list A.

Our algorithm is then

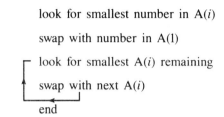

look for smallest number in A(*i*)

swap with number in A(1)

look for smallest A(*i*) remaining

swap with next A(*i*)

end

This method is then called an **exchange sort** which is very little different from the minimum in pass method, but uses only one list.

Now consider the $N = 10$ example in detail, and see how this works in practice.

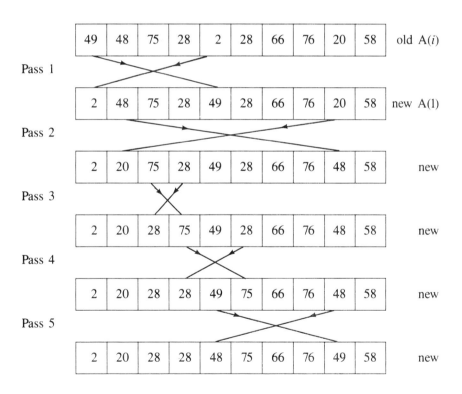

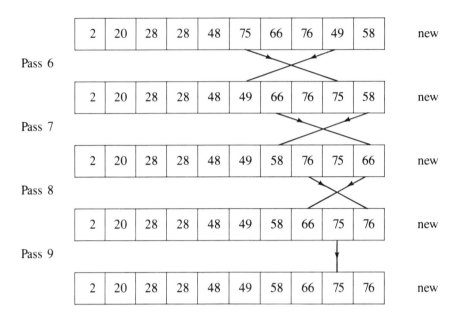

Pass 6

Pass 7

Pass 8

Pass 9

We will eventually be using this on a microcomputer, so at this stage we write
out the procedure in BASIC.

```
                                    FOR i = 1 TO N − 1

                                        minimum = i

         Loop to find                     FOR j = i + 1 TO N

         smallest                             IF A(j) < A(minimum) THEN minimum = j
Loop to
         A(i)                                 NEXT j
try all
                   swap                   temporary = A(i)
the boxes
                   A(i) and               A(i) = A(minimum)

                   A(minimum)             A(minimum) = temporary

                                        NEXT i
```

If you have access to a micro, now is clearly a good time to incorporate this piece
of coding into your own program; you will have to add

some way of inputting the original list
a DIMension statement for the array A(i)
some way of outputting the sorted list

and you may have to avoid the long variable names (minimum and temporary) if your micro cannot cope with these. If possible, it would also be a good idea to include a means of timing, to see how long the minimum in pass algorithm takes to sort N numbers.

If you have not got access to a micro, however, you can still do most of what follows by labelling 10 counters (such as pieces of card or tiddly-winks) with the numbers from the original list and swapping the counters round as the algorithm proceeds. In fact, it is by far the best way to understand what is going on. So from now on we will assume that the boxes are actually counters, and that you are moving the counters around as you learn the algorithms.

What we are eventually hoping to do is to find the best algorithm to use to sort a particular data set. What do we mean by 'best', though? It is clear that timing is important; if one algorithm is 30% faster than another, and that is the sort of difference we will be discovering later, then this will be very important when sorting a large number of items. Another aspect, though, is how 'muddled' the original data set is. It will turn out that some algorithms perform well on data sets which are slightly out of order, but do very badly on data sets in almost the opposite to the required order.

To give us some feeling for how well a particular algorithm copes with a particular data set, what we will do in future is to note the number of comparisons (i.e. is $A(i) < A(j)$?) and the number of exchanges (i.e. swop $A(i)$ and $A(j)$) carried out. This information, together with timings of the computer sorts whenever possible, will allow us to discuss the 'best' algorithms for a particular job.

Exercise 3.1 Work through the minimum in pass and exchange sort methods for the $N = 10$ example, and note down the total number of comparisons and exchanges carried out. Would these numbers change for a different $N = 10$ example?

Exercise 3.2 Use the exchange sort method to sort the following sets of numbers into numerical order (smallest to largest).

   (i)   (56, 61, 19, 38, 76, 45)
   (ii)   (12, 98, 67, 56, 84, 34, 67, 85, 89, 34, 24, 6)
   (iii) (23, 90, 78, 56, 87, 45, 72, 15, 18)

In each case note down the number of comparisons and exchanges carried out.

Exercise 3.3 Consider the exchange sort method for sorting N numbers. What are the total number of comparisons and exchanges in each of the cases $N = 3, 6, 9, 12$?
Generalize the result for j numbers.

1.4 BUBBLE SORTS

The essential idea of a bubble sort is that each pass places one number in its correct position in the final list; after the first pass the first element is in its final position, after the second pass the second element is in its correct position and so on.

There are several different types of bubble sort available, but we will show how each one improves on the previous one.

Primitive Bubble Sort

Let us take our $N = 10$ example and describe how the primitive bubble sort works when putting these numbers into ascending order.

49	48	75	28	2	28	66	76	20	58

Pass 1 is designed to get the smallest number (2) into the 1st position. It does this by comparing successive pairs of numbers, starting from the right-hand end. So, it

compares | 20 | 58 | and leaves them alone

compares | 76 | 20 | and exchanges them to give | 20 | 76 |

compares | 66 | 20 | and exchanges them to give | 20 | 66 |

compares | 28 | 20 | and exchanges them to give | 20 | 28 |

compares | 2 | 20 | and leaves them alone

compares | 28 | 2 | and exchanges them to give | 2 | 28 |

compares | 75 | 2 | and exchanges them to give | 2 | 75 |

compares | 48 | 2 | and exchanges them to give | 2 | 48 |

compares | 49 | 2 | and exchanges them to give | 2 | 49 |

where 2 is now in the 1st position. Notice that we have carried out 9 (= $N-1$) comparisons and (in this particular case) 7 exchanges on pass 1; we can write this down as $c_1 = 9$, $e_1 = 7$.

Pass 2 now starts, where we are aiming to bring the 2nd smallest number (20) into the 2nd position.

The sequence of comparisons this time is

| 20 | 58 | and leaves them alone

| 76 | 20 | with an exchange

| 66 | 20 | with an exchange

| 28 | 20 | with an exchange

| 28 | 20 | with an exchange

| 75 | 20 | with an exchange

| 48 | 20 | with an exchange

| 49 | 20 | with an exchange

| 2 | 20 | and leaves them alone

We then have $c_2 = 9$ and $e_2 = 7$ (in this particular case). You can probably see now how the algorithm proceeds; at each pass, we have $c_i = N - 1 = 9$ and $e_i \leqslant N - 1 = 9$, so the total number of comparisons is given by

$$C = \sum_{i=1}^{N-1} c_i = \sum_{i=1}^{N-1} (N - 1) = (N - 1)(N - 1) = 81$$

and the total number of exchanges is given by

$$E = \sum_{i=1}^{N-1} e_i \leqslant (N - 1)(N - 1) = 81$$

Simple Bubble Sort

You have probably realised already why we called the previous method a primitive bubble sort; at the end of each pass it compares numbers which it already knows are in the correct order. The 'simple' bubble sort avoids this:

on pass 1 it does $N - 1$ comparisons

on pass 2 it does $N - 2$ comparisons

and so on.

So the total number of comparisons is

$$C = \sum_{i=1}^{N} c_i = \sum_{i=1}^{N} (N - i)$$

and the total number of exchanges is

$$E = \sum_{i=1}^{N} e_i \leqslant \sum_{i=1}^{N} (N - i)$$

In fact, we can simplify these expressions by noting that $\sum_{i=1}^{N} (N - i)$ is an example of an arithmetic progression:

$$a + (a + d) + (a + 2d) + \ldots + (a + (N - 1) d)$$

$$= \frac{N}{2} [2a + (N - 1)d]$$

So $\sum_{i=1}^{N} (N - i) = 0 + 1 + 2 + \ldots + (N - 1)$

$$= \frac{N}{2} [0 + (N - 1) 1]$$

$$= \frac{1}{2} N(N - 1)$$

With $N = 10$ in this example, the simple bubble sort has

$$C = 45 \quad \text{and} \quad E \leqslant 45,$$

and we have managed to halve the total number of comparisons with respect to the primitive bubble sort.

Intelligent Bubble Sort

We can improve on $C = \frac{1}{2}N(N - 1)$ quite easily, though. Think of doing a particular pass in which no exchanges at all are made (i.e. $e_i = 0$); if this happens, the numbers must already be in the correct order and we can stop immediately. So $C \leqslant \frac{1}{2}N(N - 1)$, and the saving involved depends on the data set in use at the time.

Exercise 4.1   At the beginning of this section we worked through our $N = 10$ example in two ways: (i) completely for the primitive bubble sort, (ii) partially for the simple bubble sort. Complete the simple bubble sort example.

Exercise 4.2   Now do the same using the intelligent bubble sort. Note down the total number of comparisons (C) and the total number of exchanges (E).

Exercise 4.3   Try out all three bubble sorts on the following data sets, and note down C and E.

```
Data set 1      1  2  3  4  5  6  7  8  9  10
Data set 2     10  9  8  7  6  5  4  3  2   1
Data set 3     10  2  3  4  5  6  7  8  9   1
```

Exercise 4.4   In section 1.3 we gave the important part of a BASIC program for the exchange sort. Do the same for the three methods of bubble sorting, and work through your programs by hand for our $N = 10$ example to ensure that they agree with the previous working.

Exercise 4.5   If you have access to a micro, run the programs you have just written! Can you incorporate a method of counting C and E into the programs, and a means of timing the whole process?

Try using your programs on all four data sets.

Exercise 4.6   When we ran our programs, written in procedures on a BBC micro, we obtained the following values for C, E and the time T (s).

Data set	Primitive			Simple			Intelligent		
	C	E	T	C	E	T	C	E	T
Standard	81	22	0.45	45	22	0.35	42	22	0.33
1	81	0	0.29	45	0	0.19	9	0	0.06
2	81	45	0.62	45	45	0.52	45	45	0.52
3	81	17	0.43	45	17	0.31	45	17	0.31

If we make the rather simplistic assumption that only comparisons and exchanges use up any time, we should be able to work out how long this time is. Let the time taken (in seconds) to complete a comparison be c and the time for an exchange be e. Now look at the times taken for the primitive and simple bubble sorts on our standard example. We can say that:

$$81c + 22e = 0.45$$
$$45c + 22e = 0.35$$

Using these simultaneous equations to work out values for c and e gives $c = 0.00\ 278$ and $e = 0.01\ 023$. Do similar approaches based on the above table give roughly the same answers?

Exercise 4.7 The time taken in any sort must depend on N, as well as on the other factors discussed above. Adapt your programs for the three bubble sorts to run with $N = 100$, and obtain timings for the data set below.

Data set:

```
435  860   67  121  699  868  319   40  481  971  218  649   78  275  521   98
613  729  621  608  968  863  952  388  405  308  157  389  597  414  603  452
960  161  348   32  508   38  253  792  991  649   45  330  756  365  431  901
500  957  129  927  431  870  516  983  880  431   57  886  618  245  385  808
696  659  279  749  532  465  162  678  643  137  134  940  710  686  325  549
471  745  592  930  373  776  600  234  453  587  279  640  275  739  114  571
481  116  982  796
```

1.5 SHUTTLE AND SHELL SORTS

Shuttle Sort

An extremely simple and effective alternative to the bubble sort is known as **the Shuttle Sort**. As in the bubble sorts, pairs of items are compared and if the second item of a pair is found to be smaller than the first, the positions are reversed. At this point the two methods differ. The shuttle sort now works towards the end of the list until that item which has just been exchanged is promoted to its correct position in the list.

We will look at the shuttle sort, working on our standard set of 10 numbers, to see how it works.

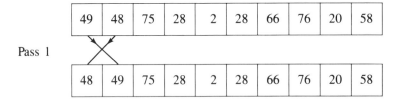

The first pass compares the first two elements of the array, A(1) and A(2), and exchanges them if necessary. The second pass begins by comparing A(2) with A(3), exchanging if necessary. We then compare A(1) with A(2), and exchange if necessary. In our example, no exchanges are required in pass 2.

The third pass begins by comparing A(3) with A(4) and exchanging if necessary. We now compare A(2) with A(3) and A(1) with A(2), exchanging if necessary at each stage. In our example, exchanges are necessary at each stage of pass 3, as illustrated below:

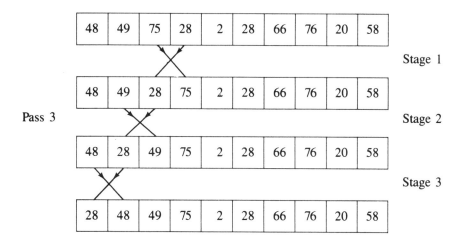

The fourth pass begins by comparing A(4) with A(5) and exchanging if necessary. We now compare A(3) with A(4), A(2) with A(3) and A(1) with A(2), exchanging if necessary at each stage. Carry out the fourth pass and show that the array will now look like:

2	28	48	49	75	28	66	76	20	58

Continue with passes 5, 6, 7, 8, 9 to complete the sort.

The number of comparisons made at each pass increases from 1 to 9 in steps of 1, so the total number of comparisons is given by

$$1 + 2 + 3 + 4 + 5 + 6 + 7 + 8 + 9 = \frac{9 \times 10}{2} = 45.$$

The number of exchanges made during the sort will depend on the set of numbers chosen for the array. Show that the number of exchanges in this example is 22.

You will have noticed that during the sixth pass, after A(6) and A(7) were exchanged, no further exchanges were necessary. The fact that A(5) and A(6) are not exchanged means that no further comparisons are required, since the first 5 elements were ordered in pass 5. Hence the number of comparisons can be reduced below 45. Show that the number of comparisons required under this intelligent approach is now only 28.

The number of comparisons in pass i will either equal i (if the number of exchanges in pass i, e_i, equals i) or $e_i + 1$ (if $e_i < i$).

In general, the maximum number of comparisons that will be required will be $\frac{1}{2}N (N - 1)$, a figure which can often be improved upon by making the sort intelligent.

Shell Sort

We have seen that the number of comparisons required for both bubble and shuttle sorts can be as high as $\frac{1}{2}N(N-1)$. The time taken to sort a small set of numbers is quite acceptable, but since real applications often involve a large set of data, the efficiency of the sort, in terms of the number of comparisons that could be made, is a crucial factor in determining which type to employ.

A method which, for large values of N, is appreciably quicker is one which was proposed by D.L. Shell in 1959. We employ a series of shuttle sorts on carefully chosen subsets of the numbers. The number of subsets in each phase decreases and the number of items in each subset increases correspondingly until finally, a shuttle sort is performed on the total set of items. By this time, however, the earlier phases have produced a high degree of order in the array and the number of exchanges needed on the last phase is considerably reduced over those needed for a straight shuttle sort.

We will describe how a Shell sort works by considering how it is applied to our standard set of numbers. The number of subsets in phase 1 is $N_1 = \text{INT}(\frac{1}{2}N)$ where INT means 'take the whole number part', so in our case the number of subsets is 5. The first subset consists of A(1) and A(6), the second subset consists of A(2) and A(7), etc. A shuttle sort is now carried out on each subset independently. The final part of phase 1 is to merge the sorted subsets back into the array.

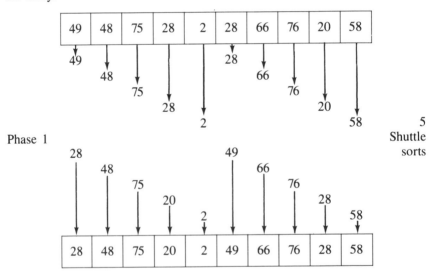

Phase 1

The number of subsets in phase 2 is $N_2 = \text{INT}(\frac{1}{2}N_1) = \text{INT}(2.5) = 2$. Since the array contains 10 elements, each subset in phase 2 will contain 5 elements, the first subset containing A(1), A(3), A(5), A(7) and A(9). The second subset will contain elements A(2), A(4), A(6), A(8) and A(10). Shuttle sorts are now carried out on each subset separately, following which the subsets are merged back into the array.

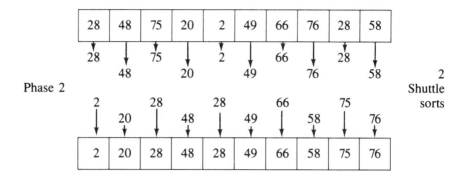

Phase 2

Shuttle
sorts

The final phase is phase 3, since the number of subsets here is given by $N_3 =$ INT($\frac{1}{2}N_2$) = INT(1) = 1. A shuttle sort is now carried out on the whole array. You can see that after phase 2, relatively few elements need to be exchanged in order to complete the sort.

In order to make the Shell sort efficient, each shuttle sort of the various subsets should be intelligent. On this assumption, check that the following figures apply:

	Phase 1	Phase 2	Phase 3	
No. comparisons	5	13	11	29
No. exchanges	2	7	2	11

The comparable totals for the intelligent shuttle sort give us 28 comparisons and 22 exchanges. You can see that, although the number of comparisons has increased by 1, the number of exchanges required has decreased by 11.

In terms of efficiency we can compare the two methods more realistically if we allocate 'time' units to the operations of comparison and exchanging. In practice, each exchange will take approximately 3 times as long as a comparison. If we suppose each comparison takes 1 time unit and each exchange 3 time units, then the total time units used in sorting our data set is as follows:

	Shuttle	Shell
Comparison time units	28	29
Exchange time units	66	33
Total	94	62

In this example, the shuttle sort takes over half as long again as the Shell sort.

Exercise 5.1 Use the algorithms for both shuttle and Shell sorts on the following data sets, and note down the total number of comparisons (C) and the total number of exchanges (E) in each case.

Data set 1	1	2	3	4	5	6	7	8	9	10
Data set 2	10	9	8	7	6	5	4	3	2	1
Data set 3	10	2	3	4	5	6	7	8	9	1

Using the 'timing' formula $T = C + 3E$, compare timings for both types of sorts. Is the Shell sort always more efficient?

Exercise 5.2 Using the BASIC exchange sort program segment in section 3, modify it to produce both a simple and intelligent shuttle sort. Trace through the program using the given data set to ensure that it works.

Exercise 5.3 Modify your program for the shuttle sort so that it can be incorporated into a program to perform the Shell sort.

Exercise 5.4 If you have access to a computer, run the programs for the shuttle and Shell sorts with $N = 100$ for the following data set:

Data set:

435	860	67	121	699	868	319	40	481	971	218	649	78	275	521	98
613	729	621	608	968	863	952	388	405	308	157	389	597	414	603	452
960	161	348	32	508	38	253	792	991	649	45	330	756	365	431	901
500	957	129	927	431	870	516	983	880	431	57	886	618	245	385	808
696	659	279	749	532	465	162	678	643	137	134	940	710	686	325	549
471	745	592	930	373	776	600	234	453	587	279	640	275	739	114	571
481	116	982	796												

Use the 'timing' formula from Exercise 5.1 to compare the efficiency of the two methods for this data set. Also compare the timings with those obtained for the bubble sorts in Exercise 4.7. Which type of sort seems to be most efficient for relatively large N ?

1.6 QUICKSORT

In section 1.5 we discovered a method of sorting, the Shell sort, that proved to be relatively efficient, especially when N is large. We now examine an alternative method, **the quicksort**, which is also relatively fast, especially for large N. Quicksort takes a set of numbers and first finds the number which is physically located in the middle of the set and then divides the rest into two sets:

(i) those numbers smaller than the middle
(ii) those numbers larger than the middle.

(If there are even number of numbers then we choose either of the pair of middle numbers.)

To sort out the numbers into two subsets, we use the following rule:

Step 1 start at the left-hand end and move right until we arrive at a number greater than the middle, a say,

Step 2 now start at the right-hand end and move left until we arrive at a number smaller than the middle, *b* say,
Step 3 interchange *a* and *b*,
Step 4 repeat these three steps until the middle number is met in both passes — from left and right.

At the end of this process the numbers in the left subset are all smaller than the middle number and the numbers in the right subset are all bigger than the middle number.

Now we repeat the rule on each of the two subsets, and so on. Consider the following set of data to see how the quicksort method works.

$$47 \quad 9 \quad 83 \quad 2 \quad 27 \quad 4 \quad 17$$

The number physically in the middle is 2.
Now split the numbers into two subsets using steps 1–3

Step 1 47 is larger than 2 $a = 47$
Step 2 17 is larger than 2
          4 is larger than 2
          27 is larger than 2
          2 is equal to 2 $b = 2$
Step 3 interchange 47 and 2 to give

$$\text{empty} \quad 2 \quad 9 \quad 83 \quad 47 \quad 27 \quad 4 \quad 17$$
$$<2 \qquad\qquad\qquad\qquad >2$$

One subset is empty (there are no numbers smaller than 2), the other contains all the numbers larger than 2.
Now we apply the method to this subset.
47 and 27 are in the middle, so we choose either as 'the middle'. Consider 47.

Step 1   9 is smaller than 47
          83 is larger than 47 $a = 83$
Step 2 17 is smaller than 47 $b = 17$
Step 3 interchange 83 and 17 to give

$$2 \quad (9 \quad 17 \quad 47 \quad 27 \quad 4 \quad 83)$$

Step 1   9 and 17 are smaller than 47
          47 is equal to 47 $a = 47$
Step 2 83 is larger than 47
          4 is smaller than 47 $b = 4$
Step 3 interchange 47 and 4 to give

$$2 \quad 9 \quad 17 \quad 4 \quad 27 \quad 47 \quad 83$$
$$<47 \qquad\qquad\qquad >47$$

Now we have two subsets A and B; A contains numbers smaller than 47 and B contains the number larger than 47. So 2, 47 and 83 are in the correct position. Repeat steps 1−3 on the subset smaller than 47. Choose 17 as the middle number. Steps 1−3 lead to interchanging 17 and 4 to give

$$2 \quad (9 \quad 4) \quad (17 \quad 27) \quad 47 \quad 83$$
$$\underset{<17}{\qquad} \qquad \underset{>17}{\qquad}$$

Finally dividing again requires interchanging 9 and 4: the final order is then given by

$$2 \quad 4 \quad 9 \quad 17 \quad 27 \quad 47 \quad 83$$

The following table summarises the Quicksort method in this case.

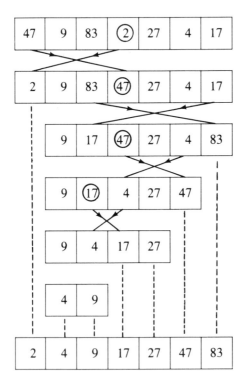

Exercise 6.1 Use the quicksort method to sort the following numbers into ascending order

  (i) 56, 61, 19, 38, 76, 45
 (ii) 23, 90, 78, 56, 87, 45, 72, 15, 18
(iii) 49, 48, 75, 28, 2, 28, 66, 76, 20, 58

1.7 OTHER SORTS

Although we seem to have looked at an enormous number of different sorts in the previous sections, there are plenty more. A lot of these are minor variations on the methods we have seen, so there are probably few essentially new ideas around. Other ones you might come across are:

> insertion sort
> merge sort
> heap sort

but there are many more.

1.8 SUMMARY

In each of the individual sections we have looked at efficiency in two ways:

  (i) By noting the total number of comparisons (C), the total number of exchanges (E), and the time (T).
  (ii) By trying the algorithm on different data sets.

The data sets used were:

Standard	49	48	75	28	2	28	66	76	20	58
Set 1	1	2	3	4	5	6	7	8	9	10
Set 2	10	9	8	7	6	5	4	3	2	1
Set 3	10	2	3	4	5	6	7	8	9	1

Set 4

435	860	67	121	699	868	319	40	481	971	218	649	78	275	521	98
613	729	621	608	968	863	952	388	405	308	157	389	597	414	603	452
960	161	348	32	508	38	253	792	991	649	45	330	756	365	431	901
500	957	129	927	431	870	516	983	880	431	57	886	618	245	385	808
696	659	279	749	532	465	162	678	643	137	134	940	710	686	325	549
471	745	592	930	373	776	600	234	453	587	279	640	275	739	114	571
481	116	982	796												

The ideas behind the choice of these data sets were as follows.

Standard	10 random numbers in [0, 99], to include a repeated element
Set 1	10 numbers in correct order
Set 2	10 numbers in exactly the opposite order — a test case for which we can often work out a formula for C and E
Set 3	10 numbers in almost the correct order — a common example of how sorting is used, which should not take too long
Set 4	100 random numbers in [0, 999] — a bigger sort, to see how C, E, T varied with N

The algorithms we have looked at really fall into three different groups — intelligent bubble sort, Shell sort, quicksort — and so if we now wish to develop an overview of sorting, we can concentrate on just these three. The results we obtained using a BBC microcomputer were as follows.

Data set	N	Bubble sort			Shell sort			Quicksort		
		C	E	T	C	E	T	C	E	T
Standard	10	42	22	0.33	29	11	0.28	41	8	0.29
1	10	9	0	0.05	22	0	0.78	81	0	0.38
2	10	45	45	0.52	27	13	0.27	76	5	0.42
3	10	45	17	0.31	27	9	0.25	80	1	0.40
4	100	4830	2659	33.74	850	400	6.96	911	157	5.09
5	1000	497420	251708	3273.84	15255	7750	125.56	14726	233	76.59

Here we have included the results for Set 5 : 1000 random numbers [0, 999] so that the dependence on N becomes very clear. If you have access to a micro, you should now extend this table of results. Try special data sets (like 2 and 3) with $N = 100$, or random data sets (like standard, 4 and 5) with $N = 200$ and $N = 500$.

It seems quite likely that the efficiency of each algorithm will depend on a power of N in some way. An easy way to see if this is true is to draw a log−log graph. If we suspect that $y = aN^b$, then

$$\log y = \log a + b \log N,$$

so plotting $\log y$ against $\log N$ should give a straight line of slope b and intercept $\log a$.

To apply this in our case we can draw the following graphs for data sets: Standard, 4 and 5.

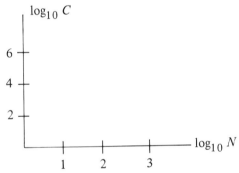

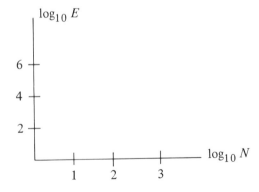

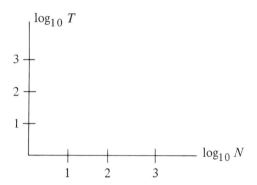

Draw these graphs for yourself, using the data in the table above and any data you have generated, putting three lines on each graph (one for bubble sort, one for Shell sort, and one for quicksort).

You should eventually arrive at values for a and b which are close to the following.

$y = aN^b$	Bubble sort			Shell sort			Quicksort		
	C	E	T	C	E	T	C	E	T
a	0.39	0.35	0.0033	1.4	0.46	0.14	2.3	2.3	0.018
b	2.0	1.9	2.0	1.4	1.4	1.3	1.3	0.73	1.2

It should be clear now which is the 'best' sorting algorithm; the quicksort is consistently better than either the bubble or Shell sorts, and really comes into its own for large data sets.

Strings

So far, all the examples we have used contain numbers. We have not tried to sort names into alphabetical order, for instance. In computing terms, things like names and addresses are called strings, and sorts on strings are a very important application of the theory.

Fortunately, there is very little extra work involved to make our existing programs work for strings! This is because computers store letters as particular numbers (often according to the ASCII convention), and 'A < D' is exactly the same statement as 'A comes before D in the alphabet'.

To make the necessary changes on the BBC micro, for instance, we merely have to store our original list in the string array A$(i) rather than the numerical array A(i). Then changing every occurrence of A(i) in the program to A$(i) should produce a program which will sort a list of names into alphabetical sort.

Try this for one of your own programs, and test it with the following data set:

```
                        JOHN
                        ROGER
                        MORAG
                        DAVID
                        BOB
                        NIGEL
                        RON
                        IAN
                        ROBIN
                        GRAHAM
```

1.9 MISCELLANEOUS EXERCISES

M1   Use both the Shell and quicksort methods to sort the data sets into ascending order.
 (i) 15, 71, 36, 44, 82, 35, 44, 25
 (ii) 436, 379, 352, 217, 195, 184, 187, 101, 42, 7

M2   Calculate the number of comparisons (C) and exchanges (E) for each sort and each data set in question M1. Using the formula $T = C + 3E$, compare the efficiency of the two methods for the two data sets. What conclusions can you draw?

M3   Write a program that will generate a set of 20 random integers in the range 1 to 100. Add this to your programs for the intelligent bubble sort, shuttle sort and Shell sort. Run the programs and compare the efficiency of these three methods.

M4   Modify your program in question M3 so that the number of random numbers generated is (i) 100, (ii) 200, (iii) 500.
 As the number of items in the data set increases, how does the relative efficiency of the three methods compare?

M5   Modify one of your sorting programs to sort a set of names into alphabetic order, as suggested in section 1.8. Test it with the names of students in your class.

M6   Write a program that reads in a set of names and numbers, and then sorts them into (i) alphabetical order of names, (ii) descending numerical order of numbers. Use the following data set to test your program, which should employ one of the sorting procedures you have written already.

John	72
Roger	51
Morag	88
David	60
Bob	32
Nigel	63
Ron	52
Ian	40
Robin	61
Graham	63

M7   Extend the program from question M6 to sort a list of candidates and their examination marks into (i) alphabetical order, (ii) merit order. Use data from your class (e.g. a recent test or examination) to test your program.

2

Packing

2.1 INTRODUCTION

In this chapter we will be dealing with problems that can be reduced to the problem of *bin packing* — that is, we want to pack bins (of given size) with various items — and we are looking for a procedure or algorithm that does this as efficiently as possible, using a minimum number of bins.

As an example, consider the problem of finding the minimum number of workers required to complete a project in 15 days, where the project consists of the following activities:

Activity	A	B	C	D	E	F	G	H	I	J	K
Duration (in days)	8	7	4	9	6	9	5	5	6	7	8

This is a bin packing problem, since we want to pack the activities above into bins (workers) of size 15 (days), using a minimum number of such bins.

As a guide to the number of bins needed, we can add up the total number of bins and divide by the bin size. In this example, we have

$$\frac{8 + 7 + 4 + 9 + 6 + 9 + 5 + 5 + 6 + 7 + 8}{15} = \frac{74}{15} = 4 \frac{14}{15}$$

A *lower* bound for the number of bins needed is the lowest integer greater than or equal to the number, i.e. 5 bins. So we know that *at least* 5 workers are needed, but we are not guaranteed that there will be a solution using just 5 bins.

Exercise 1.1 Show that there is a solution to the problem above which only uses 5 workers.

Exercise 1.2 A small car ferry, operating between the Isle of Harris and North Uist in the Outer Hebrides, has 3 lanes each 20 m long on its car deck.

On one trip the vehicles waiting to use the ferry are:

Item A	car 4 m long
Item B	car 4 m long
Item C	a car and trailer tent 7 m long
Item D	a car and caravan 10 m long
Item E	a camper 6 m long
Item F	a lorry 10 m long
Item G	a lorry 12 m long
Item H	a van 7 m long

Can these all be loaded on board?

Exercise 1.3   The timber department of a hypermarket receives the following order
for lengths of wood of dimension $3'' \times 2''$:

4 lengths of 10'
3 lengths of 7'
5 lengths of 5'
6 lengths of 3'
2 lengths of 2'

If standard 12' lengths are cut to complete this order, show that 9 is a lower bound
for the number of lengths needed. Is there a solution using just 9 standard lengths?

2.2 FULL−BIN COMBINATIONS

What methods have you used in solving the problems above? With examples that
are relatively simple, we tend to look for combinations of items that fill the bins
exactly. So for the problem in section 2.1, we see that:

A + B fill completely bin 1
D + E fill completely bin 2
F + I fill completely bin 3
J + K fill completely bin 4

which leaves   C + G + H = 14

to be packed in bin 5.

Exercise 2.1   A factory has a rush order to complete in 16 hours. The activities
and times are given below. The jobs are independent, in that they can be done
in any order, and none can be speeded up by using more than one worker.

Activity	A	B	C	D	E	F	G	H	I	J	K	L
Time required (hours)	5	7	10	8	9	11	7	4	2	6	8	3

By looking for full−bin combinations, find the number of workers needed.

Exercise 2.2   A project consists of eight activities whose durations are as follows:

Activity	A	B	C	D	E	F	G	H
Duration (hours)	1	2	3	4	4	3	2	1

Use the full−bin combination method to determine the minimum number of workers needed to finish the project in 5 hours.

2.3 FIRST FIT ALGORITHM

Although looking for full−bin combinations works well for smallish problems, it is not so easy to use for more complicated problems, or problems for which full−bin combinations do not exist. So we clearly need a more general way of dealing with bin−packing problems.

The first fit algorithm is such a method. In this method we fit each activity in turn into the first available bin. By first available, we mean the first bin that has sufficient room for the activity, starting from bin 1 in each case. So for the example in section 2.1 we have

Activity	A	B	C	D	E	F	G	H	I	J	K
Duration (days)	8	7	4	9	6	9	5	5	6	7	8

We fit, in turn,

A into Bin 1
B into Bin 1
C into Bin 2
D into Bin 2
E into Bin 3
F into Bin 3
G into Bin 4
H into Bin 4
I into Bin 5
J into Bin 5
K into Bin 6

giving the solution

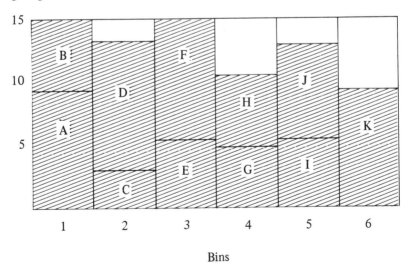

Bins

Fig 2.1

So this algorithm has produced a solution using 6 workers, although the best (optimum) solution needs only 5.

As a second example, suppose a computer software producer has developed 18 programs of size below, and wishes to store them on single-sided floppy discs, each capable of 100K bytes of storage.

Program	Size (K bytes)
A	17
B	15
C	26
D	12
E	15
F	28
G	47
H	16
I	7
J	32
K	17
L	35
M	17
N	22
O	24
P	20
Q	19
R	26

We will use the first fit algorithm to store the programs. Applying the method, we pack:

A, B, C, D, E	onto disc 1
F, G, H	onto disc 2
I	onto disc 1
J, K, L	onto disc 3
M, N, O, P	onto disc 4
Q, R	onto disc 5

This is illustrated in Fig. 2.2.

(Note that I is packed into Disc 1, as there is still room for it — in each case, you start at disc 1 and search each disc in turn until room is found for the item). Again, we will see (in Exercise 3.3) below that this solution is not optimal.

It is possible to find a solution which uses just 4 discs.

Exercise 3.1   Use the first fit method to obtain a solution to the following problem:

A plumber requires the following lengths of copper pipe to be cut from standard 12′ lengths:

Piece	A	B	C	D	E	F	G	H	I	J	K	L
Length (feet)	4	6	7	3	3	3	3	7	4	2	4	2

How many standard lengths are needed?

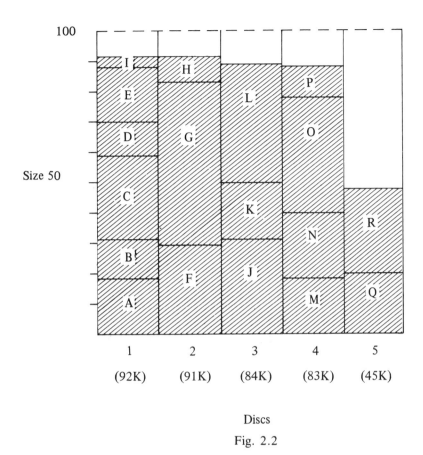

Fig. 2.2

Exercise 3.2 Use the first fit algorithm to find a solution to the problem described in Exercise 2.2

Exercise 3.3 Find a solution to the computer disc storage problems described above, which uses just 4 discs.

2.4 FIRST FIT DECREASING ALGORITHM

Working through the examples and exercises in the above section, you will probably have realised that the first fit algorithm is more likely to give the optimal solution if we first reorder the items in descending order before allocating to the bins. So this algorithm can be summarised as:

1. Reorder the items in decreasing order of size
2. Apply the first fit algorithm to this reordered list

We will see how it works using the first example in section 2.1, where we need to pack

Activities	A	B	C	D	E	F	G	H	I	J	K
Size	8	7	4	9	6	9	5	5	6	7	8

in bins of size 15. We first reorder as:

Activities	D	F	A	K	B	J	E	I	G	H	C
Size	9	9	8	8	7	7	6	6	5	5	4

and then apply the first fit algorithm

D into Bin 1
F into Bin 2
A into Bin 3
K into Bin 4
B into Bin 3
J into Bin 4
E into Bin 1
I into Bin 2
G into Bin 5
H into Bin 5
C into Bin 5

giving the solution in Fig. 2.3.

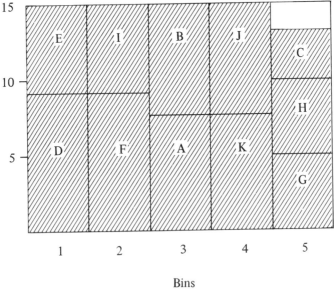

Bins

Fig. 2.3

So this time, this algorithm gives an optimal solution. Unfortunately, although this algorithm is generally more effective than the first fit algorithm it does not guarantee to always achieve the optimum solution. This is illustrated in the example below.

Example A carpenter wishes to cut the following sections from standard planks of wood, each of length 12 feet:

Section	A	B	C	D	E	F	G	H	I	J	K	L
Length	2	2	3	3	3	3	4	4	4	6	7	7

Find a solution using:
  (i) the first fit algorithm
  (ii) the first fit decreasing algorithm

Solution

  (i) The first fit algorithm gives the solution illustrated in Fig. 2.4
      and so needs 6 planks

  (ii) The first fit decreasing algorithm reorders as 7, 7, 6, 5, 5, 5, 4, 4, 4,
      4, 2, 2 and gives the solution illustrated in Fig. 2.5
      and so requires 5 planks.

We can, though, do better, and the optimal solution uses only 4 planks as shown in Fig. 2.6

Figure 2.6 shows that the first fit decreasing algorithm, although more likely to give a better solution than the first fit algorithm, does not necessarily give the optimal solution. There are, though, methods which will guarantee getting the optimal solution — for example, we could consider every combination possible (we call this the method of exhaustion!) and so find the best possible solution. This would involve an enormous amount of computation. As the example gets more complex (i.e. more items to pack), we clearly need an effective method, which gets near to the optimal solution without too much computation. In practice, we have to achieve a balance between an effective solution and computational time. The first fit decreasing is an algorithm which will normally achieve a reasonable solution (i.e. close to the optimal) whilst it is quick and easy to apply.

Exercise 4.1 Use the first fit decreasing algorithm to pack the items below into bins of capacity 12:

Items	A	B	C	D	E	F	G	H
Size	2	6	3	7	4	7	2	4

Does this give an optimal solution?

Exercise 4.2 Use the first fit decreasing algorithm for the computer storage problem, described in section 2.3.

Exercise 4.3 Solve the ferry problem, described in Exercise 1.2, by using the first fit decreasing algorithm.

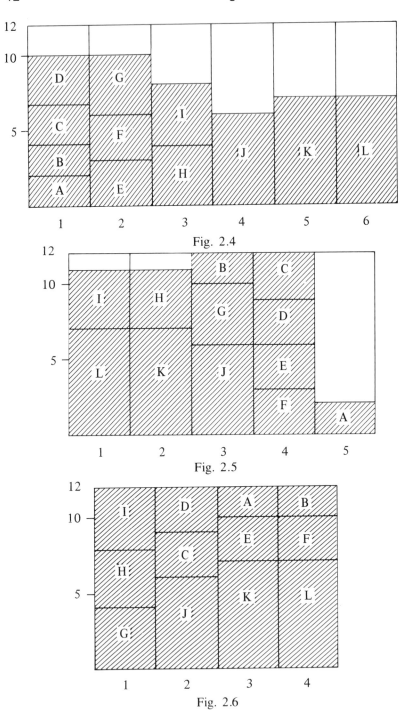

Fig. 2.4

Fig. 2.5

Fig. 2.6

2.5 MISCELLANEOUS EXERCISES

M1   A rack is designed to take small storage boxes with a standard length and width but with different heights. The rack is 20 cm high. Find optimum arrangements (i.e., using the minimum number of slots in the rack) for the following:

(i)
Item	A	B	C	D	E	F	G
Height (cm)	12	8	10	12	6	4	6

(ii)
Item	A	B	C	D	E	F	G
Height (cm)	9	6	10	15	11	12	4

(iii)
Item	A	B	C	D	E	F	G
Height (cm)	4	10	15	12	8	6	5

M2   For the return journey of the Isle of Harris − North Uist ferry, (which has 3 lanes each 20 m long on the car deck), the following vehicles are waiting to be loaded:

Vehicle	Length (m)
Car	3
Car	4
Van	4
Landrover	5
Furniture van	10
Petrol tanker	14
Car and boat on a trailer	8
Breakdown lorry and car	11

Can all these be taken on one trip?

M3   A project consists of 9 activities whose durations are given below:

Activity	P	Q	R	S	T	U	V	W	X
Duration (hours)	7	12	3	9	6	2	11	10	4

Find the minimum number of workers needed to complete the project in 16 hours.

M4   Over Christmas John wants to record the following programmes on his video recorder — the lengths of the programmes (in minutes) are shown:

Queen's Speech	10 min.	Top of the Pops 2	40 min.
Mike Yarwood Show	50 min.	Disney time	30 min.
James Bond Film	120 min.	Coronation Street (Mon)	30 min.
Tom and Jerry	10 min.	Coronation Street (Wed)	30 min.
Top of the Pops 1	40 min.	Superman film	110 min.

He has four 2 hour tapes; can he record all the programmes?

M5 A DIY householder is installing a shower unit. In order to connect the shower to the main water supply he needs the following lengths of copper piping:

80 cm, 45 cm, 50 cm, 85 cm, 35 cm, 65 cm, 70 cm, 25 cm

The piping can be bought in standard lengths of 1 m, costing £2 each, or 1.5 m, costing £2.80 each. Find his cheapest cost

(i) if he buys only 1 m standard lengths
(ii) if he buys only 1.5 m standard lengths

Can he reduce his cost by buying a mixture of the two standard lengths?

M6 A programmer has produced 8 software packages, containing 33 programs in all. Details of the program lengths in each package are given below (in kilobytes)

	Programs/Lengths							
Packages	1	2	3	4	5	6	7	8
A	7	14	4	8	6	9	12	11
B	18	6	5	14	—	—	—	—
C	7	3	6	8	7	5	—	—
D	9	8	2	5	11	10	7	—
E	13	6	—	—	—	—	—	—
F	11	5	—	—	—	—	—	—
G	12	5	—	—	—	—	—	—
H	12	7	—	—	—	—	—	—

(i) Assuming that the discs are single-sided (capable of 100K bytes of storage), and that any program can be stored on any disc, find the minimum number of discs needed to store all 33 programs.

(ii) Is it possible, without using any extra discs, to store the software in such a way that all programs in a particular package are stored on the same disc?

3

Linear Programming

3.1 PROBLEMS

Since World War II there has been a tremendous development in the application of linear programming (LP) to decision-making processes. The impact of LP on modern scientists has been compared with the impact of calculus on 17th century scientists. The widespread use of LP is partly due to its ability to solve problems in a wide variety of areas (e.g. planning, design, finance, control) and also partly due to the efficiency of this technique for solving problems. There are now many commercial software packages available which can be readily implemented on microcomputers, thereby giving a relatively cheap tool for solving a wide variety of practical problems.

We will introduce this topic through two practical examples. We will use one of these examples when developing a graphical solution to LP problems and also we will use the same example to illustrate the simplex technique. This technique, which is a general method of solving LP problems, will then be used to solve the other example.

A. Pelican Margarine

A food manufacturer makes a brand of margarine from two kinds of oils; vegetable and non-vegetable oils. The raw oils are refined by the manufacturer and blended to form the margarine. One objective of the manufacturer is to make as large a profit as possible; however, there are various constraints. It is important that the raw oils are refined separately to avoid contamination and the final blend of oils must be soft enough to spread but not too runny. To achieve this quality each ingredient and the final product has a hardness factor. The following table gives the cost and hardness of the raw materials used to make Pelican margarine.

	Oil	Cost £/Kg	Hardness
	Ground nut	0.50	1.2
Vegetable	Soya bean	0.80	3.4
	Palm	0.80	8.0
	Lard	1.15	10.8
Non-vegetable	Fish	1.00	8.3

The selling price of the margarine is £1.25 per kg and its hardness is between 5.6 and 7.4. The objective is to maximise the manufacturer's profit. The manufacturer can refine up to 40 000 kg of vegetable oils and up to 32 000 kg of non-vegetable oils per day.

We can formulate this problem mathematically in the following way. Suppose we begin by defining the following variables:

Variable	Amount (in kg)
x_1	Ground nut
x_2	Soya bean
x_3	Palm
x_4	Lard
x_5	Fish
X	Pelican margarine
P	Profit

Then the total profit is the difference between income and costs of raw oils. Thus

$$P = 1.25X - (0.5x_1 + 0.8x_2 + 0.8x_3 + 1.15x_4 + 1.00x_5)$$

where

$$X = x_1 + x_2 + x_3 + x_4 + x_5$$

The manufacturer intends to maximise P. However, there are *constraints*.

Hardness   The total hardness limitations give

$$7.4X > 1.2x_1 + 3.4x_2 + 8x_3 + 10.8x_4 + 8.3x_5 > 5.6X$$

Refining capacity   The manufacturer is restricted in how much oil can be refined per day.

$$x_1 + x_2 + x_3 \leqslant 40\ 000$$

$$x_4 + x_5 \leqslant 32\ 000$$

If we eliminate X the mathematical problem becomes

$$\text{maximise } P = 0.75x_1 + 0.45x_2 + 0.45x_3 + 0.1x_4 + 0.25x_5$$

subject to

$$L_1 \quad 4.4x_1 + 2.2x_2 - 2.4x_3 - 5.2x_4 - 2.7x_5 \leqslant 0$$

$$L_2 \quad -6.2x_1 - 4x_2 + 0.6x_3 + 3.4x_4 + 0.9x_5 \leqslant 0$$

$$L_3 \qquad\qquad\qquad\qquad x_1 + x_2 + x_3 \leqslant 40\ 000$$

$$L_4 \qquad\qquad\qquad\qquad\qquad x_4 + x_5 \leqslant 32\ 000$$

is an example of a *linear programming* problem. Problems of this type are very common in industry and commerce. All linear programming problems consist of the following components:

   (i)   *variables* — this is standard to most problems in applications.
  (ii)   *an objective function* — this is the essence of the problem.
 (iii)   *the constraints* — these are equalities or inequalities restricting the values of the variables.

We could attempt to solve the margarine problem by trial and error. The following table of values shows the start of such a strategy.

x_1	12 000	40 000	0	0	0	20 000
x_2	12 000	0	40 000	0	40 000	10 000
x_3	12 000	0	0	40 000	0	10 000
x_4	12 000	32 000	32 000	32 000	0	10 000
x_5	12 000	0	0	0	32 000	20 000
L_1	OK	No	OK	OK	No	OK
L_2	OK	OK	OK	No	OK	OK
L_3	OK	OK	OK	OK	OK	OK
L_4	OK	OK	OK	OK	OK	OK
P	24 000	—	21 000	—	—	30 000
Comment		too soft		too hard	too soft	

B. Precision Tool Company

The Precision Tool Company is a manufacturer of precision screws. It has two main lines, wood screws and metal screws, which it sells for £20 and £25 respectively per box. The material costs for each box are £10 and £8 respectively and overhead costs are £5000 per week. All the screws have to pass through a slotting and threading machine. A box of wood screws requires 3 minutes on the slotting machine and 2 minutes on the threading machine, whereas a box of metal screws requires 2 minutes on the slotting machine and 8 minutes on the threading machine. In a week, each machine is available for 60 hours. The company wishes to maximise its weekly earnings.

If we let

$$x = \text{number of wood screws produced per week}$$
$$y = \text{number of metal screws produced per week}$$

then

$$\text{Profit} = (20-10)x + (25-8)y - 5000$$
$$= 10x + 17y - 5000 \text{ (in£)}$$

For the slotting machine, we have the time constraint per week

$$3x + 2y \leqslant 3600 \text{ (in minutes)}$$

and for the threading machine, similarly

$$2x + 8y \leqslant 3600$$

So we require to maximise the profit

$$P = 10x + 17y - 5000$$

subject to the constraints

$$3x + 2y \leqslant 3600$$
$$2x + 8y \leqslant 3600$$
$$x, y \geqslant 0$$

Try a few values of x and y which satisfy these constraints.

Find the profit made. Can you change the values of x and y and increase the value of P? We will develop a precise method for solving this in the next section.

More complicated problems are dealt with using the simplex algorithm which is outlined in the following sections. The margarine problem is a fairly complex problem, since it involves 5 variables and 4 constraints, and is best dealt with by using an appropriate algorithm on a computer.

Exercise 1.1 Suppose a factory produces two different types of toy: a bicycle and a truck. Three machines (a moulder, a lathe and an assembler) are used in the production of the toys. The manufacture of one bicycle requires 1 hour on the moulder, 3 hours on the lathe and 1 hour on the assembler, while to produce one truck the moulder is not used, the lathe is required for 1 hour and the assembler is also required for 1 hour. However, the moulder can only operate for 3 hours per day, the lathe is available for 12 hours per day and the assembler for 7 hours. Everything made in this factory is sold; a profit of £8 is made on each bicycle, whereas each truck yields a £5 profit. The problem is to allocate the use of the three machines in order to maximise profits.

Formulate this problem as a linear programming problem.

Exercise 1.2   Formulate the following problem as a linear programming problem.

A diet-conscious housewife wishes to ensure that her family's daily intake of vitamins A, B and C does not fall below certain levels, say 24 units, 30 units and 18 units respectively. For this she relies on two fresh foods which respectively provide 8, 5 and 2 units of vitamin per 25 grams of foodstuff and 3, 6 and 9 units per 25 grams. If the first foodstuff costs 3 pence per 25 grams and the second only 2 pence per 25 grams, how many grams of each foodstuff should the housewife purchase daily in order to keep her food bill as low as possible?

3.2 THE GRAPHICAL METHOD

For linear programming problems with two variables we can represent the constraints by straight line graphs which define a region of acceptable points (acceptable in the sense that all the constraints are satisfied). At one of these points the objective function can be optimised. As an example of the approach, consider Problem B in section 3.1 concerning the Precision Tool Company. The linear programming problem is

$$\text{maximise } z = 10x + 17y - 5000$$

subject to the constraints

$$3x + 2y \leqslant 3600$$
$$2x + 8y \leqslant 3600$$
$$x \geqslant 0 \quad y \geqslant 0$$

Consider the constraint $3x + 2y \leqslant 3600$.

If we draw a graph of the line $3x + 2y = 3600$ (Fig. 3.1), then the points in the region below the line satisfy the given constraint. We can repeat this for each constraint, constructing a polygonal region of acceptable points (Fig. 3.2).

The only part of the plane that contains points satisfying all four constraints is called the *feasible region* shown shaded in Fig. 3.2.

Drawing the feasible region is the first step in the graphical method of solution.

The second step is to find the point (or points) within the feasible region at which the objective function achieves a maximum value.

The objective function is $z = 10x + 17y - 5000$. Now for any given value of z, $z = z_1$ say, the points on the line $10x + 17y = z_1 + 5000$ give the same weekly earnings.

Changing the value of z to $z = z_2$ say gives a straight line parallel to $z = z_1$. So different values of z give a set of parallel straight lines, larger values of z giving lines further from the origin, as shown in Fig. 3.3.

If we imagine a ruler to slide over the feasible region, so that it is always parallel to the family of straight lines, then the largest value of z will occur at the furthest point in the feasible region from the origin (Fig. 3.4).

The feasible point which gives the maximum value of z ($= 10x + 17y - 5000$) is the vertex *B*. The coordinates of point B gives the optimal *solution* of the linear programming problem.

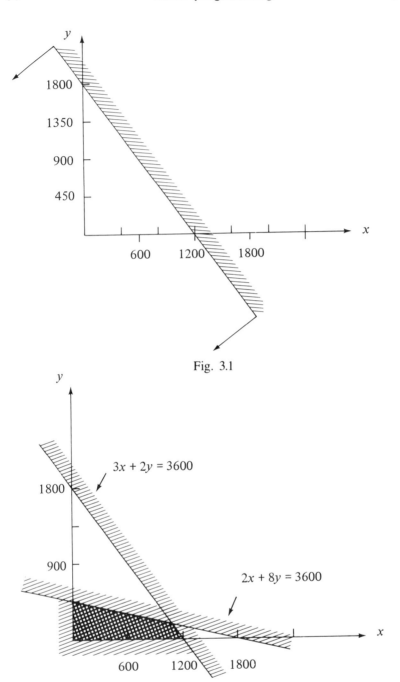

Fig. 3.1

Fig. 3.2

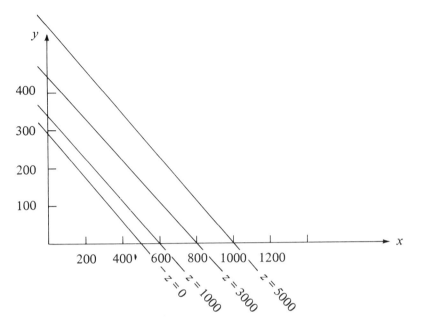

Fig. 3.3

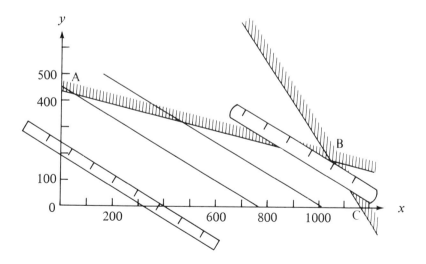

Fig. 3.4

Solving the pair of equations

$$3x + 2y = 3600$$
$$2x + 8y = 3600$$

gives $x = 1080$ and $y = 180$. The maximum weekly earnings of the tool company is thus £8860.

Exercise 2.1   A manufacturer makes two kinds of chairs, high-back and rockers. A high-back requires 3 hours on the lathe and 2 hours on the sander. Each rocker requires 2 hours on the lathe and 4 hours on the sander. The profit from high-back chairs is £14 each, and the profit on each rocker is £12. If the lathe operates 12 hours daily and the sander operates 16 hours daily, how many chairs should be produced to maximise the profit?

Exercise 2.2   Find the solutions to Exercises 1.1 and 1.2 by using the graphical method to solve the LP problems formulated.

Exercise 2.3   Solve by the graphical method, the following LP problem

$$\text{maximise } P = x + y$$

subject to

$$2x + y \leqslant 6$$
$$2x + 3y \leqslant 12$$
$$4x + y \leqslant 10$$
$$x, y \geqslant 0$$

3.3 THE SIMPLEX METHOD

The graphical method described in the last section works well for problems with two basic variables (x and y). Most practical problems though will have many more variables and we clearly need a method of solution which will cope with this.

To develop a technique for solving problems involving many variables, we first note some of the characteristics of the solution to two-dimensional problems. Firstly we note that the inequalities define a feasible region — which must be a *convex* polygon, and secondly we note that the solution to the LP problem must occur at a *vertex* of the polygon. This is shown for the Precision Tool Company in Fig. 3.5.

One way to solve LP problems would be to find the coordinates of each vertex and then evaluate the function you are trying to maximise (or minimise) at every vertex. The solution occurs at the one with largest (smallest) value. For the Precision Tool problem, where

$$z = 10x + 17y - 5000$$

we have the vertices

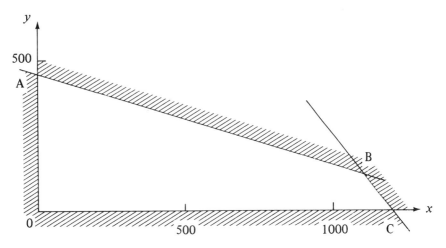

Fig. 3.5

O (0, 0),	$z = -5000$	
A (0, 450)	$z = -2650$	
B (1080, 180)	$z = +8860$	maximum value
C (1200, 0)	$z = +7000$	

The simplex method is more efficient than this, since it will start at one vertex and move round in sequence with the objective function increasing each time until the maximum is reached. So, in this problem, if we started from the origin O, we move O—A—B or O—C—B, reaching the solution at B. The simplex algorithm is a method of carrying out this procedure without reference to a diagram, and it can be readily generalised to more variables. It is clearly a very suitable procedure for using on a computer. We will first illustrate the procedure with the Precision Tool Company problem:

$$\text{maximise } z = 10x + 17y - 5000$$

subject to

$$3x + 2y \leqslant 3600$$
$$2x + 8y \leqslant 3600$$
$$x \geqslant 0$$
$$y \geqslant 0$$

We start by introducing *slack* variables, s and t, so that

$$s = 3600 - 3x - 2y$$
$$t = 3600 - 2x - 8y$$

and the inequalities now take the form

$$s \geqslant 0$$
$$t \geqslant 0$$
$$x \geqslant 0$$
$$y \geqslant 0$$

We call s, t slack variables since they represent the amount of slack between the time used on each machine and that available for use.

Our problem now involves 4 variables, *one of which* is *zero* along each edge of the feasible region, since the lines making up the feasible region have the slack variables equal to zero as equations.

Each vertex corresponds to two of the variables being zero, i.e.

$$\begin{array}{ll} O & x = y = 0 \\ A & t = x = 0 \\ B & s = t = 0 \\ C & y = s = 0 \end{array}$$

We will start the simplex procedure at the origin. Here $x = y = 0$ and

$$z = 10x + 17y - 5000$$

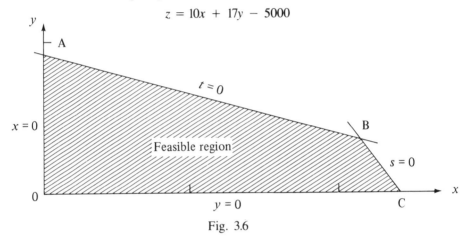

Fig. 3.6

It is clear that if we increase either x or y, the value of z must increase. So we can choose to increase either x or y — let us take y while keeping $x = 0$. (In Fig. 3.6 we are now moving from O to A).

We must now locate the next vertex. This will occur when either the line $s = 0$ or $t = 0$ cuts the line $x = 0$. Now from our definitions, we can see that this occurs at 1800 for $s = 0$ and 450 for $t = 0$. So A must be the point (0, 450) and defined by $t = x = 0$. (The line $s = 0$ does cut the line $x = 0$ although this is not shown in Fig. 3.6).

Before we proceed further, we need to know if this is the solution vertex. To find out, we must express z in terms of the variables x and t, which are zero at A. Now

$$z = 10x + 17y - 5000$$

and substituting for y from the equation for t gives,

$$z = 10x + 17\frac{(-t - 2x + 3600)}{8} - 5000$$

$$z = \frac{23}{4}x - \frac{17}{8}t + 2650$$

We see that increasing x (while keeping $t = 0$) will increase z. This corresponds to moving along the edge AB. We must now locate the coordinates of B. This will correspond to the intersection of either $s = 0$ or $y = 0$ with the line $t = 0$. To best see this we rewrite the equation for s and y in terms of x and t;

So that
$$s = 3600 - 3x - 2\,\frac{(3600 - 2x - t)}{8}$$
$$s = 2700 - \frac{5}{2}x + \frac{1}{4}t$$

and
$$y = 450 - \frac{1}{4}x - \frac{1}{8}t$$

Remember that we are keeping $t = 0$, and then looking for the value of x when either $s = 0$ or $y = 0$. We obtain $x = 1080$ for $s = 0$ and $x = 1800$ for $y = 0$. So we first intersect the line $s = 0$, and B is characterised by $t = s = 0$.

Again, we must test to see if we have reached the maximum, and we do this by expressing z in terms of t and s. Now

$$z = \frac{23}{4}\,(2700 + \frac{1}{4}t - s)\,\frac{2}{5} - \frac{17}{8}t + 2650$$
$$z = 8860 - \frac{23}{10}s - \frac{31}{20}t$$

This time, we can see that the coefficients of both s and t are negative and so moving away from B will *not* increase the value of z. We have reached the *maximum*!

From the equation above, we see that at $s = t = 0$

$$x = 1080$$
$$y = 180$$

Although this might appear to be a rather long-winded approach to solving LP problems, we will see in the next section how we can perform these calculations in a more systematic way.

Exercise 3.1   Use the simplex method to solve the problem above, but this time by starting at the origin and first increasing x.

Exercise 3.2   Find the vertices of the feasible region defined by

$$5x + 2y \leqslant 30$$
$$5x + 7y \leqslant 35$$
$$2x + 5y \leqslant 20$$
$$x, y \geqslant 0$$

Evaluate the function

$$z = 40x + 50y$$

at these vertices, and hence find its maximum value subject to the inequalities above.

Exercise 3.3

(i)   Solve the problem

$$\text{maximum } z = 2x + 4y$$

subject to

$$
\begin{aligned}
x + 5y &\leqslant 10 \\
4x + y &\leqslant 8 \\
x, y &\geqslant 0
\end{aligned}
$$

by evaluating z at each vertex of the feasible region.

(ii) Introduce slack variables r and s, and hence apply the simplex method to solve the problem.

Exercise 3.4 Determine the vertices of the feasible region for the LP problem

$$\text{maximise } z = x + y$$

subject to

$$
\begin{aligned}
x + 4y &\leqslant 8 \\
2x + 3y &\leqslant 12 \\
3x + y &\leqslant 9 \\
x, y &\geqslant 0
\end{aligned}
$$

Hence find the solution.

Exercise 3.5

(i) By using the graphical approach, solve the LP problem

$$\text{maximise } z = 10x + 15y$$

subject to

$$
\begin{aligned}
4y + 10x &\leqslant 40 \\
10y + 3x &\leqslant 30 \\
5y + 4x &\leqslant 20 \\
x, y &\geqslant 0
\end{aligned}
$$

(ii) Introduce slack variables r, s and t so that

$$
\begin{aligned}
4y + 10x + r &= 40 \\
10y + 3x + s &= 30 \\
5y + 4x + t &= 20
\end{aligned}
$$

Identify the variables which are zero along each edge of the feasible region. Now apply the simplex method to solve the problems, each time expressing z and the other variables in terms of the two variables which are zero at each vertex.

3.4 THE SIMPLEX TABLEAU

The Simplex method introduced in the previous section consists basically of the following steps:

First we introduce slack variables so that along each boundary of the feasible region one of the slack variables is zero, then we move round the boundaries of the feasible region in a systematic way finding the coordinates of each vertex, then we find the formula for the objective function z in terms of the current variables. We stop when the coefficients of the current variables in the formula for z are negative.

At various stages of the method we are solving linear equations and eliminating variables. These processes can be done without reference to the diagram of the feasible region and in more than two dimensions this is essential.

Consider the same problem solved in section 3.3 but this time we set the solution out as a series of linear equations.

At the start we have

$$
\begin{aligned}
z - 10x - 17y \quad\quad &= -5000 & &(1) \\
3x + 2y + s &= 3600 & (s=0 \text{ on BC}) \quad &(2) \\
2x + 8y + t &= 3600 & (t=0 \text{ on AB}) \quad &(3) \\
x \quad\quad &= 0 & (\text{on OA}) \quad &(4) \\
y \quad\quad &= 0 & (\text{on OC}) \quad &(5)
\end{aligned}
$$

This set of equations gives the objective function to be maximised and the boundaries of the feasible region.

We start at the origin $x=y=0$; clearly z is not a maximum here. As we increase x or y then z will increase.

We set off choosing $x=0$ and allow y to vary. The first vertex we meet is either on the $s=0$ or $t=0$ lines. In equation (2) we have $x=s=0$ so that $y=3600/2$ and in equation (3) we have $x=t=0$ so that $y=3600/8$. Clearly we arrive at $y=3600/8$ first so that $t=0$ meets $x=0$ first and we use equation (3) (i.e. the one involving t) to eliminate y from equation (1).

(Notice that we can decide on this quickly by looking at the two equations (2) and (3) and finding the one with largest y coefficient — this is important later.)

Dividing equation (3) by 8 gives

$$ \frac{x}{4} + y + \frac{t}{8} = \frac{3600}{8} $$

Now eliminating y from equation (1) we have the following set of equations

$$
\begin{aligned}
z - \frac{23}{4}x + \frac{17}{8}t \quad &= 2650 & &(1a) \\
3x + 2y + s \quad &= 3600 & (s=0 \text{ on BC}) \quad &(2) \\
\frac{x}{4} + y + \frac{t}{8} \quad &= \frac{3600}{8} & (t=0 \text{ on AB}) \quad &(3a) \\
x \quad &= 0 & (\text{on OA}) \quad &(4) \\
y \quad &= 0 & (\text{on OC}) \quad &(5)
\end{aligned}
$$

Now we can see from equation (1a) that as we move along $t=0$ then x increases so that z increases.

The next vertex we arrive at is given by the intersection of $t=0$ with either $s=0$ or $y=0$.

If it is $t=0$ and $y=0$ then from (3a) $x=1800$.

If it is $t=0$ and $s=0$ then we find the x coordinate of the intersection by solving equations (2) and (3a) for x.

Eliminating y from equation (2) gives

$$\frac{5x}{2} + s - \frac{t}{4} = 2700$$

and when $s=0$ and $t=0$ we have $x=1080$. Clearly as we move along $t=0$ with x increasing we arrive at the point $x=1080$ before the point 1800, so that the intersection of $s=0$ and $t=0$ is the next vertex. Notice that in this last calculation we had to eliminate y from equation (2). That means we have used equation (3a) to eliminate y from equations (1) and (2) to give the set of equations

$$z - \frac{23x}{4} + \frac{17t}{8} \quad = \quad 2650 \qquad\qquad (1a)$$

$$\frac{5x}{2} + s - \frac{t}{4} \quad = \quad 2700 \quad (s=0 \text{ on } BC) \quad (2a)$$

$$\frac{x}{4} + y + \frac{t}{8} \quad = \quad \frac{3600}{8} \quad (t=0 \text{ on } AB) \quad (3a)$$

$$x \quad\qquad\qquad = \quad 0 \quad (\text{on } OA) \qquad (4)$$

$$y \quad\qquad\qquad = \quad 0 \quad (\text{on } OC) \qquad (5)$$

(Notice again that with this set of equations we can quickly decide which equations intersect first by looking at the coefficients of x in the two equations (2a) and (3a) — it is the equation with the largest coefficient of x.)

Now we can use equation (2a) to eliminate x from equation (1a) to give

$$z + \frac{23s}{10} + \frac{31t}{20} = 8860$$

Now we see that as we increase s and t the value of z will decrease. The largest value of z is at the vertex given by the intersection of $s=0$ and $t=0$. The largest value is thus 8860. Equation (2a) gives the value of x as 1080 (i.e. when $s=t=0$) To find the corresponding value of y we eliminate x from equation (3a) to give

$$y - \frac{s}{10} + \frac{3t}{20} = 180$$

Thus when $s=t=0$ we have $y=180$.

The solution to the problem is that the maximum value of z is 8860 and this occurs for $x=1080$ and $y=180$.

Note that in this final step we have eliminated x from equation (3a), so that we may as well carry out this operation while eliminating x from equation (1a). If we do then we finish with the following set of equations

$$z + \frac{23s}{10} + \frac{31t}{20} = 8860 \qquad (1b)$$

$$x + \frac{2s}{5} - \frac{t}{10} = 1080 \qquad (2b)$$

$$y - \frac{s}{10} + \frac{3t}{20} = 180 \qquad (3b)$$

$$x \qquad\qquad = 0$$

$$y \qquad\qquad = 0$$

These equations give the maximum value of z and the values of x and y immediately.

The technique described can be written out in a much more convenient tabular form using matrices. We can write equations (1), (2) and (3) in matrix form as

$$
\begin{array}{ccccc}
 & & & z & \\
1 & -10 & -17 & 0 & 0 & x & & -5000 \\
0 & 3 & 2 & 1 & 0 & y & = & 3600 \\
0 & 2 & 8 & 0 & 1 & s & & 3600 \\
 & & & & & t &
\end{array}
$$

We will work with the augmented matrix

z	x	y	s	t	
1	-10	-17	0	0	-5000
0	3	2	1	0	3600
0	2	8	0	1	3600

The first calculation was to divide equation (3) by 8 and then eliminate y from equation (1).

Equation (1a) so formed and equations (2) and (3) can be written in augmented form as

z	x	y	s	t	
1	$\dfrac{-23}{4}$	0	0	$\dfrac{17}{8}$	2650
0	3	2	1	0	3600
0	$\dfrac{1}{4}$	1	0	$\dfrac{1}{8}$	450

Now this matrix can be formed from the previous one by carrying out operations on the elements of the rows.

We have row $1 + 17/8$ times row 3.

In what follows, we will work with the augmented matrix, performing what are called 'elementary row operations'. This means that we can

(i) subtract (add) multiples of any row from any other row (or rows)
(ii) multiply (divide) any row by any number

Note that we *cannot* and *must not* perform similar column operations. These would not hold.

So we now return to the simplex method outlined above, and see how it works in terms of the augmented matrix. We start by writing the first augmented matrix

z	x	$\downarrow$ y	s	t	
1	-10	-17	0	0	-5000
0	3	2	1	0	3600
0	2	8	0	1	3600

We start the procedure at the origin O, $x = y = 0$, and we arbitrarily decide to keep $x = 0$, but allow y to increase. To see whether we meet $s = 0$, or $t = 0$ first, we divide the final column entries by the y column entry for rows 2 and 3. This gives 3600/2 and 3600/8. The second value is smallest, that is $t = 0$ meets $x = 0$ first and so we express the variables z and s in terms of x and t rather than x and y. The 8 entry is circled and each element in the final row is divided by 8 to give

z	x	$\downarrow$ y	s	t	
1	-10	-17	0	0	-5000
0	3	2	1	0	3600
0	$\dfrac{1}{4}$	1	0	$\dfrac{1}{8}$	450

Now we add 17 times row 3 to row 1 and subtract 2 times row 3 from row 2 to give

z	x	$\downarrow$ y	s	t	
1	$\dfrac{-23}{4}$	0	0	$\dfrac{17}{8}$	2650
0	$\dfrac{5}{2}$	0	1	$\dfrac{-1}{4}$	2700
0	$\dfrac{1}{4}$	1	0	$\dfrac{1}{8}$	450

This is the augmented matrix representing equations (1a), (2a) and (3a).

The first row gives z in terms of x and t, and we can immediately see from the entry in the x column ($-23/4$) that we have not yet reached the maximum. So we must now increase x, keeping $t = 0$, and we look to find whether we reach $s = 0$ or $y = 0$ first. We do this by dividing the final column entries by the corresponding x entries, i.e. 2700/(5/2) and 450/(1/4) giving 1080 or 1800. So we reach $s = 0$ line first, and the 5/2 entry is circled. Dividing all entries in row 2 by 5/2 gives

z	x	y	s	t	
1	$-23/4$	0	0	17/8	2650
0	1	0	2/5	$-1/10$	1080
0	1/4	1	0	1/8	450

Eliminating x from 1st and 3rd rows gives the augmented matrix representing equations (1b), (2b) and (3b).

z	x	y	s	t	
1	0	0	23/10	31/20	8860
0	1	0	2/5	$-1/10$	1080
0	0	1	$-1/10$	3/20	180

Since both s and t entries in the first row are now positive, we have revealed the maximum value of z. Indeed, since this occurs at $s = t = 0$, we can immediately see that the final column entry in the first row gives the maximum value as 8860. We can also read off the corresponding values of x and y. Since $s = t = 0$, these will also be the entries in the final column of rows 2 and 3,

$$x = 1080, \ y = 180$$

In practice we can write out the simplex tableau, without any of the words but just simply the calculation. We will do this for the following problem (but with explanations on the R H S).

Example 1

$$\text{Maximise } P = 5x + 7y$$

subject to

$$3x + 2y \leqslant 42$$
$$2x + 5y \leqslant 50$$
$$x, y \geqslant 0$$

Solution   As in the previous example, we introduce slack variables s and t so that

$$3x + 2y + s = 42$$
$$2x + 5y + t = 50$$

and we can write the augmented matrix as

P	$\downarrow$ x	y	s	t		
1	−5	−7	0	0	0	(we first choose to increase x)
0	3	2	1	0	42	(42/3 ≤ 50/2)
0	2	5	0	1	50	
1	−5	−7	0	0	0	
0	1	2/3	1/3	0	14	(row 2/3)
0	2	5	0	1	50	
1	0	−11/3	5/3	0	70	(row 1 + 5 row 2)
0	1	2/3	1/3	0	14	
0	0	11/3	−2/3	1	22	(row 3 − 2 row 2)
1	0	−11/3	5/3	0	70	$\left(\dfrac{22}{11/3} < \dfrac{14}{2/3}\right)$
0	1	2/3	1/3	0	14	
0	0	1	−2/11	3/11	6	(row 3/(11/3))
1	0	0	1	1	92	(row 1 + $\dfrac{11}{3}$ row 3)
0	1	0	5/11	−2/11	10	(row 2 − $\dfrac{2}{3}$ row 3)
0	0	1	−2/11	3/11	6	

We have now reached the maximum value of P, since both non-zero entries (for r and s) are positive. So the maximum value of P is given by 92, and this occurs at $x = 10$, $y = 6$.

Exercise 4.1 Solve each of the problems above, using the simplex tableau, but in the first problem take x increasing initially, and in the second take y increasing initially.

Exercise 4.2 Solve, using the simplex tableau

$$\text{maximise } P = 6x + 9y$$

subject to

$$6x + 3y \leqslant 36$$
$$2x + 3y \leqslant 24$$
$$x, y \geqslant 0$$

Exercise 4.3   Using the simplex tableau, solve the following LP problem

$$\text{maximise } P = 2x + y$$

subject to

$$5x + y \leqslant 15$$
$$2x + 3y \leqslant 12$$
$$x, y \geqslant 0$$

Exercise 4.4   Solve the LP problem

$$\text{maximise } P = x + 2y$$

subject to

$$4x + y \leqslant 16$$
$$x + 3y \leqslant 12$$
$$x, y \geqslant 0$$

by (i) the graphical method, (ii) the simplex tableau.

3.5 SIMPLEX ALGORITHM

We are now in a position to write down the precise algorithm for solving LP problems. Before doing so, we will show how the method works for a slightly more complex problem, for example we will consider the problem

$$\text{maximise } P = x + 2y$$

subject to

$$x + 4y \leqslant 20$$
$$x + y \leqslant 8$$
$$5x + y \leqslant 32$$
$$x, y \geqslant 0$$

So we now have three inequalities in x and y (as well as the usual $x, y \geqslant 0$), so we will need three slack variables r, s and t. We define these by

$$x + 4y + r = 20$$
$$x + y + s = 8$$
$$5x + y + t = 32$$

and we can write the augmented matrix as

P	$\downarrow$ x	y	r	s	t		Comments
1	-1	-2	0	0	0	0	We choose to increase x initially
0	1	4	1	0	0	20	Compare $\dfrac{20}{1},\ \dfrac{8}{1},\ \dfrac{32}{5}$
0	1	1	0	1	0	8	
0	5	1	0	0	1	32	$\uparrow$ smallest positive value
1	-1	-2	0	0	0	0	
0	1	4	1	0	0	20	
0	1	1	0	1	0	8	
0	1	$\dfrac{1}{5}$	0	0	$\dfrac{1}{5}$	$\dfrac{32}{5}$	$R_4/5$
1	0	$-\dfrac{9}{5}$	0	0	$\dfrac{1}{5}$	$\dfrac{32}{5}$	$R_1 + R_4$
0	0	$\dfrac{19}{5}$	1	0	$-\dfrac{1}{5}$	$\dfrac{68}{5}$	$R_2 - R_4$
0	0	$\dfrac{4}{5}$	0	1	$-\dfrac{1}{5}$	$\dfrac{8}{5}$	$R_3 - R_4$
0	1	$\dfrac{1}{5}$	0	0	$\dfrac{1}{5}$	$\dfrac{32}{5}$	
1	0	$-\dfrac{9}{5}$	0	0	$\dfrac{1}{5}$	$\dfrac{32}{5}$	Compare $\dfrac{68/5}{19/5},\ \dfrac{8/5}{4/5},\ \dfrac{32/5}{1/5}$
0	0	$\dfrac{19}{5}$	1	0	$-\dfrac{1}{5}$	$\dfrac{68}{5}$	$\uparrow$ smallest positive value
0	0	1	0	$\dfrac{5}{4}$	$-\dfrac{1}{4}$	2	$R_3/(4/5)$
0	1	$\dfrac{1}{5}$	0	0	$\dfrac{1}{5}$	$\dfrac{32}{5}$	
1	0	0	0	$\dfrac{9}{4}$	$-\dfrac{1}{4}$	10	$R_1 + \dfrac{9}{5}R_3$
0	0	0	1	$-\dfrac{19}{4}$	$\dfrac{3}{4}$	6	$R_2 - \dfrac{19}{5}R_3$
0	0	1	0	$\dfrac{5}{4}$	$-\dfrac{1}{4}$	2	
0	1	0	0	$-\dfrac{1}{4}$	$\dfrac{1}{4}$	6	$R_4 - \dfrac{1}{5}R_3$
1	0	0	0	$\dfrac{9}{4}$	$-\dfrac{1}{4}$	10	Compare $\dfrac{6}{3/4},\ \dfrac{2}{-1/4},\ \dfrac{6}{1/4}$
0	0	0	$\dfrac{4}{3}$	$-\dfrac{19}{3}$	1	8	$\uparrow$ smallest positive value
0	0	1	0	$\dfrac{5}{4}$	$-\dfrac{1}{4}$	2	
0	1	0	0	$-\dfrac{1}{4}$	$\dfrac{1}{4}$	6	
1	0	0	$\dfrac{1}{3}$	$\dfrac{2}{3}$	0	12	$R_1 + \dfrac{1}{4}R_2$
0	0	0	$\dfrac{4}{3}$	$-\dfrac{19}{3}$	1	8	
0	0	1	$\dfrac{1}{3}$	$-\dfrac{1}{3}$	0	4	$R_3 + \dfrac{1}{4}R_2$
0	1	0	$-\dfrac{1}{3}$	$\dfrac{4}{3}$	0	4	$R_4 - \dfrac{1}{4}R_2$
P	x	y	r	s	t		

Since the first row now has positive coefficients, we conclude that we have reached the maximum. This has value 12 and occurs at

$$x = y = 4$$

We can now state the simplex algorithm in a precise form

Step 1 Write the LP problem in the form including slack variables and formulate the augmented matrix.

Provided all the elements (except possibly the top one) in the right-hand column are all non-negative, we proceed as follows.

Step 2 Select a column (except the last) for which the top entry is negative; let its elements be

$$a_0$$
$$a_1$$
.
.
.
$$a_n$$

Step 3 Choose as pivot the *positive* a_p for which b_p/a_p is least, where

$$b_0$$
$$b_1$$
.
.
.
$$b_n$$

is the final column. Divide each element in row p by a_p.

Step 4 Take appropriate multiples of the pth row in order to change the pivot elements to 1, and all other elements in that column to 0.

Step 5 If the top row still contains negative entries (excluding the final entry) return to step 2. If not, the maximum has been reached, and we can read off the maximum value in the top right-hand corner, and the value of variables which contain a single 1 entry in the right-hand column opposite the appropriate 1. The rest of the variables are equal to zero when the maximum is reached.

This is the basic algorithm, and we will finish this section by using the procedure to solve a problem in three variables, which cannot be readily solved using the graphical approach.

Example 2   Maximise $P = 4x + 5y + 3z$
subject to $8x + 5y + 2z \leqslant 3$
                             $3x + 6y + 9z \leqslant 2$
                               $x, y, z \geqslant 0$

Solution We first introduce two slack variables, r and s, defined so that

$$8x + 5y + 2z + r = 3$$
$$3x + 6y + 9z + s = 2$$

and we now require, $x, y, z, r, s \geqslant 0$. So, as before, we write the augmented matrix as

P	x	y	z	r	s		Comments
1	-4	-5	-3	0	0	0	We choose to increase x initially
0	8	5	2	1	0	3	Compare $\dfrac{3}{8}$, $\dfrac{2}{3}$
0	3	6	9	0	1	2	$\uparrow$ smaller
1	-4	-5	-3	0	0	0	
0	1	$\dfrac{5}{8}$	$\dfrac{2}{8}$	$\dfrac{1}{8}$	0	$\dfrac{3}{8}$	$R_2/8$
0	3	6	9	0	1	2	
1	0	$-\dfrac{5}{2}$	-2	$\dfrac{1}{2}$	0	$\dfrac{3}{2}$	$R_1 + 4R_2$
0	1	$\dfrac{5}{8}$	$\dfrac{2}{8}$	$\dfrac{1}{8}$	0	$\dfrac{3}{8}$	
0	0	$\dfrac{33}{8}$	$\dfrac{33}{4}$	$-\dfrac{3}{8}$	1	$\dfrac{7}{8}$	$R_3 - 3R_2$
1	0	$-\dfrac{5}{2}$	-2	$\dfrac{1}{2}$	0	$\dfrac{3}{2}$	We choose to increase y
0	1	$\dfrac{5}{8}$	$\dfrac{2}{8}$	$\dfrac{1}{8}$	0	$\dfrac{3}{8}$	so compare $\dfrac{3/8}{5/8}$, $\dfrac{7/8}{33/8}$
0	0	1	2	$-\dfrac{1}{11}$	$8/33$	$\dfrac{7}{33}$	$\uparrow$ smaller $\quad R_3/(33/8)$
1	0	0	3	$\dfrac{3}{11}$	$\dfrac{20}{33}$	$\dfrac{67}{33}$	$R_1 + \dfrac{5}{2}R_3$
0	1	0	-1	$\dfrac{2}{11}$	$-\dfrac{5}{33}$	$\dfrac{8}{33}$	$R_2 - \dfrac{5}{8}R_3$
0	0	1	2	$-\dfrac{1}{11}$	$\dfrac{8}{33}$	$\dfrac{7}{33}$	

The first row now has positive coefficients which shows that we have reached the maximum. This has value 67/33 and occurs at $x = 8/33$, $y = 7/33$, $z = 0$ (and $r = s = 0$).

Exercise 5.1 Use the simplex algorithm to solve the following problems.

Maximise $P = 4x + 6y$

subject to
$$x + y \leqslant 8$$
$$7x + 4y \leqslant 14$$
$$x, y \geqslant 0$$

Exercise 5.2

$$\text{Maximise } P = 3x + 2y$$

subject to
$$x + 5y \leqslant 10$$
$$2x + 3y \leqslant 12$$
$$4x + y \leqslant 12$$
$$x, y \geqslant 0$$

Exercise 5.3

$$\text{Maximise } P = 10x + 12y + 8z$$

subject to
$$2x + 2y \leqslant 5$$
$$5x + 3y + 4z \leqslant 15$$
$$x, y, z \geqslant 0$$

Exercise 5.4

$$\text{Maximise } P = 3x + 8y - 5z$$

subject to
$$2x - 3y + z \leqslant 3$$
$$2x + 5y + 6z \leqslant 5$$
$$x, y, z \geqslant 0$$

Exercise 5.5 Solve the following LP problem.

$$\text{Maximise } P = x_1 + 4x_2 + 10x_3$$

subject to
$$x_1 + 4x_2 + 2x_3 \leqslant 100$$
$$2x_1 + 8x_3 \leqslant 40$$
$$x_1, x_2, x_3 \geqslant 0$$

Exercise 5.6 Use the simplex algorithm to maximise

$$3x + 6y + 2z$$

subject to
$$3x + 4y + z \leqslant 2$$
$$x + 3y + 2z \leqslant 1$$
$$x, y, z \geqslant 0$$

3.6 RELATED PROBLEMS

There are many complications in applying the simplex algorithm. We will deal with just one of them — that of finding a minimum rather than maximum. The procedure for dealing with this is quite straightforward; for example, the LP problem

$$\text{Minimise } P = -2x - 4y$$

subject to
$$3x + 4y \leqslant 1700$$
$$2x + 5y \leqslant 1600$$

and
$$x, y \geqslant 0$$

can clearly be converted to

$$\text{Maximise } Q = -P = 2x + 4y$$
$$3x + 4y \leqslant 1700$$
$$2x + 5y \leqslant 1600$$
$$x, y \geqslant 0$$

We can solve this, either by using the graphical method or the simplex algorithm. Using the simplex method, we introduce slack variables r and s, so that

$$3x + 4y + r = 1700$$
$$2x + 5y + s = 1600$$
$$x, y, r, s \geqslant 0$$

The simplex tableau is

Q	x	y	r	s		Comments
1	-2	-4	0	0	0	We choose to increase x initially
0	3	4	1	0	1700	Compare $\dfrac{1700}{3}$, $\dfrac{1600}{2}$
0	2	5	0	1	1600	smaller
1	-2	-4	0	0	0	
0	1	$\dfrac{4}{3}$	$\dfrac{1}{3}$	0	1700/3	$R_2/3$
0	2	5	0	1	1600	
1	0	$-\dfrac{4}{3}$	$\dfrac{2}{3}$	0	3400/3	$R_1 + 2R_2$
0	1	$\dfrac{4}{3}$	$\dfrac{1}{3}$	0	1700/3	Compare $\dfrac{1700/3}{4/3}$, $\dfrac{1400/3}{7/3}$
0	0	$\dfrac{7}{3}$	$-\dfrac{2}{3}$	1	1400/3	smaller $R_3 - 2R_2$
1	0	$-\dfrac{4}{3}$	$\dfrac{2}{3}$	0	3400/3	
0	1	$\dfrac{4}{3}$	$\dfrac{1}{3}$	0	1700/3	
0	0	1	$-\dfrac{2}{7}$	$\dfrac{3}{7}$	200	$R_3/(7/3)$
1	0	0	$\dfrac{2}{7}$	$\dfrac{4}{7}$	1400	$R_1 + \dfrac{4}{3}R_3$
0	1	0	$\dfrac{5}{7}$	$-\dfrac{4}{7}$	300	$R_2 - \dfrac{4}{3}R_3$
0	0	1	$-\dfrac{2}{7}$	$\dfrac{3}{7}$	200	

Since we have positive entries in the top row, we have reached the maximum of Q, i.e. minimum of P, which has value -1400 and occurs at $x = 300$, $y = 200$.

We are now in a position to return to our original problems posed in section 3.1. The first problem, concerned with Pelican margarine, has five variables and four constraints, and although we could apply the simplex tableau, it would be a fearsome task in manipulation. There are many available LP computer packages (see, for example, Bunday (1984)) and we suggest that the interested reader solves the problem this way. In fact, the optimal solution is given by

$$x_1 = 26\ 823.5 \quad x_2 = 0 \quad x_3 = 13\ 176.5 \quad x_4 = 0 \quad x_5 = 32\ 000$$

with profit $P = £34\ 047$

There are many other complications in applying the simplex algorithm, but they can be readily overcome. For example, the initial starting point (the zero solution) might not be in the feasible region. We will not deal with these problems here as we are aiming only to give an outline of the simplex algorithm, but interested readers may refer to the many texts now available on LP (for example, Bunday (1984)).

Exercise 6.1 A firm manufactures three products (A, B, C), each of which requires time on all of the four manufacturing facilities I, II, III, IV. The manufacturing times and profit margin per unit amount of the products are shown below.

	Time (hours)				
	I	II	III	IV	Profit (£)
A	1	3	1	2	3
B	6	1	3	3	6
C	3	3	2	4	4

If the production times available on the facilities I, II, III and IV are 84, 42, 21 and 42 hours, respectively, determine which products should be made and in what quantities. (You may assume there to be an unlimited market for each product, set-up times prior to a change of product being manufactured are negligible and maximisation of profit is the only consideration. (Bunday (1984).)

Exercise 6.2 A manufacturer of soft drinks has two bottling machines A and B. Machine A is designed for ½ litre bottles and machine B for 1 litre bottles, but each can be used for both sizes of bottle with some loss in efficiency as shown in the table below, which gives the rates at which the machines work.

Machine	½ litre bottles	1 litre bottles
A	50 per minute	20 per minute
B	40 per minute	30 per minute

Both machines run for 6 hours each day. The profit on a ½ litre bottle is 4 pence and on a 1 litre bottle 10 pence.

The manufacturer wishes to use his bottling plant so as to maximise his profit. Formulate this problem as a linear programming problem and find an optimum solution. (Bunday).

Exercise 6.3 A manufacturer of central heating components makes radiators in 4 models. The constraints on his production are the limits on his labour force (in man hours), and the steel sheet from which the radiators are pressed. The sheet is delivered each week by a regular supplier. The data in the table below gives information on the four models.

Radiator model	A	B	C	D	Available
Man hours needed	0.5	1.5	2	1.5	500 hours
Steel sheet (m^2) needed	4	2	6	8	2500 m^2
Profit/radiator (£)	5	5	12.5	10	

He sets up the problem as a linear programming problem with profit maximisation as his objective. Obtain the problem he formulates and solve it using the simplex method. (Bunday).

Exercise 6.4 A small firm produces two types of bearing, A and B, which each have to be processed on three machines, namely lathes, grinders and drill presses. The time taken for each stage in the production process is shown in the table below.

Bearing type	Time required (hours)			Profit per bearing
	Lathe	Grinder	Drill press	
A	0.01	0.02	0.04	80p
B	0.02	0.01	0.01	125p
Total time available	160	120	150	

The firm wishes to produce bearings in quantities in order to maximise its profit. Formulate this problem as a linear programming problem and obtain the solution using the simplex method. Verify the solution graphically. (Bunday).

Exercise 6.5 A firm can advertise its products using four media, television, radio, newspapers and posters. From various advertising experiments which they have carried out in the past they estimate that there are increased profits of £10, £3, £7 and £4 per pound spent on advertising via these media. The allocation of the advertising budget to the various media is subject to the following restrictions:

(i) The total budget must not exceed £500 000.
(ii) The policy is to spend at most 40% of the budget on television and at least 20% on posters.
(iii) Because of the appeal of the products to teenagers the policy is to spend at least half as much on radio as on television.

Formulate the problem of allocating the available money to the various media as a linear programming problem and use the simplex method to obtain a solution. (Bunday).

3.7 MISCELLANEOUS EXERCISES

M1 A firm of biscuit bakers make two varieties of custard creams: (i) type A, in packets of 12; (ii) type B, in packets of 20. The type A biscuits are for the upper end of the market, having twice as much filling as type B biscuits. If only type A biscuits were made, there would be enough filling to make 2000 packets per day.

Each type A biscuit requires 25% more biscuit crumbs for its manufacture than does a type B biscuit. If only type A biscuits were made, there would be enough crumbs for 2400 packets per day.

Customer demand requires that for every two packets of type A biscuits, there must be at least one packet of type B biscuits. The profit on each packet of biscuits sold is 10p regardless of type, and the firm wishes to maximise its profits. Assuming that every packet produced is sold, formulate and solve the linear programming problem that would help decide how to do this. (Open University).

M2 David Lass is the production manager at Startek Enterprises. He would like to determine which production mix of these products, A, B and C should be scheduled for the next month. There are only 6000 units of materials and 3680 man−hours available for the month. Product A uses 4 units of materials and 4 man−hours. Product B uses 48 units of materials and 32 man−hours; and Product C needs 60 units of materials and 24 man−hours. The contribution to profit is £7.00, £8.50 and £9.00 for Product A, B and C respectively. How many units of each product should David manufacture? (Lev and Weiss).

M3 Agatha Christin is the library manager of Presley University. With a budget of £1400 she is considering the purchase of book stacks to cover 720 square feet of floor space. There are basically two models in the market. Model A has a storage capacity of 80 cubic feet, requires 60 square feet of floor space, and costs £100 per book stack; Model B stores 120 cubic feet of books, requires 80 square feet, and costs £200 per book stack. How many book stacks of each model should she buy in order to maximise storage capacity? (Lev and Weiss).

M4 A firm requires coal with a phosphorus content no more than 0.03%, and no more than 3.25% ash impurity. Three grades of coal A, B, C are available at the prices shown.

Grade	% Phosphorus	% Ash	Cost (£/tonne)
A	0.06	2.0	30
B	0.04	4.0	30
C	0.02	3.0	45

How should these be blended to meet the impurity restrictions at minimum cost?
(*Hint:* if we let one tonne of the blend contain x_1, x_2, x_3 tonnes of A, B, C respectively. $x_1 + x_2 + x_3 = 1$. Thus this three−dimensional problem can easily be reduced to two−dimensional form by eliminating x_3). (Bunday)

M5 A company produces bathroom cabinets in two sizes A and B. Their sales staff tell them that the market can absorb up to 500 cabinets per week. Each cabinet of type A needs 2 m^2 of material and each cabinet of type B needs 3 m^2 of material. The company can obtain up to 1200 m^2 of material weekly. Each A cabinet needs 12 minutes of machine time and each B cabinet 30 minutes of machine time. Each week 160 hours of machine time is available. If the profit on each A cabinet is £3, and on each B cabinet £4, how many of each should be made each week? (Bunday)

M6 A car factory produces two models, the Caprice and the (cheaper) Fiasco. The factory has 1000 unskilled workers and 800 skilled workers, each of whom is paid for a 40−hour week. A Caprice requires 30 hours of unskilled labour and 50 hours of skilled labour. A Fiasco requires 40 hours of unskilled and 20 hours of skilled labour. Each Fiasco requires an outlay of £500 for raw materials and parts, whilst each Caprice requires an outlay of £1500; the total outlay must not exceed £900 000 per week. The delivery workers work a five—day week and can only remove 210 cars per day from the factory. The firm makes a profit of £1000 on each Caprice and £500 on each Fiasco. What output of each model would you recommend? What possibilities etc. etc.

M7 A small mine works two coal seams and produces three grades of coal. It costs £10 an hour to work the upper seam, obtaining in that time 1 ton of anthracite, 5 tons of best quality coal and 2 tons of ordinary coal. The lower seam is more expensive to work, at a cost of £15 per hour, but it yields in that time 4 tons of anthracite, 6 tons of best coal and 1 ton of ordinary coal. Faced with just one order, for 8 tons of anthracite, 30 tons of best coal and 8 tons of ordinary coal each day, how many hours a day should each seam be worked so as to fill this order as cheaply as possible?

4

Game Theory

4.1 THE PRISONER'S DILEMMA

Two men are arrested by the police and each found to be in possession of a number of forged £20 notes. They are taken to the police station and put into different rooms for interrogation. The CID inspector, in charge of the investigation, is convinced that these two men are not just guilty of passing the forged notes but are the actual counterfeiters. At the moment, though, he has no evidence that will stand up in court to prove his conjecture. So he puts the same proposition *separately* to each of the arrested men:

> if neither of you confesses to being a counterfeiter, then we will charge both of you with attempting to pass forged notes—I expect you will each get about $1\frac{1}{2}$ years for that crime. Should you *both* confess to being forgers, then we will do our best to get a lenient sentence—I would expect about 3 years. But if *only* you confess to forgery, then we will get you a free pardon, but we will throw the book at your fellow prisoner—and I expect he will get about 7 years.

Now let us consider how the first prisoner might argue. If he refuses to talk, then he will only get $1\frac{1}{2}$ years provided his fellow prisoner does the same. On the other hand, he risks getting 7 years if his colleague talks! So to play safe, he would confess; at best he would get a free pardon and, at worst, he

73

would get 3 years. We can summarise his choices in the following matrix table.

| | | Prisoner B | |
		Confess	Refuse
Prisoner A	Confess	(3, 3)	(0, 7)
	Refuse	(7, 0)	$(1\frac{1}{2}, 1\frac{1}{2})$

This table gives the outcomes in the form (Prisoner A, Prisoner B). So Prisoner A, by playing safe, will confess. But Prisoner B has the same options, and if he argues in the same way, he will also confess. So we end up with both prisoners confessing, getting 3 years each, and the inspector gets promotion!

Although this example is rather far-fetched, it does bring out the important aspects of game theory. Essentially two players are competing against each other and one strategy is to play safe, that is to minimise the worst outcome. This is illustrated in the table below.

| | | Prisoner B | | Worst outcome for Prisoner A |
		Confess	Refuse	
Prisoner A	Confess	(3, 3)	(0, 7)	3
	Refuse	(7, 0)	$(1\frac{1}{2}, 1\frac{1}{2})$	7 minimum value = 3

So, by playing safe, Prisoner A looks for his *maximum* value in each row, and then takes the decision corresponding to the row with minimum value.

While 'life', in general, is not as simple as this, we can see that we do indeed play something like game theory. Whether it is in school, college, work or sports, we are very often competing against friends and colleagues, and the situation can often be represented as a 'game' like the one above. We will look at a number of practical situations in the latter part of this chapter, but first we will develop the mathematical theory to cope with more involed situations.

Exercise 1.1 The results of a two person game are shown below.

| | | Player B | |
		1	2
Player A	1	(1, −1)	(2, −2)
	2	(4, −4)	(3, −3)

The entry in row 1, column 1, (1, −1) means that if Player A chooses option 1, and Player B chooses option 1, then Player A wins 1, and Player B loses 1.

Find the best strategies for each player, assuming that they will be playing this game many times, the positive numbers are *gains* and the negative numbers are losses.

Exercise 1.2   Two players, A and B, play the following game which results in the pay-off matrix below. The entry (a, b) means that A *wins* a, and B *wins* b if this is the outcome.

		Player B		
		1	2	3
	1	(8, 2)	(0, 9)	(7, 3)
Player A	2	(3, 6)	(9, 0)	(2, 7)
	3	(1, 7)	(6, 4)	(8, 1)
	4	(4, 2)	(4, 6)	(5, 1)

Analyse each player's strategy. What is the outcome if they both play safe? Would it be advantageous for the players to collaborate?

4.2   COLLABORATION

In the prisoner's dilemma, described in Section 4.1, it is clear that the prisoners would have achieved a better outcome if they had been allowed to collaborate. They would have agreed between themselves not to confess, so that they would have achieved the result of $1\frac{1}{2}$ years each. Unless, of course, one of them changed his mind and decided to shop his fellow prisoner.

The same is true in Exercise 1.2. Here the pay-off matrix is

		Player B		
		1	2	3
	1	(8, 2)	(0, 9)	(7, 3)
Player A	2	(3, 6)	(9, 0)	(2, 7)
	3	(1, 7)	(6, 4)	(8, 1)
	4	(4, 2)	(4, 6)	(5, 1)

If Player A plays safe then he will see that his worst outcomes for each row are 0, 2, 1, 4; that is the *minimum* value in each row (as these numbers represent winnings). So he would choose row 4, since this is the maximum value of the four options. So he is guaranteed to win at least 4, but could win 5. Similarly for Player B. His worst outcomes are 2, 0, 1 for each column. So, in playing safe, he would opt for column 1 and so guarantee a win of at least 2. We can tabulate these results as shown below.

	Player B			Worst outcomes for Player A	
Player A	(8, 2)	(0, 9)	(7, 3)	0	
	(3, 6)	(9, 0)	(2, 7)	2	maximum value = 4
	(1, 7)	(6, 4)	(8, 1)	1	
	(4, 2)	(4, 6)	(5, 1)	4 ←	
Worst outcomes for Player B	2	0	1		
	↑ maximum value = 2				

So the outcome becomes (4, 2), that is A wins 4, and B wins 2. But, again collaboration will help improve *total* winnings. For example, if Player A plays row 3, and Player B plays column 2, the result is (6, 4)—both players improve their winnings. So, if collaboration is allowed, there are many ways of achieving *total* winnings of 10.

This is not true of all such games. For example, consider the game with pay-off matrix.

	Player B			Worst outcomes for Player A	
Player A	(8, 2)	(1, 9)	(7, 3)	1	
	(4, 6)	(9, 1)	(3, 7)	3	maximum value = 4
	(2, 8)	(6, 4)	(9, 1)	2	
	(6, 4)	(4, 6)	(6, 4)	4 ←	
Worst comes for Player B	2	1	1		
	↑ maximum value				

Playing 'safe' by both players will result in (6, 4), that is A wins 6 and B wins 4. In this case collaboration will not help as the *total* winnings for any outcome are 10.

On the other hand, if either Player A or B is adventurous, he (or she) might *not* play safe. For example, if A assumes that B is bound to play column 1, he can increase his personal winnings by playing row 1—with outcome (8, 2). Equally, B might decide that A is bound to play row 4, and so will play column 2 in order to increase his winnings from 4 to 6. Of course, if both play adventurously, A will play row 1, and B column 2 giving an outcome of (1, 9); sad for Player A, but a real bonus for B.

In games, such as the one above, which offer no incentive for collaboration, the game can be simplified by taking 5 from all the outcomes. This gives

		Player B	
	(3, −3)	(−4, 4)	(2, −2)
Player A	(−1, 1)	(4, −4)	(−2, 2)
	(−3, 3)	(1, −1)	(4, −4)
	(1, −1)	(−1, 1)	(1, −1)

The two entries in each cell add to *zero*. What one player gains the other loses. The game is purely competitive between the two players. We call such games *zero-sum* games, and we will concentrate on strategies for these games in the next sections.

As the two entries in each cell are always the negative of each other, we can drop one of the values (say the second) and write the pay-off matrix for the example above as

$$\begin{bmatrix} 3 & -4 & 2 \\ -1 & 4 & -2 \\ -3 & 1 & 4 \\ 1 & -1 & 1 \end{bmatrix}$$

We must remember though that these numbers represent A's winnings, whilst B's winnings are the *negative* of each number in the table.

Exercise 2.1   For which of the following games is collaboration of benefit to both players?

(i)

		B	
		1	2
A	1	(4, 6)	(1, 10)
	2	(3, 5)	(2, 2)

(ii)

	B	1	2
A	1	(4, 7)	(1, 10)
	2	(8, 3)	(5, 6)

(iii)

		B		
		1	2	3
	1	(6, 2)	(4, 4)	(7, 1)
A	2	(5, 3)	(1, 7)	(2, 6)
	3	(2, 6)	(0, 8)	(3, 5)
	4	(4, 4)	(2, 6)	(5, 3)

Exercise 2.2   For the games in Exercises 1.1 and 1.2, find the outcomes in each case if players always play safe.

Exercise 2.3   For the following zero-sum games, determine if a play-safe strategy will always benefit both players.

(i) $\begin{bmatrix} 1 & 2 \\ 4 & 3 \end{bmatrix}$

(ii) $\begin{bmatrix} 4 & -2 & -5 \\ -2 & 8 & -3 \\ -5 & -3 & 14 \end{bmatrix}$

(iii) $\begin{bmatrix} -2 & -3 & 2 \\ 5 & 4 & 3 \\ 0 & 6 & 1 \end{bmatrix}$

Exercise 2.4   In the children's game of 'stone–scissors–paper' the two players simultaneously thrust forth

(a) clenched fist (stone)
(b) two fingers (scissors)
(c) flat palm (paper)

If both players present the same object, the play is drawn; otherwise the winner is determined by,

stone blunts scissors; scissors cut paper; paper wraps stone.

Construct the pay-off matrix for this game, assuming that the loser pays the winner one unit.

How would you rate the merits of the three possible moves?

4.3 ZERO-SUM GAMES

In this section, we will analyse zero-sum games and begin to find appropriate strategies. We start by looking again at the game with pay-off matrix.

$$
\begin{array}{c}
 & \quad\quad\quad B \\
A \;
\begin{array}{|rrr}
3 & -4 & 2 \\
-1 & 4 & -2 \\
-3 & 1 & 4 \\
1 & -1 & 1
\end{array}
\end{array}
$$

Remember that these entries are Player A's gains, whilst the negatives of each entry are Player B's gains. So, for example, if Player A plays row 2, and B plays column 3, then the outcome is -2. This means that A wins (-2), that is *loses 2*, whilst B loses (-2) that is *wins 2*.

To find the play safe strategy for A, we find the *minimum* entry in each row, and then look for the *maximum* amongst these values. This is shown below.

			Row minimum	
3	-4	2	-4	
-1	4	-2	-2	
-3	1	4	-3	maximum value $= -1$
1	-1	1	$-1 \leftarrow$	

For B, the play safe strategy is to find the *minimum* entry for its own pay-off matrix; which would be the negative of all the values in above table—so, using the above table, we now look for the *maximum* entry in each column. This is equivalent to finding the *minimum* entry of the negative values. Having found the maximum entries, we then choose the column with the minimum value.

$$
\begin{array}{rrr}
3 & -4 & 2 \\
-1 & 4 & -2 \\
-3 & 1 & 4 \\
1 & -1 & 1
\end{array}
$$

Column maximum	3	4	4
	$\uparrow$		

minimum value $= 3$

To see that this really does give B's play-safe strategy, we can check our result using B's actual pay-off matrix. This is:

	B		
	-3	4	-2
	3	-4	2
	3	-1	-4
	-1	1	1

Worst outcomes for Player B	-3	-4	-4

maximum value $= -3$

As we can see, to play safe, B will play column 1, which will keep his losses to at most 3.

We have already seen (Section 4.2) that in this example, it might pay for one or other of the players *not* to play safe. There are though some games in which there is no incentive to move away from a play-safe strategy. For example, if we consider the game with pay-off matrix:

$$A \begin{bmatrix} 4 & -1 & 2 & 3 \\ 4 & 6 & 3 & 7 \\ 1 & 2 & -2 & 4 \end{bmatrix} \quad B$$

To find the play-safe strategies, we follow the usual procedure.

		B			Row minimum
	4	-1	2	3	-1
A	4	6	3	7	3 ← maximum value $= 3$
	1	2	-2	4	-2
Column maximum	4	6	3	7	

minimum value $= 3$

So the play safe strategy is: A play row 2—guarantees win of at least 3
                                      B play column 3—guarantees loss of no more than 3

Now consider A's strategy. Will it be advantageous to change his play-safe policy? If he assumes that B will always play safe (i.e. play column 3), then A will not gain by playing either of the alternatives, row 1 or row 3. Similarly for B. If he assumes A plays safe, that is row 2, then losses will get worse if he changes to any of the alternatives, columns 1, 2 or 4. So for both players, there is little incentive to change their play-safe strategy. We say that this game has a **stable** *solution* (or is in equilibrium).

Exercise 3.1 Determine if the following zero-sum games have stable solutions.

(i) $\begin{bmatrix} 1 & 2 \\ 4 & 3 \end{bmatrix}$

(ii) $\begin{bmatrix} 4 & -3 \\ -4 & 3 \end{bmatrix}$

(iii) $\begin{bmatrix} -3 & -2 & -1 & 0 \\ 4 & 3 & 2 & 1 \\ 3 & 2 & 1 & 0 \\ -4 & -3 & -2 & -1 \end{bmatrix}$

(iv) $\begin{bmatrix} 1 & 2 & 3 \\ 0 & 3 & 5 \\ -1 & 2 & -2 \end{bmatrix}$

(v) $\begin{bmatrix} -2 & 0 \\ 2 & 4 \\ 6 & 8 \end{bmatrix}$

Exercise 3.2 For the game with pay-off matrix

$$\begin{bmatrix} 1 & 3 \\ 2 & -1 \end{bmatrix}$$

show that there is *not* a stable solution. If the players are going to play this game 100 times, what strategies would you advise each to use?

4.4 STABLE SOLUTIONS FOR $m \times n$ GAMES

Before proceeding further, we need to introduce a general notation for zero sum games. Suppose that Player A has m options to choose from, and Player B has n options, then the pay-off matrix will be of size $m \times n$, and take the form below:

Player B

column j

$\downarrow$

Player A $\qquad \begin{bmatrix} a_{11} & a_{12} & \cdots & a_{1j} & \cdots & a_{1n} \\ a_{21} & a_{22} & \cdots & a_{2j} & \cdots & a_{2n} \\ \cdot & \cdot & \cdot & \cdot & \cdot & \cdot \\ \cdot & \cdot & \cdot & \cdot & \cdot & \cdot \\ a_{i1} & a_{i2} & \cdots & a_{ij} & \cdots & a_{in} \\ \cdot & \cdot & \cdot & \cdot & \cdot & \cdot \\ \cdot & \cdot & \cdot & \cdot & \cdot & \cdot \\ a_{m1} & a_{m2} & \cdots & a_{mj} & \cdots & a_{mn} \end{bmatrix} \leftarrow$ row i

So if Player A plays row i, and B plays column j, we have the outcome that

$$A \text{ wins } a_{ij}, \text{ and B wins } (-a_{ij})$$

If A plays row i, the smallest amount he wins will be the minimum entry in this row

$$\min_j a_{ij}$$

which means the minimum of $a_{i1}, a_{i2}, \ldots, a_{in}$. He then looks at all those values, one for each row, and chooses the row which has the largest value; so he will win at least

$$\mu = \max \left(\min_j a_{1j}, \min_j a_{2j}, \ldots, \min_j a_{nj} \right)$$

i.e. $$\mu = \max_i \left(\min_j a_{ij} \right)$$

This is shown below.

						Row minimum
a_{11}	a_{12}	$\cdots$	a_{1j}	$\cdots$	a_{1n}	$\min_j a_{1j}$
a_{21}	a_{22}	$\cdots$	a_{2j}	$\cdots$	a_{2n}	$\min_j a_{2j}$
.	.	. . . . .	.	. .	.	. . .
a_{i1}	a_{i2}	$\cdots$	a_{ij}	$\cdots$	a_{in}	$\min_j a_{ij}$
.	.	. . . . .	.	. .	.	. . .
a_{mi}	a_{m2}	$\cdots$	a_{mj}	$\cdots$	a_{mn}	$\min_j a_{mj}$

Column maximum $\qquad \max_i a_{i1} \quad \max_i a_{i2} \qquad \max_i a_{ij} \qquad \max_i a_{in}$

Similarly the play-safe strategy for Player B is to find the maximum in each column, that is $\max_i a_{ij}$, and then to find the minimum of these values. So B is sure to win at least

$$v = -\min_j \left(\max_i a_{ij} \right)$$

(the negative value, since B's winnings are the negative of all the entries).

So for the game below, we determine μ and v

					Row minimum	
1	-3	-2	0	3	-3	
4	2	3	2	6	$2 \leftarrow$	
3	-1	5	-4	0	-4	$\mu = \max(-3, 2, -4, 2, -3, -4)$
7	2	8	2	2	$2 \leftarrow$	$\underline{\mu = 2}$
0	1	-3	-2	-1	-3	
5	-4	1	-1	3	-4	

Column
maximum   7   2   8   2   6
$\qquad\quad\uparrow\qquad\quad\uparrow$

$v = -\min(7, 2, 8, 2, 6)$
$\underline{v = -2}$

We have two play-safe solutions, and they are both *stable*. In fact, if we look back at Exercise 3.1, we see that in all cases

$$\mu + v \leqslant 0$$

and in the case of stable solutions,

$$\mu + v = 0$$

Both these results are true in general, as we shall now prove.

Theorem 1   For a zero-sum game, $\mu + v \leqslant 0$

Proof
If both players play safe, A gains at least μ, and B gains at least v; so that together they gain at least $\mu + v$. But in a zero sum game, the total gain is always zero. Hence $\mu + v$ cannot exceed zero, that is $\mu + v \leqslant 0$.

So, for any zero sum game, $\mu + v \leqslant 0$. We now move onto games with stable solutions.

Theorem 2   A zero-sum game has a stable solution if and only if

$$\mu + v = 0$$

Proof
We have two results to prove here

(i) *If $\mu + v = 0$, we must show that there is a stable solution.*

By definition of μ, there is a row, say the rth, in which the smallest entry is μ. Similarly there is a column, say the sth, in which the largest entry is $-v$

(remember the definition earlier). So $a_{rs} \geqslant \mu$, and $a_{rs} \leqslant -v$. But we are assuming that $\mu + v = 0$, so we have $a_{rs} \geqslant \mu$ and $a_{rs} \leqslant -v = \mu$.

*s*th column

↓

$$
\begin{array}{ccccc}
a_{11} & \cdots & a_{1s} & \cdots & a_{1n} \\
\vdots & & \vdots & & \vdots \\
a_{r1} & \cdots & a_{rs} & \cdots & a_{rn} \\
\vdots & & \vdots & & \vdots \\
a_{m1} & \cdots & a_{ms} & \cdots & a_{mn}
\end{array}
$$

*r*th row → (indicating the $a_{r1} \cdots a_{rs} \cdots a_{rn}$ row)

Thus, we must have $a_{rs} = \mu = -v$, and so a_{rs} is the minimum in the *r*th row, and the maximum in the *s*th column. If A decides that B plays the *s*th column, A cannot improve on the value a_{rs} since $a_{rs} > a_{js}$ for $j \neq r$. Similarly for B. This is thus a stable solution. (We also call a_{rs} the *value* of the game and a_{rs} is sometimes called a *saddle point*.)

(ii) *If there is a stable solution, we must show that* $\mu + v = 0$

Suppose that we now have a stable solution, say at row *r* and column *s*, i.e. at a_{rs}. Then from the definition of μ, we have

$$
\mu = \max_i \left(\min_j a_{ij} \right)
$$

$$
\geqslant \min_j a_{rj} \text{ (looking along the } r\text{th row)}
$$

$$
= a_{rs}, \text{ since } a_{rs} \text{ is a saddle point}
$$

Similarly

$$
-v = \min_j \left(\max_i a_{ij} \right)
$$

$$
\leqslant \max_i a_{is} \text{ (looking along the } s\text{th column)}
$$

$$
= a_{rs}, \text{ since } a_{rs} \text{ is a saddle point}
$$

Thus $\mu + v = 0$, and the result is proved.

We now have a precise test for stable solutions.
Find μ and v, and if $\mu + v = 0$, we have a stable solution.

Example 1   Does the following game have a stable solution?

$$\begin{bmatrix} 0 & -3 & 5 & -9 \\ 15 & -8 & -2 & 10 \\ 7 & 10 & 6 & 9 \\ 6 & 11 & -3 & 2 \end{bmatrix}$$

Solution   We first find μ and v in the usual way

				Row minimum	
0	−3	5	−9	−9	
15	−8	−2	10	−8	$\mu = \max(-9, -8, 6, -3)$
7	10	6	9	6	i.e. $\mu = 6$
6	11	−3	2	−3	

Column
maximum   15   11   6   10

$v = -\min(15, 11, 6, 10)$

i.e. $v = -6$

So $\mu + v = 0$, and we have a stable solution at $a_{33} = 6$.

Exercise 4.1   Determine if the following games have stable solutions. If so, find the value of the game.

(i) $\begin{bmatrix} -4 & 6 & -4 & 1 \\ 5 & -7 & 3 & 8 \\ -8 & 0 & 6 & -2 \end{bmatrix}$

(ii) $\begin{bmatrix} 5 & 2 \\ 7 & 3 \end{bmatrix}$

(iii) $\begin{bmatrix} 7 & -3 \\ -5 & -2 \end{bmatrix}$

(iv) $\begin{bmatrix} 2 & -2 & 0 \\ -6 & 0 & -5 \\ 5 & 2 & 3 \end{bmatrix}$

(v) $\begin{bmatrix} 1 & 3 & 2 & 4 \\ 2 & 4 & 3 & 1 \\ 3 & 1 & 4 & 2 \\ 4 & 2 & 1 & 3 \end{bmatrix}$

Exercise 4.2   Show that the game with pay-off matrix

$$\begin{bmatrix} 4 & -3 \\ -4 & 3 \end{bmatrix}$$

does *not* have a stable solution. If the players, A and B, are going to play this game 100 times, what advice would you give to either player?

Exercise 4.3   Find all the saddle points for the zero-sum game with pay-off matrix

$$\begin{bmatrix} 5 & 5 & 3 & 4 & 3 \\ 4 & 3 & 2 & 4 & 1 \\ 4 & 6 & 2 & 7 & 2 \\ 7 & 5 & 3 & 4 & 3 \end{bmatrix}$$

and determine the solution to this game.

4.5 MIXED STRATEGIES

In Exercise 4.2 we considered the game with pay-off matrix

$$
\begin{array}{c}
\qquad\qquad\quad B \\
\begin{array}{cc|c}
 & & \text{Row min.} \\
A \quad \begin{matrix} 4 & \;\;\widehat{-3} \\ -4 & 3 \end{matrix} & & \begin{matrix} -3 \\ -4 \end{matrix} \quad \mu = \max(-3, -4) = -3 \\
\hline
\text{Column max.} \quad\; 4 \quad 3 & & \\
\end{array}
\end{array}
$$

Column max.   4   3
$v = -\min(4, 3) = -3$

If both players play safe, then we have the result ringed. But if A assumes that B will play safe (i.e. column 2), it will pay him to change to row 2, and so win 3 rather than lose 3. However, if B assumes that A plays safe (i.e. row 1), it will *not* pay him to change to column 1 because then B loses 4 rather than wins 3. So it might well pay Player A to change from a play-safe strategy, since there is no stable solution. (We can check this since $\mu + v = -6 \neq 0$ hence no stable solution.)

If the players are going to play this game just once, it would be difficult to decide on their best policy. But, suppose that they are going to play the game many times. It seems likely that a mixed strategy would be the best, that is, a combination of rows (or columns). Let us look more closely at A's strategy. Suppose that

$$\text{A chooses} \begin{cases} \text{row 1 with probability } p \\ \text{row 2 with probability } 1 - p \end{cases}$$

The expected pay-off to A will depend on what choice B makes.

If, for example, B chooses column 1, then A's expected pay-off is

$$4p + (-4)(1 - p) = 8p - 4$$

Whereas if B chooses column 2, then A's expected pay-off is

$$(-3)p + 3(1 - p) = 3 - 6p$$

We can illustrate A's pay-off on a graph.

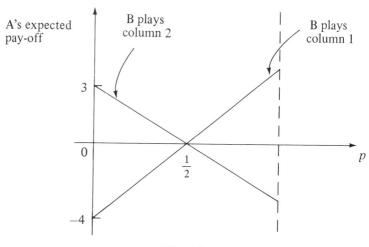

Fig. 4.1

Now we can see that if A plays with $p < 1/2$, then B, by choosing column 1 all the time, can make A's expected pay-off negative. Similarly, if A plays with $p > 1/2$, B can again make sure that A's expected pay-off is negative by always playing column 2. So, only by playing $p = 1/2$, can A hold his losses to zero. So his best mixed strategy is to play row 1 with probability 1/2 (this must of course be random, for example toss of a coin, Heads—row 1. Tails—row 2).

In the same way we can find B's best mixed strategy. Suppose B plays column 1 with probability q, and so column 2 with probability $1 - q$.

Then, if A plays row 1, B's expected pay-off is

$$-[4q + (-3)(1 - q)] = -[7q - 3] = 3 - 7q$$

But, if A plays row 2, B's expected pay-off is

$$-[-4q + 3(1 - q)] = -[3 - 7q] = 7q - 3$$

Plotting this, we obtain the graph below.

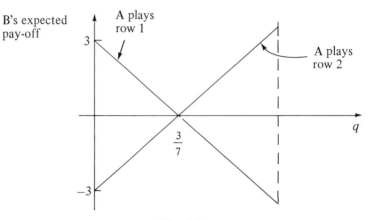

Fig. 4.2

Analysing B's strategy as we did for A, we conclude that the best mixed strategy for B is to play column 1 with probability 3/7, and so column 2 with probability 4/7 (again these must be played at random, so he will need 3 white and 4 black counters in a bag, taking one at random each time).

So we have determined the optimum mixed strategies for both A and B. With these strategies, both A and B should, in the long run, hold their losses to zero. Try playing this game a large number of times (say about 50) with a friend, and see if this strategy works in practice.

Exercise 5.1 What are the expected returns to A and B for the zero-sum game with pay-off matrix

$$\begin{bmatrix} 1 & 3 \\ 2 & -1 \end{bmatrix}$$

if

(i) A plays row 1 with probability 1/2 and B plays column 1 always;
(ii) A plays row 1 always and B plays column 1 with probability 3/4?

Determine the optimal mixed strategies for A and B and their respective gains if they are both free to choose their strategies.

Exercise 5.2 In each of the following 2 × 2 games, find the optimum mixed strategies for both players.

(i) $\begin{bmatrix} 6 & 3 \\ -1 & 4 \end{bmatrix}$ (ii) $\begin{bmatrix} 40 & 20 \\ -10 & 30 \end{bmatrix}$ (iii) $\begin{bmatrix} 3 & 7 \\ -5 & 4 \end{bmatrix}$ (iv) $\begin{bmatrix} 3 & 5 \\ 5 & 2 \end{bmatrix}$

Exercise 5.3 Analyse A's best mixed strategy for the game with pay-off matrix

$$\text{A} \quad \begin{bmatrix} 1 & -1 & 3 \\ 3 & 5 & -3 \end{bmatrix}$$

with B over the columns.

Exercise 5.4 Determine optimal strategies for both players for the zero-sum game with pay-off matrix

$$\begin{bmatrix} -2 & -2 \\ 2 & -1 \\ -1 & 2 \end{bmatrix}$$

4.6 GENERAL _m_ × _n_ GAMES

In this section, we show the way in which a general $m \times n$ game can be converted to a linear programming problem. As we have seen in Section 4.5, there is no difficulty in checking 2×2 games—they either have a saddle point, or you can determine the optimum mixed strategies. For games of different sizes, the graphical method does not work quite so easily, and the most appropriate method of solution is to convert the problem to a linear programming (LP) problem, which we can solve using the techniques already developed.

We will start by showing how we can convert a 2×2 game into an LP problem. We can of course solve any 2×2 game in the usual graphical way, however we are using a simple example here in order to illustrate the technique involved in transferring this to a LP problem. So we look again at the 2×2 game with pay-off matrix

$$\begin{bmatrix} 4 & -3 \\ -4 & 3 \end{bmatrix}$$

Our first task is to make all the entries in the matrix positive; we can achieve this here by adding 5 to every entry, that is

$$\text{A} \quad \begin{bmatrix} 9 & 2 \\ 1 & 8 \end{bmatrix}$$

with B over the columns.

This does not affect the strategies for playing this game, just the final value, that is we must remember to take 5 off at the end. Now if A plays row 1 with probability p_1, and row 2 with probability p_2, then

$$p_1 + p_2 = 1$$

and A's expected gains are

$$9p_1 + p_2 \quad \text{if B plays column 1}$$

$$2p_1 + 8p_2 \quad \text{if B plays column 2}$$

Now if p_0 represents the value of the game, that is the average gain to A, then A seeks to choose the probabilities p_1 and p_2, so that p_0 is as large as possible, and is guaranteed. So we must have

$$9p_1 + p_2 \geqslant p_0$$

$$2p_1 + 8p_2 \geqslant p_0$$

We can write the problem as

$$\text{maximise } p_0$$

subject to the constraints,

$$p_0 - 9p_1 - p_2 \leqslant 0$$

$$p_0 - 2p_1 - 8p_1 \leqslant 0$$

$$p_1 + p_2 \leqslant 1$$

and p_0, p_1, $p_2 > 0$. (p_0 will be positive, since all entries in the matrix are positive.) Note that the constraint $p_1 + p_2 = 1$ has been replaced by the weaker constraints

$$p_1 + p_2 \leqslant 1$$

$$p_1, p_2 \geqslant 0$$

In finding the maximum value of p_0, we are bound to make $p_1 + p_2$ as large as possible, and so equal to 1.

So we now have an LP problem, namely find p_0, p_1, $p_2 \geqslant 0$ such that

$$P = p_0 \text{ is a maximum, subject to}$$

$$p_1 + p_2 \leqslant 1$$

$$p_0 - 9p_1 - p_2 \leqslant 0$$

$$p_0 - 2p_1 - 8p_2 \leqslant 0$$

This a standard LP problem, and we will use the usual simplex method to solve it.

We first introduce slack variables, r, s and t, to convert the inequalities to equalities, that is

$$p_1 + p_2 + r = 1$$

$$p_0 - 9p_1 - p_2 + s = 0$$

$$p_0 - 2p_1 - 8p_2 + t = 0$$

and then we can write the simplex tableau as

P	p_0	p_1	p_2	r	s	t	
1	-1	0	0	0	0	0	0
0	0	1	1	1	0	0	1
0	1	-9	-1	0	1	0	0
0	1	-2	-8	0	0	1	0
1	0	-9	-1	0	1	0	0
0	0	1	1	1	0	0	1
0	1	-9	-1	0	1	0	0
0	0	7	-7	0	-1	1	0
1	0	0	-10	0	$-2/7$	$9/7$	0
0	0	0	2	1	$1/7$	$-1/7$	1
0	1	0	-10	0	$-2/7$	$9/7$	0
0	0	1	-1	0	$-1/7$	$1/7$	0
1	0	0	0	5	$3/7$	$4/7$	5
0	0	0	1	$1/2$	$1/14$	$-1/14$	$1/2$
0	1	0	0	5	$3/7$	$4/7$	5
0	0	1	0	$1/2$	$-1/14$	$1/14$	$1/2$

Since all the entries in the top row are positive, we have reached the optimal solution, given by $r = s = t = 0$ and

$$p_2 = 1/2. \; p_0 = 5, \; p_1 = 1/2$$

So the optimal policy for Player A is to play each row with probability $1/2$ and the value of the game is given by $p_0 - 5 = 5 - 5 = 0$ (since we added 5 onto all entries in the game matrix). So this policy for A should keep his loss to zero. This solution, as expected, confirms the solution found in the previous section. We can also find the optimal policy for B by either a similar type of LP problem (see Exercise 6.2) or by a graphical solution.

We will now see how this method works for the general $m \times n$ zero-sum game.

Consider the game with pay-off matrix

$$
\begin{array}{cc}
 & \mathbf{B} \\
\mathbf{A} & \begin{bmatrix} a_{11} & \cdots & a_{1n} \\ \cdot & \cdot & \cdot \\ \cdot & \cdot & \cdot \\ a_{m1} & \cdots & a_{mn} \end{bmatrix}
\end{array}
$$

Before proceeding, we must make all entries positive, by adding an appropriate quantity to each element. So let us assume that this has been done, and that Player A is adopting a policy of playing row i with probability p_i $(i = 1, 2, \ldots, m)$. The expected gains to A depend on the column played by B.

If B plays column 1, A's expected gain $= a_{11}p_1 + \cdots + a_{m1}p_m$

If B plays column 2, A's expected gain $= a_{12}p_1 + \cdots + a_{m2}p_m$

. . . .

If B plays column n, A's expected gain $= a_{1n}p_1 + \cdots + a_{mn}p_m$

If p_0 represents the value of the game, then A will choose the probabilities p_1, $p_2, \ldots, p_m$ so as to maximise p_0 where

$$a_{11}p_1 + \cdots + a_{m1}p_m \geq p_0$$
$$a_{12}p_1 + \cdots + a_{m2}p_m \geq p_0$$
. . . .
$$a_{1n}p_1 + \cdots + a_{mn}p_m \geq p_0$$

and of course subject to

$$p_0, p_1, \ldots, p_m \geq 0$$

and

$$p_1 + p_2 + \cdots + p_m = 1$$

(p_0 will be positive, since all entries in the matrix have been made positive). We will again replace these conditions on the p's by the weaker inequality

$$p_1 + p_2 + \cdots + p_m \leq 1,$$

and so we are left with the LP problem:

Find $p_0, p_1, \ldots, p_m \geq 0$ so that we

$$\text{maximise } p_0$$

subject to

$$p_1 + p_2 + \cdots + p_m \leq 1$$
$$a_{11}p_1 + \cdots + a_{m1}p_m \geq p_0$$
$$a_{12}p_1 + \cdots + a_{m2}p_m \geq p_0$$
. . . .
$$a_{1n}p_1 + \cdots + a_{mn}p_m \geq p_0$$

This can be solved using the simplex method.

Example 2   Find A's optimal mixed strategy for the game with pay-off matrix

$$A \quad \begin{bmatrix} 18 & 12 \\ 5 & 17 \\ -5 & 20 \end{bmatrix}$$

(with B above)

Solution We first add 6 to all entries, so that all elements are positive, i.e.

$$
A \quad \begin{array}{c} \text{B} \\ \begin{bmatrix} 24 & 18 \\ 11 & 23 \\ 1 & 26 \end{bmatrix} \end{array}
$$

Assuming A plays row i with probability p_i, then if the value of the game is p_0, we require maximum p_0 such that

$$24p_1 + 11p_2 + p_3 \geqslant p_0$$

$$18p_1 + 23p_2 + 26p_3 \geqslant p_0$$

with $p_1 + p_2 + p_3 = 1$, and $p_0, p_1, p_2, p_3 \geqslant 0$. Again using a weaker inequality

$$p_1 + p_2 + p_3 \leqslant 1,$$

we have the LP problem of finding $p_0, p_1, p_2, p_3 \geqslant 0$ such that

$$P = p_0 \text{ is maximised}$$

and subject to the inequalities

$$p_1 + p_2 + p_3 \leqslant 1$$

$$p_0 - 24p_1 - 11p_2 - p_3 \leqslant 0$$

$$p_0 - 18p_1 - 23p_1 - 26p_3 \leqslant 0$$

Using the simplex method we have

P	p_0	p_1	p_2	p_3	r	s	t	
1	-1	0	0	0	0	0	0	0
0	0	1	1	1	1	0	0	1
0	1	-24	-11	-1	0	1	0	0
0	1	-18	-23	-26	0	0	1	0
1	0	-24	-11	-1	0	1	0	0
0	0	1	1	1	1	0	0	1
0	1	-24	-11	-1	0	1	0	0
0	0	6	-12	-25	0	-1	1	0
1	0	0	-59	-101	0	3	4	0
0	0	0	3	$31/6$	1	$1/6$	$-1/6$	1
0	1	0	-59	-101	0	-3	4	0
0	0	1	-2	$-25/6$	0	$-1/6$	$1/6$	0
1	0	0	0	$11/18$	$59/3$	$5/18$	$13/18$	$59/3$
0	0	0	1	$31/18$	$1/3$	$1/18$	$-1/18$	$1/3$
0	1	0	0	$11/18$	$59/3$	$5/18$	$13/18$	$59/3$
0	0	1	0	$-13/18$	$2/3$	$-1/18$	$1/18$	$2/3$

So we have the solution $p_2 = 1/3$, $p_0 = 59/3$, $p_1 = 2/3$, and $p_3 = 0$. The value of the game is $59/3 - 6 = 41/3$ and to obtain this, A must play

row 1 with $p = 2/3$,

row 2 with $p = 1/3$,

row 3 with $p = 0$

Exercise 6.1   Convert the game with pay-off matrix

$$
\begin{array}{c}
 \quad \text{B} \\
A \quad \begin{bmatrix} 3 & 5 \\ 7 & 4 \end{bmatrix}
\end{array}
$$

to a LP problem to determine A's optimal strategy. Solve the problem, finding A's strategy and the value of the game.

Exercise 6.2   Consider B's strategy for the game with pay-off matrix

$$
\begin{array}{c}
 \quad \text{B} \\
A \quad \begin{bmatrix} 4 & -3 \\ -4 & 3 \end{bmatrix}
\end{array}
$$

(considered in this section). Convert the problem of finding B's optimal strategy to a LP problem and solve using the simplex method.

Exercise 6.3   For the game with pay-off matrix

$$
\begin{array}{c}
 \quad \text{B} \\
A \quad \begin{bmatrix} 4 & -3 & -1 \\ -2 & 3 & 0 \end{bmatrix}
\end{array}
$$

find A's optimum strategy by (i) the graphical method and (ii) conversion to an LP problem.

Exercise 6.4   Formulate as an appropriate LP problem for A's optimum strategy, the game with pay-off matrix

$$
\begin{array}{c}
 \quad \text{B} \\
A \quad \begin{bmatrix} -1 & 1 \\ 1 & -2 \\ 0 & -1 \end{bmatrix}
\end{array}
$$

Solve the problem.

4.7   APPLICATIONS

We now look at some of the many varied ways in which game theory can be used to model real situations, and how it has been used to explain observed results.

4.7.1 Competitive Strategies

Suppose that two firms, A and B, are competing for the same market. They each produce three different brands of their particular product. The management of Firm A has decided to increase by £50 000 its advertising expenditure for next year in the hope of obtaining a greater proportion of the market. However, Firm B also hopes to increase its share, not by increased advertising, but by possibly investing a similar sum of money to increase the quality of its products. Both firms, though, are undecided about which of their three brands should be promoted. So A's alternatives are

1. Increase advertising of brand 1 by £50 000
2. Increase advertising of brand 2 by £50 000
3. Increase advertising of brand 3 by £50 000

and similarly B's alternatives are

1. Increase quality of brand 1 by investing £50 000
2. Increase quality of brand 2 by investing £50 000
3. Increase quality of brand 3 by investing £50 000
4. No action

Both firms have a sales forecasting function which predicts the sales for each brand in terms of the decisions taken by each firm. For example, if A employs strategy 1 and B employs strategy 1, the net sales revenue gain for A is predicted as £120 000. The resulting gains (expressed in £000's) for firm A for the various possible strategies that can be employed by A and B are given in the matrix

		Firm B			
		1	2	3	4
	1	120	−60	300	−220
Firm A	2	140	20	180	100
	3	−60	0	−100	160

It is assumed that B's gains are the negative of A's gains for all the varying strategies. So let us apply our game theory analysis to this problem by evaluating μ and v.

					Row min.
120	−60	300	−220		−220
140	20	180	100		$20 \leftarrow \mu = 20$
−60	0	−100	160		−100
Column max.	140	20	300	160	

$$v = -20$$

So for this pay-off matrix, there is a stable solution (saddle point) and the play safe strategies are

A: strategy 2—increase advertising on product 2.
B: strategy 2—increase investment on product 2.

These are the optimal strategies, providing that both firms are playing safe.

4.7.2   Optimal Strategy in Battles

In August 1944, shortly after the invasion of Normandy, the Allied forces advanced from their beach-head position through a narrow gap at Avranches. The military positions are shown in the Fig. 4.3.

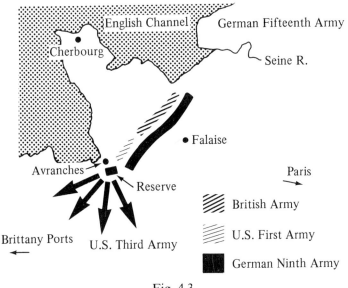

Fig. 4.3

The US First Army and the British Army were threatening the German Ninth Army, whilst the US Third Army had moved south of Avranches. The commander of the US forces was General Bradley, and the German forces commander was General von Kluge. Each had a tactical decision to take.

Von Kluge could either attack towards the west in order to secure his west flank and cut off the US Third Army, or he could withdraw to the east in order to take up a better defensive position near the River Seine.

General Bradley's problem was what to do with his reserves, which were standing just south of the gap. He could order his reserve back to defend the gap: he could send it eastwards to harass and possibly cut off the German Ninth Army's withdrawal; or he could leave it in position for a further day before committing it. So Bradley had three options, and in terms of game theory there are six possible outcomes. These are illustrated in Fig. 4.4, with the expected results for each decision.

We now construct a pay-off matrix for the game, using Bradley's figures, from one to six, for the most preferable outcome.

		General von Kluge	
		Attack	Withdraw
	Reserve ordered back to gap	2	3
General Bradley	Sent eastward	1	5
	Left in position for one day	6	4

The first thing to note is that General Bradley's row 1 choice (ordered back to the gap) is always inferior to his row 3 choice no matter what General von Kluge decides. So we can abandon it and look at the 2 × 2 game with pay-off matrix:

		Row min.	
1	5	1	
6	4	4 ←	$\mu = 4$

Column max.   6   5

$$\uparrow$$
$$v = -5$$

Now $\mu + v = -1$, so we do not have a saddle point. There is no stable solution, and we must consider mixed strategies. If the game is being played a number of times, and if Bradley plays row 1 with probability p, then his expected gain if von Kluge always plays column 1 is

$$p1 + (1 - p)6 = 6 - 5p;$$

whereas if von Kluge always plays column 2, Bradley's expected gain is

$$p5 + (1 - p)4 = 4 + p.$$

These are illustrated in Fig. 4.5.

If the game were played a number of times, Bradley's optimum strategy would be to play row 1 with probability 1/3 and row 2 with probability 2/3.

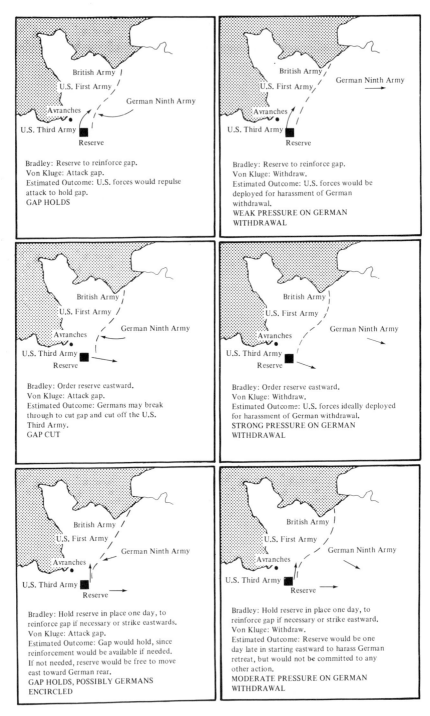

Fig. 4.4

98

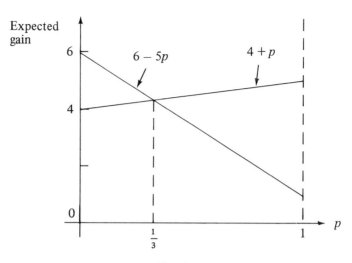

Fig. 4.5

He would then expect to gain at least 13/3. In a similar way, von Kluge's optimum strategy is to play column 1 with probability 1/6, and column 2 with probability 5/6.

So according to game theory both commanders should have played these strategies, using a random device to determine their actual decisions. Bradley, for instance, should put one red and two blue counters in a bag and choose one at random. If red, he sends his reserve eastward, and if blue, he leaves them in position for a day. Of course, this would be fine if the same battle was being played a large number of times—but this was a single very important battle, and it would hardly be likely that the commander would trust the fate of his forces to counters in a bag!

A better way to argue would be to maximise their worst positions. Bradley, for example, would choose row 2 and von Kluge column 2. In this way Bradley gets at least 4, and von Kluge will not lose more than 5. So if they both play safe, we have the outcome

'Reserve stays in position for one day, Germans withdraw'

This is, in fact, exactly what the two commanders decided to do. But the story does not end there. After von Kluge had made his decision to withdraw, Hitler countermanded it and ordered him to attack. In this way Hitler handed over to Bradley his best possible outcome. The gap held on the first day without reinforcements, so the reserve was then used to encircle the Germans. After extricating the shattered remains of his army, von Kluge committed suicide.

4.7.3 Jamaican Fishermen

William Davenport spent some time studying a fishing village of about 200 people, on the south shore of Jamaica. All the male villagers were fishermen making their living exclusively by fishing in the local waters and selling their catches. There were 26 fishing crews which fished the area in dugout canoes by setting fish pots, which were drawn and reset on three regular fishing days each week.

The fishing grounds are divided into inside and outside banks; the inside banks lie from 5 to 15 miles offshore, and the outside banks lie beyond. The distinction between inside and outside banks is made not only on their distance from the shore but on the basis of the strength of the sea currents which flow across them. The outside banks are subject to very strong currents which flow frequently and unpredictably, whereas the inside banks are almost fully protected from these currents. The fishermen have three alternatives:

1. Set their pots inside.
2. Set some inside and some outside.
3. Set their pots outside.

Each action has both advantages and disadvantages. Fishing outside is more expensive since bigger and stronger canoes are required. Pots are often swept away altogether. On the other hand, better quality fish are obtained when the current is not running. Also the price of fish varies according to quality and quantity available, which of course depend on where they are fishing and whether a current is running.

We can try to quantify these arguments by conceiving the situation as one in which the village as a whole is playing against nature. The village has three alternatives, whilst nature has two, to send a current or not to send one. Thus there are six possible outcomes, and Davenport evaluated the respective monetary pay-offs (which were the average net income per canoe during a fishing month). These are shown below, and since $\mu + v \neq 0$, we do not have a stable solution.

		Nature			
		Current	No current	Row min.	
Village	Inside	17.3	11.5	11.5	
	In and out	5.2	17.0	5.2	$\mu = 11.5$
	Outside	−4.4	20.6	−4.4	
Column max.		17.3	20.6		

$$v = -17.3$$

Since this is a 3×2 game, we can use the technique described in the last section, which converts this to an LP problem. Suppose that the village plays each row with probability p_i (i.e. 1, 2, 3) and that p_0 is the value of the game, our LP problem for the villages optimum strategy is given below.

Find $p_0, p_1, p_2, p_3 \geqslant 0$ so that

$$P = p_0 \text{ is maximised.}$$

Subject to

$$p_1 + p_2 + p_3 \leqslant 1$$

$$p_0 - 17.3p_1 - 5.2p_2 + 4.4p_3 \leqslant 0$$

$$p_0 - 11.5p_1 - 17.0p_2 + 20.6p_3 \leqslant 0$$

Using the simplex method, we have

					Slack variables				
P	p_0	p_1	p_2	p_3	r	s	t	
1	-1	0	0	0	0	0	0	0
0	0	1	1	1	1	0	0	1
0	1	-17.3	-5.2	4.4	0	1	0	0
0	1	-11.5	-17.0	-20.6	0	0	1	0
1	0	-17.3	-5.2	4.4	0	1	0	0
0	0	1	1	1	1	0	0	1
0	1	-17.3	-5.2	4.4	0	1	0	0
0	0	5.8	-11.8	-25.0	0	-1	1	0
1	0	0	-40.40	-70.17	0	-1.98	2.98	0
0	0	0	3.03	5.31	1	0.17	-0.17	1
0	1	0	-40.40	-70.17	0	-1.98	2.98	0
0	0	1	-2.03	-4.31	0	-0.17	0.17	0
1	0	0	0	0.63	40.40	0.44	0.56	13.33
0	0	0	1	1.75	0.33	0.06	-0.06	0.33
0	1	0	0	0.63	40.40	0.44	0.56	13.33
0	0	1	0	-0.76	0.67	-0.05	0.05	0.67

So we deduce that

$$p_2 = 0.33, \ p_0 = 13.33, \ p_1 = 0.67, \ p_3 = r = s = t = 0$$

giving the optimum policy for the village as

Play row 1 with probability 2/3
Play row 2 with probability 1/3
Play row 3 with probability 0

So that the optimum strategy for the village is to fish 'inside' with probability 0.67 and 'in and out' with probability 0.33 and not 'outside' at all. The village has 26 canoes, so that the number used for 'inside' fishing should be 0.67 × 26 = 17.4 and for 'in and out' fishing 8.6.

Having worked out what strategy the village should undertake, Davenport went on to see what did in fact happen. During his period of observations, 18 canoes fished 'inside', 8 fished 'in and out', and none 'outside'. The observed facts were almost in exact conformity with the optimum strategy evaluated by using game theory!

Of course, this optimum strategy assumes that nature is also playing this game, and ought to *minimise* the village's gain! Let us see what strategy nature should adopt. Rewriting the matrix in terms of *gains* to nature, we have

		Nature	
		Current	No current
Village	Inside	−17.3	−11.5
	In and Out	−5.2	−17.0
	Outside	4.4	−20.6

If nature plays 'current' with probability p, and so 'no current' with probability $1 - p$, the expected gains are given by

$$-17.3p - 11.5(1 - p) = -5.8p - 11.5 \quad \text{if village plays 'Inside'}$$

$$-5.2p - 17.0(1 - p) = 11.8p - 17.0 \quad \text{if village plays 'In and Out'}$$

$$4.4p - 20.6(1 - p) = 25.0p - 20.6 \quad \text{if village plays 'Outside'}$$

We can illustrate this on a graph, see Fig. 4.6.

Since nature is trying to maximise its pay-off, no matter what strategy is adopted by the village, it will play

send current with probability   0.31
no current with probability   0.69

Observations made by Davenport show that a current flows about 25 per cent of the time—so nature is not adopting its optimum strategy. Indeed, if we make the assumption that the current flows about 25 per cent of the time, the expected gains to the village will be maximised by putting *all* the canoes

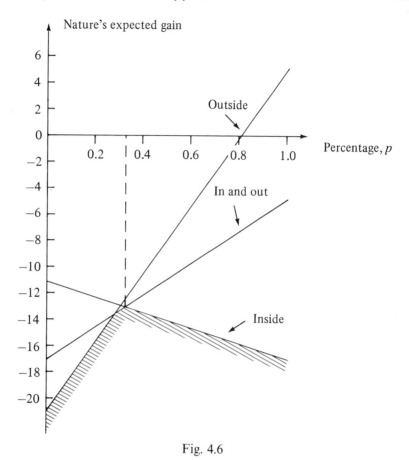

Fig. 4.6

on 'outside' fishing. So if nature is indifferent to the fisherman's problems and always plays 'current', 'no current' in the ratio 1 : 3, the village is not using an optimum strategy at all. It appears as if their strategy has been worked out over the years on the false assumption that nature was malevolent!

Exercise 7.1 The government of a small country desires to inoculate its citizens against a certain flu virus. The virus has two strains, and it is not known in what proportions the two strains occur in the virus population. Two vaccines have been developed with different effectiveness against the two strains. Vaccine 1 is 85 per cent effective against strain 1 and 70 per cent effective against strain 2. Vaccine 2 is 60 per cent effective against strain 1 and 90 per cent effective against strain 2.

What inoculation policy should the government adopt?

Exercise 7.2   Two competing television networks, A and B, are scheduling
1-hour programmes in the same peak time period. Network A can schedule
one of three possible programmes, and network B can schedule one of four
possible programmes. Neither network knows which programme the other
will schedule. Both networks ask the same outside polling agency to give
them an estimate of how all possible pairings of the programmes will divide
the viewing audience. The agency gives them each the following table, whose
(i, j)th entry is the percentage of the viewing audience that will watch network
A if network A's programme i is paired against network B's programme j.

		Network B's programme			
		1	2	3	4
Network A's programme	1	60	20	30	55
	2	50	75	45	60
	3	70	45	35	30

What programme should each network schedule in order to maximise its
viewing audience?

Exercise 7.3   Many medical procedures involve substantial risk to the
patient and should only be undertaken when the patient is exposed to greater
risk if no treatment is given. The problem is further complicated if it is not
certain that the patient does have the disease suspected.
   We can model this problem as a game theory problem with pay-off matrix

$$\begin{bmatrix} a & b \\ c & d \end{bmatrix}$$

where a, b, c and d are the expected lengths of life if the patient has the
operation and the disease, the operation and no disease, the disease and no
operation, and no disease and no operation respectively. Assuming that the
patient wishes to maximise his expected length of life, show that the operation
can be recommended if the probability that the patient has the disease is
greater than

$$\frac{d - b}{a + d - b - c}$$

(The actual probability is found by performing various tests.)

A patient has a suspected tumour on the brain. The estimated values of the parameters in years introduced above are $a = 6$, $b = 10$, $c = 1$, $d = 15$. Determine the required value of the probability that the patient has the tumour in order to recommend the operation.

4.8 MISCELLANEOUS EXERCISES

M1 For the following pay-off matrices: (a) determine the play-safe strategies and (b) decide whether collaboration would be advantageous for the players:

(i)

		B 1	2
A	1	(1, 1)	(0, 8)
	2	(2, 4)	(3, 5)

(ii)

		B 1	2
A	1	(2, 3)	(−2, 7)
	2	(5, 0)	(1, 4)

(iii)

		1	2	3
A	1	(7, 0)	(5, 3)	(0, 6)
	2	(4, 0)	(3, 5)	(3, 1)
	3	(6, 2)	(−1, 8)	(7, 1)
	4	(1, 6)	(8, −1)	(2, 5)

(iv)

		1	2	3	4
A	1	(3, 5)	(5, 3)	(8, 0)	(0, 8)
	2	(5, 3)	(8, 0)	(2, 6)	(6, 2)
	3	(5, 3)	(1, 7)	(3, 5)	(7, 1)

M2 Calculate μ and v for the following 2×2 zero-sum games, and hence decide whether they have stable solutions:

(i) $\begin{bmatrix} 2 & 5 \\ 7 & 1 \end{bmatrix}$ (ii) $\begin{bmatrix} -3 & 5 \\ 2 & -4 \end{bmatrix}$ (iii) $\begin{bmatrix} 7 & 1 \\ 3 & 2 \end{bmatrix}$ (iv) $\begin{bmatrix} 5 & -2 \\ 2 & 1 \end{bmatrix}$

M3 For each game in Exercise M2, determine the optimum strategy for each player, using the graphical technique for games without stable solutions.

M4 For each of the following zero-sum games determine which have stable
solutions and for these state the optimum strategy for each player.

(i) $\begin{bmatrix} 5 & -3 \\ 2 & 1 \\ -1 & 3 \end{bmatrix}$ (ii) $\begin{bmatrix} 0 & 1 & -3 & -3 \\ 2 & 3 & -2 & 3 \end{bmatrix}$

(iii) $\begin{bmatrix} 3 & -1 & 1 \\ -1 & 3 & 1 \end{bmatrix}$ (iv) $\begin{bmatrix} 2 & -1 & -2 \\ 1 & 0 & 1 \\ -2 & -1 & 2 \end{bmatrix}$

(v) $\begin{bmatrix} 5 & 4 & 6 \\ 3 & 4 & 8 \\ 6 & 5 & 2 \end{bmatrix}$ (vi) $\begin{bmatrix} 0 & 7 & 5 \\ 4 & 5 & 4 \\ 1 & 2 & 3 \end{bmatrix}$

(vii) $\begin{bmatrix} -3 & 0 & 2 \\ 1 & -2 & 0 \\ 0 & 3 & -1 \end{bmatrix}$

M5 For the first two of the games in Exercise M4 which do not have stable
solutions, convert to a linear programming problem, and use the simplex
method to obtain the optimum strategy for Player A for each game.

5

PLANAR GRAPHS

5.1 INTRODUCTION

In this chapter we introduce the subject of Graph Theory, and show that many practical situations can be modelled by what is called a Planar Graph.

We begin by looking at a problem that entertained the citizens of Konigsberg at the beginning of the fifteenth century (Fig. 5.1). The city was part of East Prussia and was divided into four parts by the River Pregal, the parts being joined together by seven bridges. It was said that for their Sunday afternoon walks the citizens of Konigsberg entertained themselves by trying to find a route crossing each bridge exactly once, and returning to their starting point (Fig. 5.2). Try as they might, no one could find such a route; but not until the prolific Swiss mathematician Leonhard Euler (1707–1783) solved the problem could it be conclusively stated that it was indeed impossible to find such a route.

We can easily understand Euler's proof if we represent the problem by a *graph*. We label the four land areas as A, B, C and D (see Fig. 5.2) and these become the *vertices* of our graph. The bridges between the land areas become the *arcs* (*or edges*) of the graph. Such a graph representation is shown in Fig. 5.3. The problem now is to start at any vertex and pass along every arc once and only once before returning to the starting point.

See if you can find such a path.

It should not take you long to realise that it cannot be done. If we arrive at one of the vertices, then we must also leave it. Now the total number of arcs incident at a vertex must be *even* otherwise we would have to repeat an arc. For the Konigsberg bridge graph each vertex is *odd*, and so clearly no

107

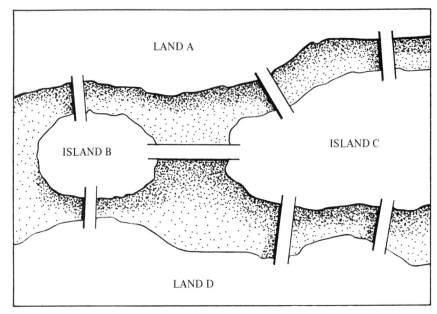

Fig. 5.1

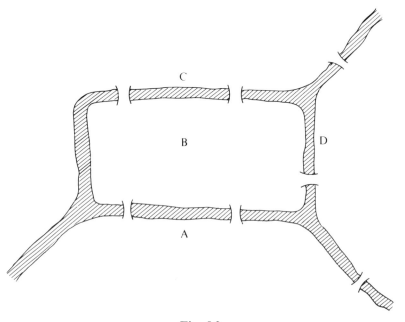

Fig. 5.2

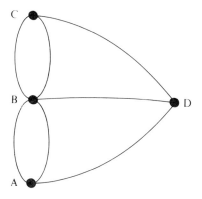

Fig. 5.3

suitable route exists. The second time we arrive at a vertex we must leave it along an arc already travelled along.

The city of Konisgsberg is now part of the Soviet Union and has been renamed Koningrad. Also, bombing during the 1939–1945 War has resulted in only four of the original bridges surviving.

This is one example of the use of the properties of graphs to solve a problem, a second more modern illustration concerns electronics. In micro-electronic circuits, such as the 'silicon chip', electronic 'components' are connected by 'channels' which conduct electricity. These channels must not cross since this would lead to undesirable electrical contact at the crossing points. In many circuits 'crossing points' cannot be avoided so the complete circuit is arranged in layers, each of which has no crossing points.

Electrical circuits can be represented diagrammatically by means of a *graph*.

The graph in Fig. 5.4 consists of six vertices, labelled A to F, representing the components, joined by arcs (or edges) representing the channels along

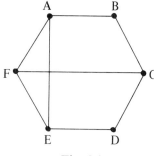

Fig. 5.4

which the electricity flows. Unfortunately the arcs AE and FC cross, but in this case the problem can easily be solved by 'bending' the arc AE around F.

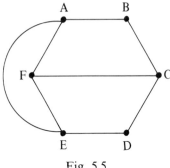

Fig. 5.5

The vertices remain connected as before but no crossing point occurs. Because Fig. 5.4 can be drawn in the plane with no arc crossing, it is called a *planar graph*.

Planar graphs can be defined as graphs which can be redrawn in the plane so that no arcs cross.

Graphs in which every vertex is *connected* (by an arc) to each of the other vertices are called *complete* graphs. Figure 5.6 is an example of a complete graph called K_5 (because there are five vertices). Is K_5 planar? Try to redraw K_5 yourself as a planar graph! You will find that you will always be left with one crossing, as in Fig. 5.7.

Exercise 1.1 Can you find a route crossing every bridge just once for the city shown in Fig. 5.8?

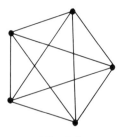

Fig. 5.6

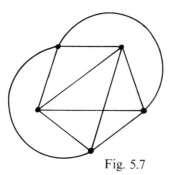

Fig. 5.7

Exercise 1.2 For Konigsberg is it possible to find a route starting from A, B, C or D, which passes through each of the land areas once and only once, returning to the starting point?

Exercise 1.3 For the city illustrated in Fig. 5.8 can you find a route starting from one of the land parts which passes through each of the land areas once and only once, returning to the starting point?

Exercise 1.4 Draw the graphs K_2, K_4 and K_6.

Exercise 1.5 How many arcs have K_2, K_3 and K_9? In terms of n how many arcs has K_n.

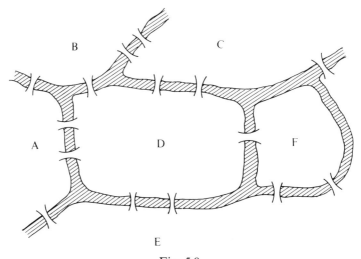

Fig. 5.8

Exercise 1.6   Show that the following graphs are planar by redrawing them in a suitable form.

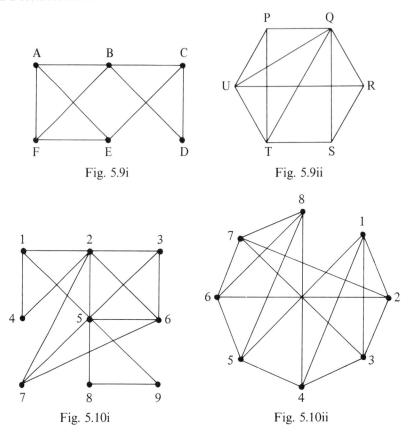

Fig. 5.9i   Fig. 5.9ii

Fig. 5.10i   Fig. 5.10ii

Exercise 1.7   Redraw these graphs with the minimum number of crossing points.

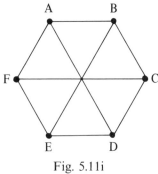

Fig. 5.11i

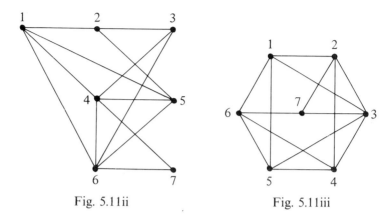

Fig. 5.11ii   Fig. 5.11iii

Exercise 1.8   For which values of n is the complete graph K_n planar?

5.2 BIPARTITE GRAPHS

A bipartite graph is one in which the vertices can be divided into two subsets where no arc connects vertices in the same subset. Figure 5.12 is an example of a bipartite graph. A *complete bipartite graph* denoted by $K_{m,n}$ is a bipartite graph in which every vertex of one subset is connected to each of the vertices of the other subset. The following diagrams (Fig. 5.13) give examples of complete bipartite graphs.

Exercise 2.1   Draw the graphs $K_{4,3}$, $K_{2,1}$, and $K_{5,2}$.

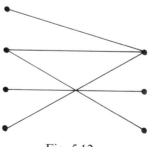

Fig. 5.12

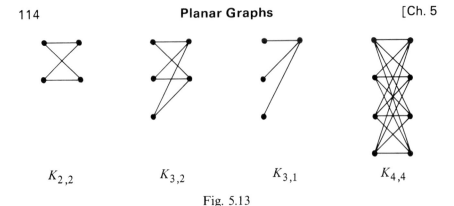

$$K_{2,2} \qquad K_{3,2} \qquad K_{3,1} \qquad K_{4,4}$$

Fig. 5.13

Exercise 2.2 In terms of n, how many arcs has $K_{n,n}$?

Exercise 2.3 Three houses (A, B, C) have to be connected to outlets for gas, electricity and water (G, E, W) as shown in Fig. 5.14. What is the name of the graph depicting this situation?

It is required that no pipe or cable cross. By attempting to redraw the graph as a planar graph try to solve this problem.

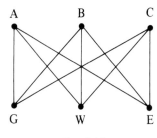

Fig. 5.14

5.3 A PLANARITY ALGORITHM

For simple graphs we can easily decide if a graph is planar or not by 'trial and error'. Electrical circuits and their associated graphs are in general very complicated. In this section we describe an algorithm which uses the concept of bipartite graphs to decide if a graph is planar or not.

To illustrate how the algorithm works consider this graph:

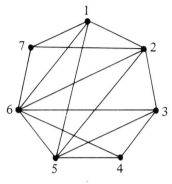

Fig. 5.15

Step 1 Starting at any vertex choose a path which passes through each vertex ending at the original vertex and which crosses no other arc. Such a path is called *a cycle*. In this case an obvious cycle is 1-2-3-4-5-6-7-1.

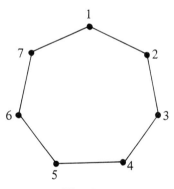

Fig. 5.16

Step 2 Choose any arc in the original graph which is not included in the cycle, for example, the arc 2-5.

List any other arcs not in the cycle which cross the arc 2-5. These arcs are 3-5 and 4-6. Now begin to construct a bipartite graph by placing the first arc (2-5) on one side as a vertex and the list of arcs which cross it (3-5 and 4-6) on the other side. Arcs which cross are

Fig. 5.17

termed *incompatible* and the lines in the bipartite graph show which arcs are incompatible for our problem.

Step 3 Choose one of the vertices on the right-hand side of the bipartite graph, say 4–6.

From the original graph list any arcs (not in the cycle) which are incompatible with (i.e. crossing) the arc 4–6. These are 2–5, 3–5 and 1–5. Insert 3–5 and 1–5 on the opposite side of the bipartite graph to 4–6 (2–5 is already there!) and draw arcs to show that 4–6 is incompatible with 3–5 and 1–5.

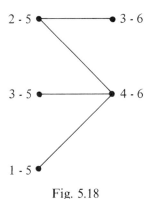

Fig. 5.18

The bipartite graph is thus beginning to show

(a) arcs on the left-hand side which are compatible with each other (i.e. do not cross each other);

(b) arcs on the right-hand side which are compatible with each other, and

(c) emphasising with lines which members of the left-hand set of vertices are incompatible with members of the right-hand side.

Step 4 Choose *any* of the vertices in the bipartite graph which are incompatible with arcs *not* already in the bipartite graph, say 3–6. List any arcs incompatible with this arc. These are 1–5 and 2–5. Place these arcs as vertices on the opposite side to 3–6 of the bipartite graph and draw lines to show their incompatibility with 3–6. (Note 2–5 is already there.)

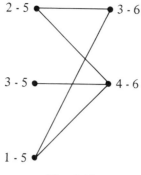

Fig. 5.19

Step 5 Repeat step 4. Choose say 1–5. 1–5 is incompatible with 2–7, 2–6, 3–6 and 4–6. Continue repeating step 4 until all arcs of the original graph (not in the cycle) occur in the bipartite graph. Choose 2–7. This crosses 1–6 and 1–5. Since in this case there are eight arcs in the original graph which are not in the cycle and there are now eight

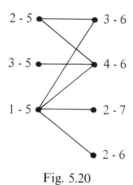

Fig. 5.20

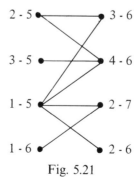

Fig. 5.21

vertices in the bipartite graph, step 4 need be repeated no longer. At this stage if a bipartite graph has been constructed then the original graph is planar.

Step 6 The planar graph can now be drawn. All arcs of one side of the bipartite graph are drawn 'inside' the cycle, and the other set of arcs is drawn 'outside' the cycle. In this case the arcs 2–5, 3–5, 1–5 and 1–6 are inside the cycle, and the arcs 3–6, 4–6, 2–7 and 2–6 are outside (see Fig. 5.22).

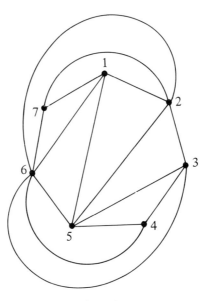

Fig. 5.22

Notes on the use of the algorithm

1. It may not be possible to draw a cycle through each vertex as required in step 1; in which case the algorithm will not work. There are alternative approaches to such graphs but we do not describe any here.

2. If a cycle can be found, but it is one which crosses other arcs of the graph, then the graph has to be completely redrawn so that the cycle does not cross any arcs. In general this is rather difficult.

3. If at some point in constructing the bipartite graph it is necessary to draw a line between vertices on the same side of the graph, then the original graph must be non-planar.

4. It may occur during the construction of the bipartite graph that there are no vertices in the bipartite graph which can be used for step 4. In this case simply choose *any* arc not yet in the bipartite graph, and not in the cycle, and continue on either side of the bipartite graph with step 4.

5. An arc which does not cross any other and is not included in the cycle will not appear in the bipartite graph. It can safely be ignored but must be included in the planar drawing of the graph.

6. The algorithm does not in general produce unique results. The resulting planar graph depends on which 'side' of the bipartite graph is chosen to go 'inside' the cycle, and also on the arcs chosen in steps 3, 4 and 5.

We illustrate note 3 by working through the algorithm for the following graph.

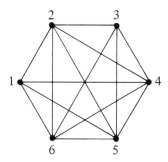

Fig. 5.23

Step 1 Choose the cycle 1–2–3–4–5–6–1

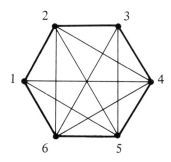

Fig. 5.24

Step 2 Choose the arc 2–5. The arcs which cross this one are 1–4, 3–6 and
4–6.

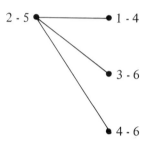

Fig. 5.25

Step 3 Choose an arc on the right-hand side, 1–4 say. The arcs which cross
1–4 are 2–6, 3–5 and 3–6.

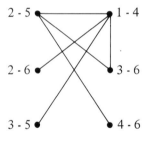

Fig. 5.26

Because 1–4 is connected to 3–6 the graph is non-planar—note 3. We
would have to draw a line between vertices on the same side of the
bipartite graph.

Use the algorithm in the following exercises.

Exercise 3.1 By choosing the cycle 1–2–3–4–5–6–1 and beginning with the
arc 1–4, perform the planarity algorithm to show that this graph is planar.
Use the bipartite graph formed to redraw the graph as a plane drawing.

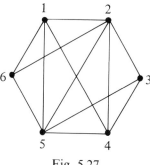

Fig. 5.27

Exercise 3.2 Perform the planarity algorithm on the following graphs to decide which are planar. Redraw the graphs which are planar as plane drawings.

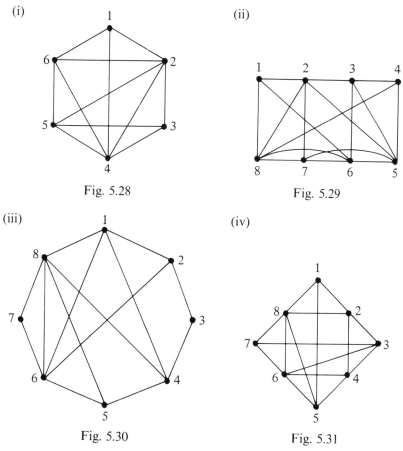

(i)

Fig. 5.28

(ii)

Fig. 5.29

(iii)

Fig. 5.30

(iv)

Fig. 5.31

Exercise 3.3 K_5 and $K_{3,3}$ are known to be non-planar. Use the planarity algorithm to confirm this.

Exercise 3.4   By redrawing the graph in Fig. 5.32 find a cycle through all the vertices which crosses no arc. Use the planarity algorithm to find a plane drawing of the graph.

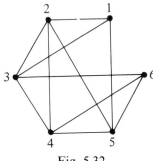

Fig. 5.32

5.4   SOME DEFINITIONS

The Planarity Algorithm is a means of not only showing that a graph is planar (or non-planar) but also indicates how a plane drawing of a graph can be made. Sometimes it is only necessary to decide whether a graph is planar or non-planar, and in the following sections we introduce tests for planarity. Although these tests do not indicate how a plane drawing should be made, they are very powerful tests, especially for large complicated graphs. First we define some further terms.

Formally *a graph* consists of a set of elements called *vertices*, and a list of unordered pairs of these elements called *arcs*. A *simple* graph is one in which there are no *multiple arcs or loops*. In Figs. 5.33 and 5.34, graph *G* is a simple graph whereas graph *H* is not simple.

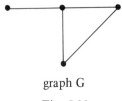

graph G

Fig. 5.33

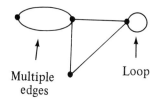

graph H

Fig. 5.34

A *connected graph* is one in which there is a path from every vertex to each of the others. Graphs *G* and *H* above are connected whereas the graph in Fig. 5.35 is not connected. Vertex A in this graph is called an *isolated* vertex. A *subgraph* is a part of a graph which is itself a graph. The subgraph of the graph in Fig. 5.36 is a non-connected subgraph.

A connected graph which contains no cycles is called *a tree*. The graph in Fig. 5.37 is an example of a tree.

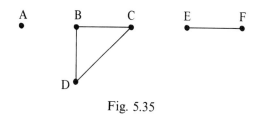

Fig. 5.35

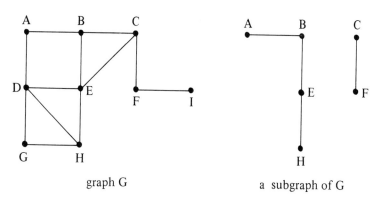

graph G   a subgraph of G

Fig. 5.36

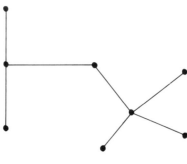

Fig. 5.37

A *spanning tree* of a graph is a subgraph which includes all the vertices of the original graph and is also a tree. Figure 5.38 shows two graphs and their spanning trees. Note that a graph can have more than one spanning tree (see Exercise 4.4).

If a graph is planar then any plane drawing divides the plane into regions called *faces*. One of the faces has no boundary and is called the *infinite face*.

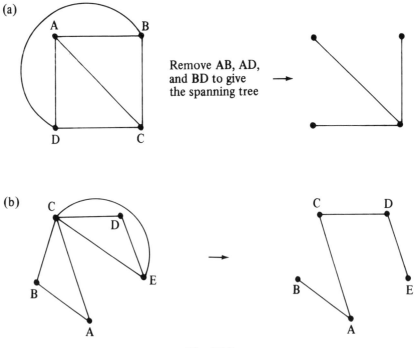

Fig. 5.38

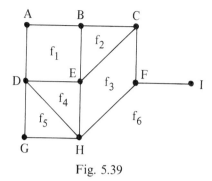

Fig. 5.39

The graph in Fig. 5.39 has six faces labelled $f_1, f_2, \ldots, f_6$, of which f_6 is the infinite face. The *degree of a vertex* is the number of arcs incident with the vertex. For example, A is a vertex of degree 2 denoted by deg A = 2, E is a vertex of degree 4 and I is a vertex of degree 1. The *degree of a face* is the number of arcs bounding the face. f_1 has degree 4 and is denoted by deg $f_1 = 4$, face 2 has degree 3 and face 6 has degree 9 (note FI is counted twice).

For a *connected planar* graph there is a simple relationship between the number of arcs, faces and vertices, originally found by the Swiss mathematician Leonhard Euler. The relationship, known as Euler's formula, is

$$v - e + f = 2$$

where v is the number of vertices, e is the number of arcs and f is the number of faces. For example, consider Fig. 5.40 which has 3 faces (one of which is an infinite face), 6 arcs and 5 vertices. Then

$$v - e + f = 5 - 6 + 3 = 2.$$

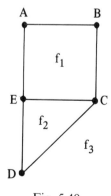

Fig. 5.40

Exercise 4.1   Which of these statements describes each of the graphs in Fig. 5.41 below?

(i) The graph is simple and connected.
(ii) The graph is simple but not connected.
(iii) The graph is connected but not simple.
(iv) The graph is not simple and not connected.

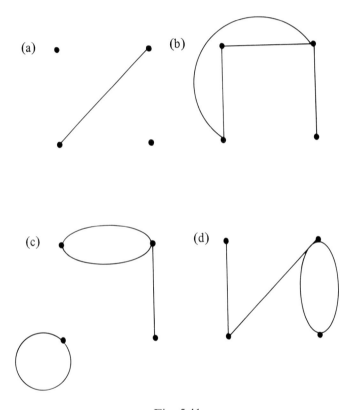

Fig. 5.41

Exercise 4.2   For each of the graphs in Fig. 5.42 below.

(i) State the number of faces and label them $f_1, f_2, \ldots$
(ii) State the degree of each face.
(iii) State the degree of each vertex.

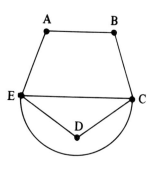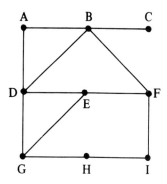

Fig. 5.42

Exercise 4.3   Redraw the graph in Fig. 5.43 as a planar graph, and find the sum of the degrees of all the faces.

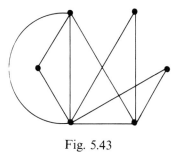

Fig. 5.43

Exercise 4.4   Draw the spanning trees of the following graph (Fig. 5.44).

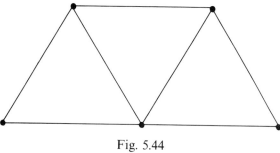

Fig. 5.44

Exercise 4.5   Show that Euler's formula holds for the graph below.

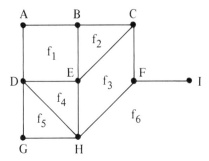

5.5   EULER'S FORMULA

Euler's formula introduced in the last section can be proved by reducing a planar graph to a spanning tree.

Theorem   For a connected planar graph, the number of vertices v, faces f and arcs e satisfies the formula $v - e + f = 2$.

Proof
We will illustrate the steps in the proof by looking at the following graph (Fig. 5.45).
   Consider any simple, connected planar graph G. Reduce G to a spanning tree. For the example we have a spanning tree (Fig. 5.46). It is obvious that in this and any other case the spanning tree has only one (infinite) face. Also a spanning tree always has one fewer number of arcs than vertices. Thus $f = 1$

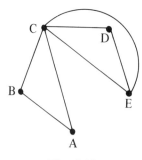

Fig. 5.45

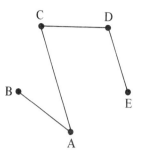

Fig. 5.46

and $v - e = 1$ so that $v - e + f = 2$. Euler's formula is therefore true for a spanning tree.

Suppose that now one of the original arcs is added to the spanning tree; the number of faces will increase by 1, since a new arc must split an existing face into 2. The number of arcs will increase by 1 whilst the number of vertices remains the same. In the example we add the arc BC.

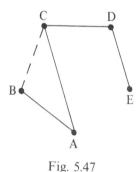

Fig. 5.47

It is obvious that Euler's formula remains true when one arc is added since now

$$f = 1 + 1 = 2 \quad \text{and} \quad v - e = 1 - 1 = 0 \quad \text{so that } v - e + f = 2 + 0 = 2.$$

Thus arcs can be continually added until the graph becomes the original graph G and Euler's formula remains true at each stage. So by induction Euler's formula is proved for the general case.

Exercise 5.1 The graphs in Fig. 5.48 are planar. Show that Euler's formula holds in each case.

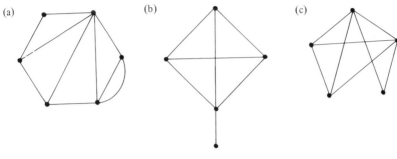

Fig. 5.48

Exercise 5.2 There are five regular solids known as Platonic solids. The three simplest, the tetrahedron, cube and octahedron, are shown in Fig. 5.49 below. (The other two are are known as the dodecahedron and icosahedron.) By drawing each as a planar graph show that Euler's formula is true for these Platonic solids.

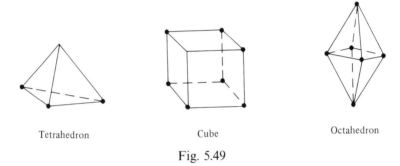

Tetrahedron   Cube   Octahedron

Fig. 5.49

Exercise 5.3 The graph in Fig. 5.50 is not simple but is connected as required by Euler's theorem. Verify that Euler's formula holds for this graph.

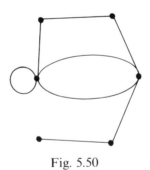

Fig. 5.50

Exercise 5.4 Verify Euler's formula for K_2 and $K_{3,2}$.

5.6   THE HANDSHAKING THEOREM FOR PLANAR GRAPHS

The theorem states: The sum of all the degrees of the faces of a connected planar graph is equal to twice the number of arcs. This result can be written as $\sum \deg f = 2e$.

Proof
Since each arc either borders two different faces or will border an infinite face twice, it must contribute 2 to the sum of the number of degrees of the faces. Hence the result. For example, in Fig. 5.51 there are 10 arcs and 4 faces.

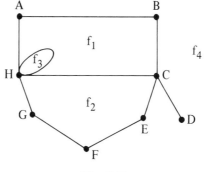

Fig. 5.51

We have

$$\deg f_1 + \deg f_2 + \deg f_3 + \deg f_4 = 5 + 5 + 1 + 9 = 20 = 2e.$$

Exercise 6.1   Show that the handshaking theorem is true for the graphs in Fig. 5.52.

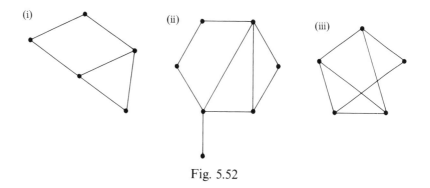

Fig. 5.52

Exercise 6.2   Make a plane drawing of the complete bipartite graph $K_{2,5}$ and verify the handshaking theorem and Euler's formula for this graph. Show with a suitable drawing that $K_{2,n}$ is planar for all values of n and verify the handshaking theorem.

Exercise 6.3   An alternative version of the handshaking theorem is: The sum of all the degrees of the vertices of a connected planar graph is equal to twice the number of arcs. Prove this statement. Show that this form of the theorem holds for each of the graphs in Exercise 6.1.

5.7   TESTS FOR PLANARITY

The handshaking theorem is normally used in conjunction with Euler's formula to show that a graph is non-planar. Be careful though, it cannot be assumed that if the handshaking theorem is true then the graph must be planar.

Example   Show that K_5 is non-planar.

Solution   In the introduction an attempt was made to make a plane drawing of K_5. It failed. Now we use Euler's formula and the handshaking theorem to show that K_5 is non-planar. We use a contradiction argument. Suppose that K_5 is planar.

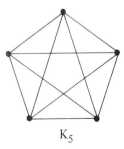

K_5

Fig. 5.53

Then $v = 5$ and $e = 10$. So using Euler's formula we have

$$v - e + f = 2,$$

solving for f,

$$f = 7.$$

Each face must have at least three arcs bordering it, so that the sum of degrees of faces $\geqslant 3f$. Thus by the handshaking theorem,

$$2e \geqslant 3f.$$

Now $e = 10$, so that

$$20 \geqslant 3f \quad \text{or} \quad f \leqslant 20/3.$$

But if the graph is planar Euler's formula gives $f = 7$, and this contradicts $f \leqslant 20/3$. Hence the original assumption that K_5 is planar is false. Thus K_5 is non-planar.

Exercise 7.1 Show that for the graphs in Fig. 5.54 both Euler's formula and the handshaking theorem are true.

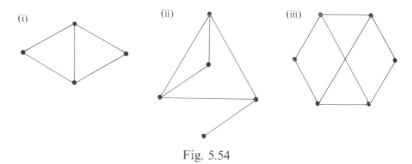

Fig. 5.54

Exercise 7.2 Prove that $K_{3,3}$ is non-planar. (*Hint:* adapt the proof in the example that K_5 is non-planar.)

Exercise 7.3 Prove that the graph G, Fig. 5.55, is non-planar.

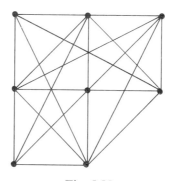

Fig. 5.55

Exercise 7.4 A part of a graph G is non-planar. Show that G is itself non-planar. (*Hint:* add arcs to the non-planar subgraph).

Exercise 7.5 If G is a planar simple graph show that

$$e \leqslant 3v - 6.$$

Exercise 7.6   If G is a planar simple graph whose shortest cycle has length n (i.e. the number of arcs in the shortest cycle is n), show that

$$e \leqslant n(v - 2)/(n - 2).$$

Exercise 7.7   Under what conditions do the inequalities in Exercises 7.5 and 7.6 become equalities.

5.8   BOUNDS ON THE NUMBER OF ARCS IN PLANAR GRAPHS

If n is the length of the shortest cycle in a connected graph then there are two inequalities which govern the number of arcs that are possible in a planar graph.

A Lower Bound

A connected graph is planar if and only if $2e \geqslant nf$ or $e \geqslant nf/2$. This result can be deduced from the handshaking theorem.

An Upper Bound

If a connected graph is planar then $e \leqslant n(v - 2)/(n - 2)$ (see Exercise 7.6). This result is more useful than the lower bound on e; unfortunately it does *not* imply that if $e \leqslant n(v - 2)/(n - 2)$ then the graph is planar. It is usually used to show that a graph is non-planar. The result can be rewritten in the following more useful way: For a connected graph with shortest cycle of length n, if $e > n(v - 2)/(n - 2)$ then the graph is non-planar. If this inequality holds then a graph is certainly non-planar; but note that for some non-planar graphs the inequality is false.

Example   Show that K_s is non-planar using the upper bound formula.

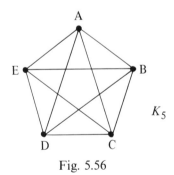

Fig. 5.56

Solution

For K_5, $e = 10$, $n = 3$ (take the cycle ABCA) and $v = 5$. Then $n(v - 2)/(n - 2) = 9$. Thus $e > n(v - 2)/(n - 2)$ and K_5 is non-planar.

Exercise 8.1 Show that for each graph in Fig. 5.57, the number of arcs exceeds the upper bound for a planar graph and therefore each graph is non-planar.

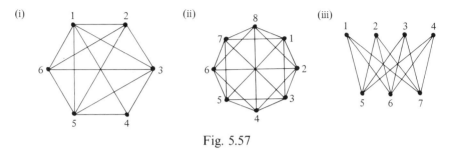

Fig. 5.57

Exercise 8.2 Prove that $K_{3,3}$ is non-planar by showing that its number of arcs exceeds the upper bound for it to be planar.

Exercise 8.3 Prove that the Petersen graph (Fig. 5.58) is non-planar.

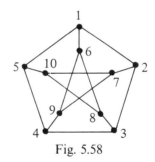

Fig. 5.58

Exercise 8.4 This graph (Fig. 5.59) is non-planar. Show that the inequality $e < n(v - 2)/(n - 2)$ is true. Use the planarity algorithm to show that the graph is non-planar.

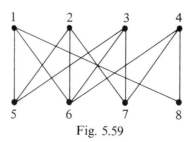

Fig. 5.59

Exercise 8.5 What is the shortest cycle length of the complete bipartite graphs $K_{r,r}$ where $r \geqslant 3$? How many arcs has $K_{r,r}$? Show that $K_{r,r}$ is always non-planar for $r \geqslant 3$.

5.9 KURATOWSKI'S THEOREM

If we take any planar graph and insert new vertices of degree 2 only along arcs of the graph then the graph will remain planar. The result of inserting vertices in this way is called *a subdivision* of the original graph. For example, in Fig. 5.60, K_4 has been subdivided to form various subdivisions. Since every

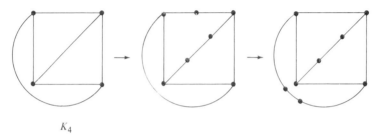

K_4

Fig. 5.60

subdivision of a planar graph is planar *every subdivision of a non-planar graph is non-planar*. For example, K_5 is non-planar and this is a non-planar subdivision of it. Also, it follows from the result in Exercise 7.4 that *if a subgraph of a graph is non-planar then the graph is non-planar*.

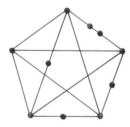

Fig. 5.61

Suppose a graph G contains (as a subgraph) a subdivision of either of the non-planar graphs K_5 or $K_{3,3}$ then the above observations imply that the original graph G must be non-planar.

In fact, the Polish mathematician Kuratowski proved that *all* non-planar graphs contain subgraphs which are subdivisions of K_5 or $K_{3,3}$. This important result is the basis of Kuratowski's theorem.

Kuratowski's Theorem

A graph is planar if and only if it does not contain K_5, $K_{3,3}$ or a subdivision of K_5 or $K_{3,3}$ as a subgraph.

More usually the theorem is used to show that a graph is non-planar and is stated as: A graph is non-planar if and only if it contains K_5, $K_{3,3}$ or a subdivision of K_5 or $K_{3,3}$ as a subgraph. For example, the graph G is non-planar because it contains a subdivision of K_5 as the subgraph G'. Check carefully and you will see that the graph G' is a subgraph of G. Arc BE has been omitted to form the subgraph and E subdivides K_5.

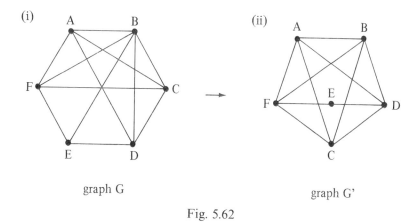

graph G   graph G'

Fig. 5.62

Exercise 9.1   Which of the graphs in Fig. 5.63 are subdivisions of $K_{3,2}$?

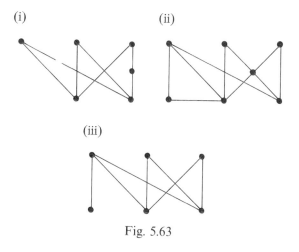

Fig. 5.63

Exercise 9.2 Which of the graphs in Fig. 5.64 (a) contains a subgraph which is K_5 and/or a subdivision of K_5 (b) contains neither K_5 nor a subdivision of K_5 as a subgraph?

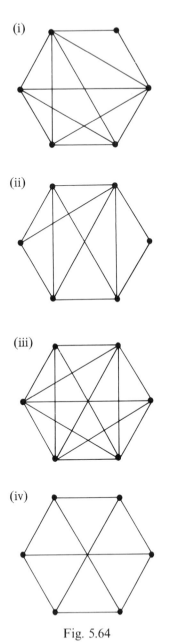

(i)

(ii)

(iii)

(iv)

Fig. 5.64

Exercise 9.3   Show that the graphs in Fig. 5.65 are non-planar because they contain subgraphs which are subdivisions of K_5 or $K_{3,3}$.

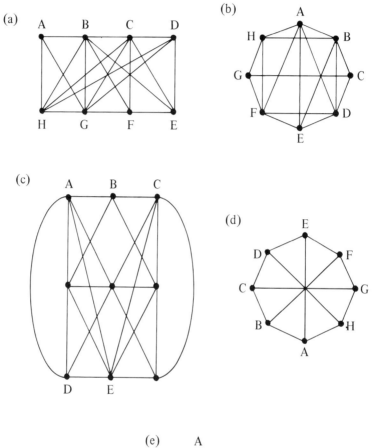

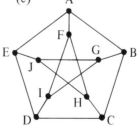

Petersen graph

Fig. 5.65

Exercise 9.4   Use Kuratowski's theorem to prove that all complete graphs K_n where $n \geqslant 5$, are non-planar.

Exercise 9.5   Prove that all complete bipartite graphs $K_{r,s}$ are non-planar where $r, s \geqslant 3$.

Exercise 9.6   In this graph (Fig. 5.66) the vertices are connected if and only if their numbers are relatively prime. It is labelled as P_7. Use Kuratowski's theorem to show that this graph is non-planar. Draw the graph P_6. Is this graph planar?

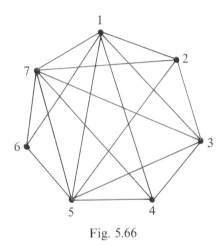

Fig. 5.66

5.10   THICKNESS OF A CONNECTED GRAPH

The original problem was to decide whether an electrical circuit was planar, and we now have a variety of techniques to test whether graphs are planar or non-planar. Suppose now that a circuit design is known to be non-planar, then it can still be produced with no 'crossing' wires if it is built up in layers. For example, the Petersen graph (see Exercise 9.3(e)) can be drawn with two layers and no crossing arcs as shown in Fig. 5.67 below. The minimum number of layers of planar graphs needed in order to have no crossings in a non-planar graph is called the *thickness* of a graph. There is no known formula which gives a value for the thickness of a graph; however, a lower bound is obtainable which often gives the correct result. The inequalities given below for the thickness involve the use of two symbols $[x]$ and $\{x\}$. $[x]$ is the largest integer not greater than x; for example, $[3.6] = 3$. $\{x\}$ is the

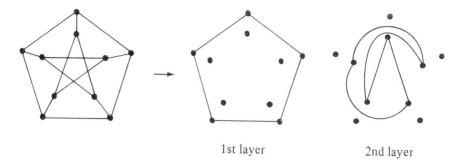

1st layer   2nd layer

Each vertex is connected to its corresponding
vertex in the other layer.

Fig. 5.67

smallest integer not less than x; for example, $\{3.6\} = 4$. It can also be shown
that for rational numbers

$$\left\{\frac{x}{y}\right\} = \left[\frac{x}{y} + \frac{y-1}{y}\right]$$

for example

$$\left\{\frac{5}{2}\right\} = \left[\frac{5}{2} + \frac{1}{2}\right] = [3] = 3.$$

Let $t(G)$ be the thickness of a simple graph G, then

$$t(G) \geqslant \left\{\frac{e}{3v-6}\right\}$$

If G is a simple graph with shortest cycle of length n, this inequality becomes

$$t(G) \geqslant \left\{\frac{e(n-2)}{n(v-2)}\right\}$$

As an example consider the graph K_8. Then using the first inequality with
$e = 28$ (see Exercise 1.5) and $v = 8$.

$$t(G) \geqslant \{28/(24 - 6)\} = \{28/18\} = 2$$

Thus $t(G) \geqslant 2$. (Note that $t(G)$ must be an integer.) K_8 therefore needs at least
two layers of planar graphs in order to be drawn without crossings. Note that
by showing $t(K_8) \geqslant 2$ we have an alternative way of showing that K_8 is
non-planar.

Exercise 10.1   Try to draw each of the non-planar graphs in Fig. 5.68 in two layers.

(a)

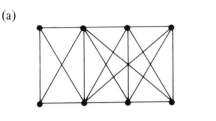

(b)

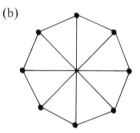

Fig. 5.68

Exercise 10.2   Draw the non-planar graphs K_6 and $K_{4,4}$ in two layers.

Exercise 10.3   Find (i) [4.2]
(ii) $\{0.6\}$
(iii) $[-1.5]$
(iv) $\{1\}$

Exercise 10.4   Show that

$$\{x\} = -[-x]$$

Exercise 10.5   Show that

$$\left\{\frac{a}{a+1}\right\} = \left[\frac{2a}{a+1}\right]$$

Exercise 10.6   Find a lower bound for the thickness of the graphs in Fig. 5.69.

(i)

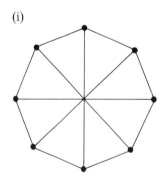

(ii)

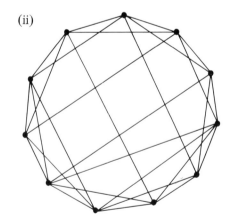

Fig. 5.69

Exercise 10.7   Find a lower bound for the thickness of K_6, K_{20} and $K_{30,30}$.

Exercise 10.8   Find the smallest value of n for which K_n has a thickness of lower bound more than 3.

Exercise 10.9   Show that if a solid has triangular faces and n vertices then $t(G) \geqslant 1$.

5.11   SUMMARY

Six important results listed below occur in this chapter for connected (not necessarily simple) graphs.

1. The planarity algorithm
2. Euler's formula for planar graphs
3. The handshaking theorem for planar graphs } used together
4. An upper bound on the number of arcs of a planar graph.
5. Kuratowski's theorem.
6. The thickness $t(G)$ of a non-planar graph G.

In order to show that a graph is planar the planarity algorithm is the only option available. It has the additional advantage that the resulting bipartite graph shows how a plane drawing of the graph can be made.

Euler's formula and the handshaking theorem, Kuratowski's theorem, and the upper bound on the number of arcs of a planar graph can all be used to show that a graph is non-planar. Although the most powerful test for non-planarity, Kuratowski's theorem is perhaps the most difficult to apply, as in general a large number of subgraphs must be considered.

On knowing that a graph is non-planar the thickness of a graph gives a degree to the non-planarity of the graph. There is no known formula which will give the thickness of a graph so we must be content with a lower bound. However, as noted before, this lower bound often gives the actual thickness.

As a final example we shall look at an electrical circuit.

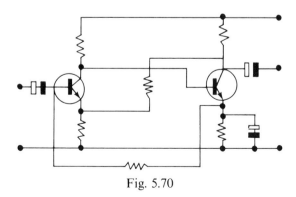

Fig. 5.70

Example   Consider the electrical circuit in Fig. 5.70. Can it be made as a single layer with no crossing wires? If not how many layers are needed and which parts of the circuit need to be put in each layer?

Solution   First the circuit needs to be redrawn as a graph before any analysis can take place.

Junctions marked • obviously become vertices, and wires become arcs. The components may become vertices or arcs depending on their type. A resistor (-ww-) or a capacitor (-| |-), for example, can be treated as arcs, whereas a transistor (⊗) having three wires leaving it must be treated as a vertex of degree 3. The resulting graph is shown in Fig. 5.71. It can be seen that arcs AB

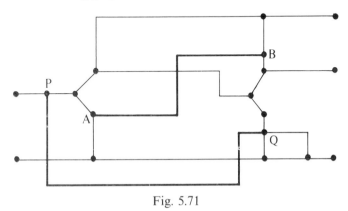

Fig. 5.71

and PQ cross other arcs and if removed the remaining graph would be planar. However, these two arcs cannot both be included in the whole graph if it is to remain planar.

This non-planar graph thus needs to be drawn in two layers, the second layer which can conveniently contain the arcs AB and PQ. These layers are shown below.

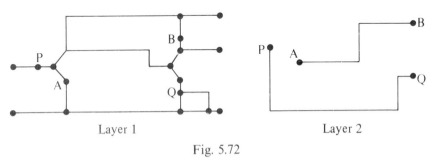

Layer 1   Layer 2

Fig. 5.72

For larger, more complex circuits than this example a computer would be used utilising some of the ideas developed in this chapter.

5.12 MISCELLANEOUS EXERCISES

M1 Show, using the planarity algorithm that the graph *G* is planar and produce a plane drawing of *G*.

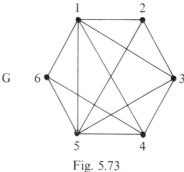

Fig. 5.73

M2 Make a plane drawing of the graph in Fig. 5.74 and verify Euler's theorem and the handshaking theorem for this graph.

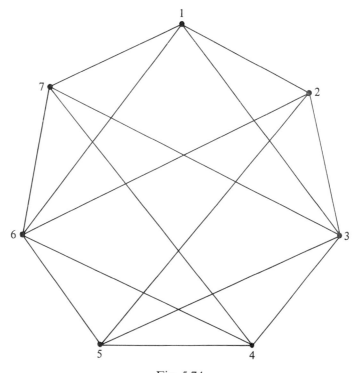

Fig. 5.74

M3 A dodecahedron is a regular solid with 20 vertices and each face is a regular pentagon. Make a plane drawing of this figure and verify Euler's formula for the figure.

M4 Give examples of:
(a) A planar graph in which every face has degree 5.
(b) A non-simple planar graph in which every vertex has degree 4 (the degree of a vertex is the number of arcs incident with it).
(c) A planar graph in which each face has degree 4 and each vertex has degree 3.
(d) A planar graph with eight vertices and a shortest cycle of length 4.

M5 Classify these statements as **true** or **false**. In each case give reasons for your choice.
(a) Every subgraph of a planar graph is planar.
(b) Every graph which has only planar subgraphs is planar.
(c) Every subgraph of a non-planar graph is non-planar.
(d) Every graph which contains a non-planar graph is non-planar.
(e) Every subdivision of a non-planar graph is non-planar.
(f) Every non-planar graph has a subgraph (not itself) which is non-planar.
(g) All non-planar graphs have K_5 or $K_{3,3}$ as subgraphs.
(h) If Euler's formula is true then a graph is planar.

M6 Which of the graphs in Fig. 5.75 are planar? For those which are, find a plane drawing and verify Euler's formula. For those which are not verify Kuratowski's theorem by finding a subgraph which is subdivision of K_5 or $K_{3,3}$.

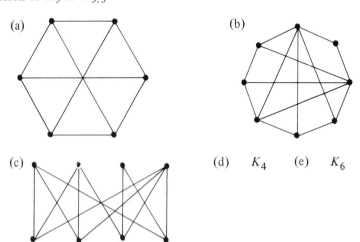

(a)   (b)

(c)   (d) K_4 (e) K_6

Fig. 5.75

M7 For which values of r and s is the complete bipartite graph $K_{r,s}$ planar $(r \leqslant s)$?

M8 Redraw the graph in Fig. 5.76 so that a cycle of length 6 exists which does not cross any arcs of the graph. Use the planarity algorithm to show that the graph is planar and to find a planar drawing.

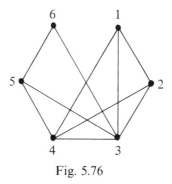

Fig. 5.76

M9 Verify the handshaking theorem for the graphs in Fig. 5.77.

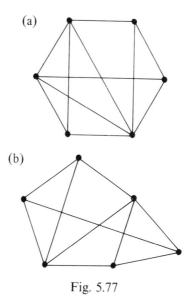

Fig. 5.77

Why is it not possible *to attempt* to verify the handshaking theorem for non-planar graphs?

M10 Find two different spanning trees for the graph in Fig. 5.78.

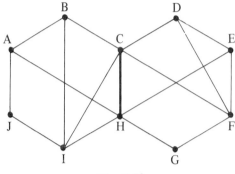

Fig. 5.78

M11 Find two distinct spanning trees of the graph in Fig. 5.79 which together form the original graph (i.e. disjoint spanning trees)

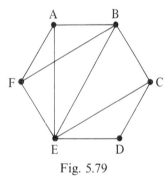

Fig. 5.79

M12 Let G be a simple, connected planar graph with v vertices and e arcs. Show that $e \leqslant 3v - 6$. If G has a shortest cycle of length n show that $e \leqslant n(v - 2)/n - 2$.

    When would the inequality $e \leqslant 3v - 6$ become an equality? (i.e. $e = 3v - 6$).

M13 The degree of a vertex is equal to the number of arcs incident with the vertex. What is the degree of each vertex in (a) K_5 (b) K_n (c) $K_{r,r}$?

M14 By considering vertex degrees of a graph an alternative form of the handshaking theorem for a planar graph can be formed. If each vertex has degree d or more, then $2e \geqslant dv$ or $e \geqslant dv/2$.

    Use this result together with Euler's formula in the form $v - e + f = 2$ to find an inequality giving an upper bound of e in terms of d and f.

M15 Deduce that if G is a simple, connected planar graph then G contains at least one vertex of degree 5 or less. (*Hint:* Use the result of M14 above and the upper bound on $e(\S5)$ with $n = 3$.)

M16 Show that the graph below is non-planar. With suitable diagrams show that the graph in Fig. 5.80 can be drawn as two connected planar graphs on separate layers.

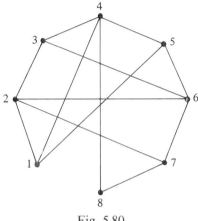

Fig. 5.80

M17 By finding a subgraph which is subdivision of K_5 or $K_{3,3}$ show that the graph in Fig. 5.81 is non-planar.

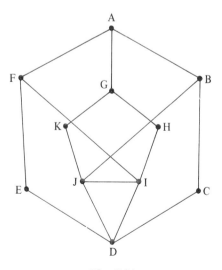

Fig. 5.81

M18 Use the planarity algorithm to show that the graph in Fig. 5.82 is planar. Make a plane drawing and verify Euler's formula for the graph.

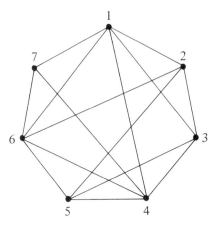

Fig. 5.82

M19 If G is a simple connected planar graph with v vertices, e arcs, and f faces show that if $v < 12$ then G has at least one vertex of degree 4 or less.

M20 The crossing number of a graph G (cr(G)) is an alternative measure of the non-planarity of a graph. It is simply the smallest number of crossings (of arcs) when a graph is drawn in the plane. Find the crossing numbers of (a) K_5 (b) $K_{3,3}$ (c) $K_{6,6}$.

M21 Let G be the graph formed by the vertices, arcs and principal diagonals of a $2n$-sided polygon ($n \geqslant 3$). Show that G is always non-planar. Find cr(G). Find a lower bound on $t(G)$.

M22 Use Kuratowski's theorem to show that the Petersen graph (Fig. 5.29) is non-planar. Find the crossing number of the Petersen graph.

M23 Can K_5 be drawn without crossings (a) on the surface of a sphere (b) on the surface of a torus (doughnut shape!)?

M24 Can K_5 be drawn without crossings (a) in 3-space (b) on the surface of a Möbius band?

M25 Prove Euler's formula for a simply connected planar graph.

M26 Redraw the circuits in Fig. 5.83 on plane drawings.

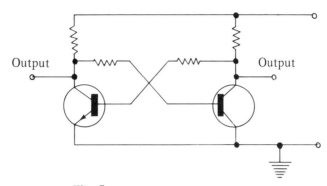

Flip-flop

Fig. 5.83a

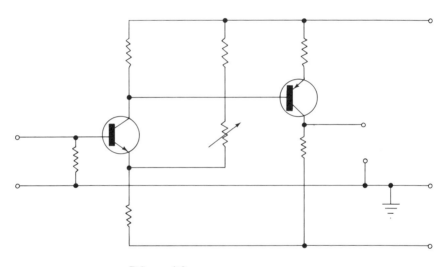

DC amplifier

Fig. 5.83b

6

NETWORKS

6.1 EXAMPLES OF NETWORK PROBLEMS

In this chapter we introduce the idea of a network and show that many practical problems can be reduced to problems in network theory.

We illustrate the ideas by looking at a road system in the East Midlands (with mileages indicated along each road—see Fig. 6.1).

Suppose a leading TV company is setting up a new cable TV network based at Leicester which has connections either direct or indirect to all the towns shown. A possible layout is given in Fig. 6.2. The total length of cable needed is 94 miles. Can you find another layout which uses less total length of cable? If so, what is the shortest total length that could be used? It should not take you too long to find the answer to this problem—which for obvious reasons is called a minimum connector problem. But if we have a more complicated network we need a systematic method of solving the problem. In this example we have used the word 'network' in an everyday sense. For instance, we might think of a television network as a number of transmitters linked by landlines.

In this chapter we give the word *network* a mathematical meaning. We say that *a network* is a *graph* in which each arc (or edge) is assigned a number called *its weight*.

We can represent the road system in Fig. 6.1 by the network shown in Fig. 6.3. Each town is represented by a vertex of the network and the roads connecting the towns are the arcs (or edges) of the network. The weights are the distances between the towns. There are many different systems which may be modelled by network theory.

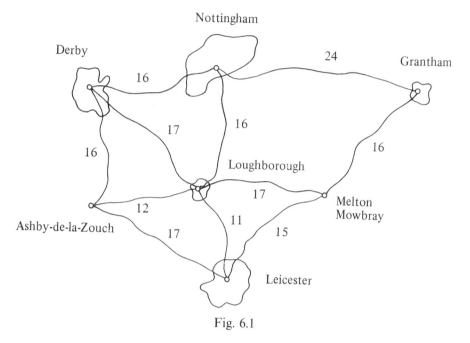

Fig. 6.1

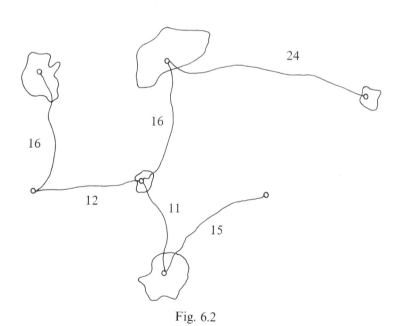

Fig. 6.2

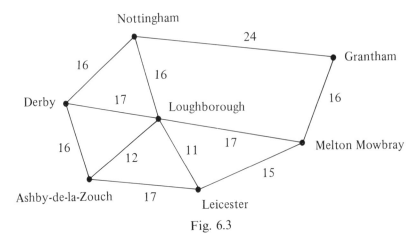

Fig. 6.3

The problem of finding the minimum length of cable is an example of a *minimum connector problem*. We introduce algorithms for such problems in sections 6.4 and 6.5.

In sections 6.2 and 6.3 we investigate a slightly different problem. Suppose we wish to find the shortest route between two particular towns in Fig. 6.1. This is an example of a *shortest path problem*—find the path with the lowest possible total weight. A related problem is the *longest path problem*—find the path with the largest possible total weight.

In sections 6.6 and 6.7 we investigate a class of problems called *the travelling salesman problem*. For example, suppose that you start and finish at Derby (in Fig. 6.1) and each day you have to visit a shop in each of the other towns shown, what is the route that has the minimum total distance?

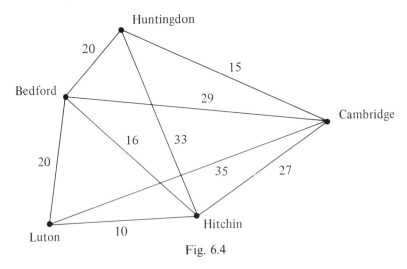

Fig. 6.4

Finally in section 6.8 we consider the problem of travelling along every arc in a network so as to cover the smallest total distance. This is often called 'the Chinese postman problem'—a postman has to deliver mail along all the roads in an area. How can the route be planned so as to cover the least distance?

Exercise 1.1   Cable TV is being piped from Bedford to the towns shown in Fig. 6.4. Find the shortest length of cable needed to connect all the towns to the system.

Exercise 1.2   Fig. 6.5 shows the distances in kilometres between cities along main roads. A new national cable TV company wants to connect all these

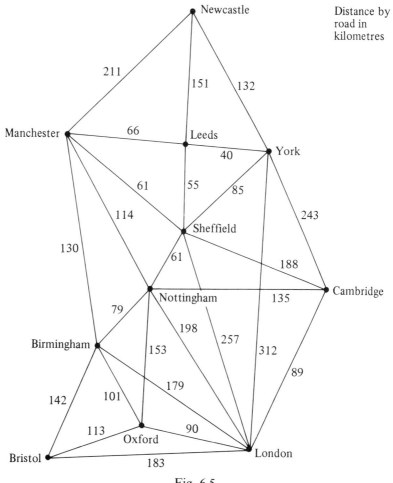

Fig. 6.5

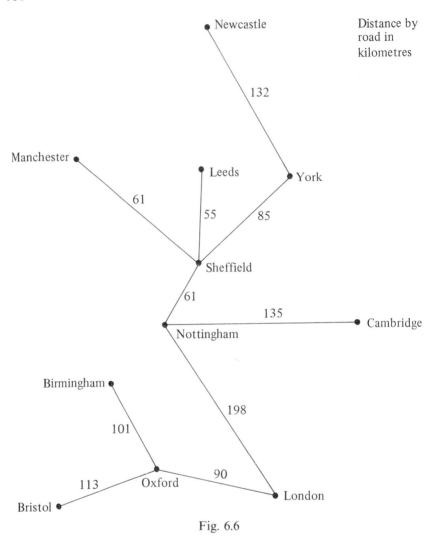

Fig. 6.6

cities to London by laying cables alongside main roads. A possible layout is shown in Fig. 6.6. This uses 1031 km of cable. Can you find a layout which uses less cable?

Exercise 1.3   The road system in Fig. 6.1 is represented by the network in Fig. 6.7. Use the network to find the shortest route between Derby and Grantham.

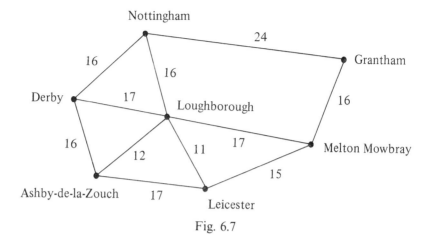

Fig. 6.7

Exercise 1.4   Solve the travelling salesman problem for a shop retailer who lives in Derby, owns a chain of shops in the towns shown in Fig. 6.7 and visits each shop each day.

6.2   SHORTEST PATH ALGORITHM

In Exercise 1.3 you probably used trial and error, investigating different routes through the network, to find the shortest route. In this section we give a more systematic approach developed by E. Dijkstra.

Consider the problem of finding the shortest path from S to T in the network in Fig. 6.8. In this network the weight may denote, for instance, the expenditure in pounds or time in hours. Probably though it will be easiest to think of the weight as a distance. Now in developing the algorithm, we assign a *value* to each vertex as the shortest distance up to that vertex. In this way we find the shortest route through the network in stages. Start at the vertex S; the value at S is 0 and this is shown in a box at S. (Clearly this is the shortest distance from S to itself.)

In the second stage, we assign a number to each vertex connected directly to S equal to the weight of the arc. The vertices A, B, C and D are connected directly to S, so we assign numbers 4, 7, 4 and 2 to these vertices respectively. Now among these we select the least which is 2. So we assign the value 2 to the vertex D—putting it in a box. (See Fig. 6.9). Thus we have found that the shortest distance from S to D is 2 that is the value of D. The next step is to consider all the vertices connected directly to D. These are C and T. Then add

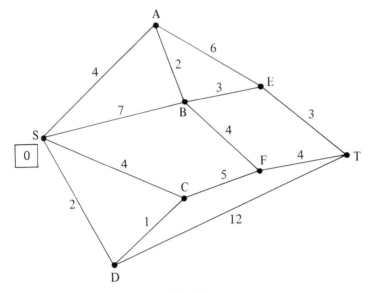

Fig. 6.8

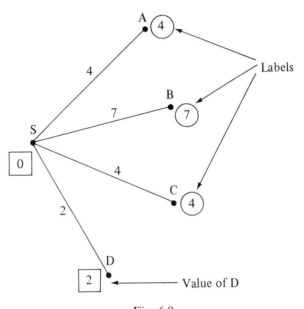

Fig. 6.9

the weight on the connecting arc and assign these numbers to the vertex. So the vertex C is assigned 3 (= value of D + weight on arc DC = 2 + 1) and the vertex T is assigned 14 (= value of D + weight on arc DT = 2 + 12). Now C has two labels assigned to it, 4 (from the last stage in Fig. 6.9) and 3 from this stage. Since 3 is the smaller we cross out the label 4 (i.e. the route S–D–C is shorter than S–C.) We now scan all the unboxed labels of the labelled nodes and select the least. This is at C. We assign the value 3 to the vertex C—this is the shortest distance from S to C. (See Fig. 6.10). A similar procedure is now applied to the vertices connected directly to C; there is only one, F, and this is assigned the label 8 (= value of C + weight on arc CF). Again we scan all the unboxed labels and find that A's (4) is the least and assign to the vertex A the value 4. Figure 6.11 shows the result after this stage. Repeating these steps, the final picture is shown in Fig. 6.12. Every vertex has now been given a value, which is its shortest distance from S.

Finally the shortest path from S to T is found by tracing back from T to S including an arc MN in the route whenever

$$\text{Value of M} + \text{weight on arc MN} = \text{value of N.}$$

Starting at T gives three possible routes ET, FT or DT.

For ET we have: value of E + weight on arc ET = 9 + 3 = 12.
For FT we have: value of F + weight on arc FT = 8 + 4 = 12.
For DT we have: value of D + weight on arc DT = 2 + 12 = 14.

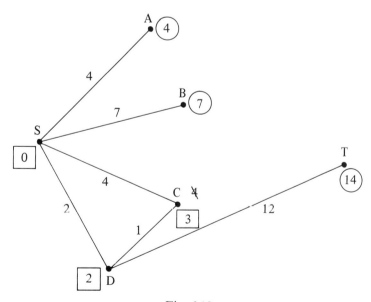

Fig. 6.10

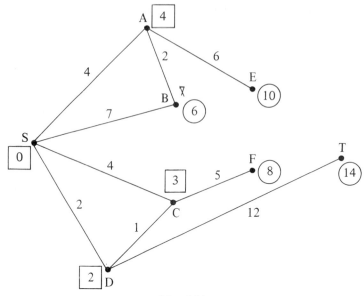

Fig. 6.11

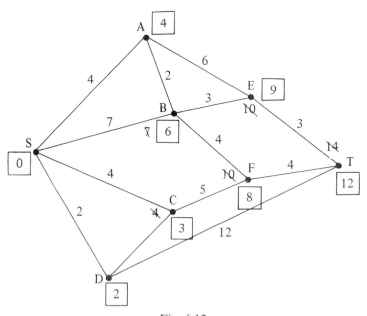

Fig. 6.12

Thus the arc DT is not included, but ET and FT are possible parts of the route.

Repeating the backwards process from E we have BE as a possible part of the route, and the shortest path from S to B is S–A–B. So one shortest path through the network is S–A–B–E–T. Alternatively, for the backwards process from F we have CF as a possible part of the route, and the shortest path from S to C is S–D–C. An alternative shortest path from S to T is S–D–C–F–T. In this case we find that there are two possible shortest paths, S–A–B–E–T and S–D–C–F–T. The first of these is shown in Fig. 6.13.

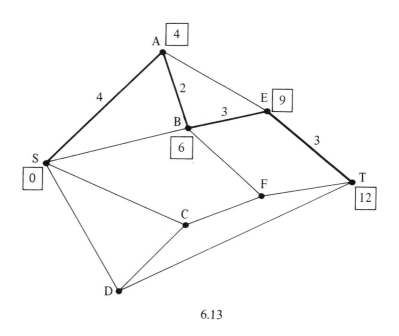

6.13

The shortest path algorithm is summarised in the following five steps:

Step 1 Assign the value 0 to the vertex S.

Step 2 For every vertex M just assigned a value, for every vertex N joined directly to M, assign to N the label = value of M + weight on arc MN.

Step 3 Choose the least label which has not already been assigned as a value, and assign it as the value at each vertex where it occurs.

Step 4 Repeat steps 2 and 3 until T has been assigned a value.

Step 5 Trace back from T to S to find the shortest path, including an arc MN in the route whenever

Value of M + weight on arc MN = value of N.

Try this procedure on the following exercises.

Exercise 2.1   Find the shortest path from S to T in each of the networks shown in Figs. 6.14 and 6.15.

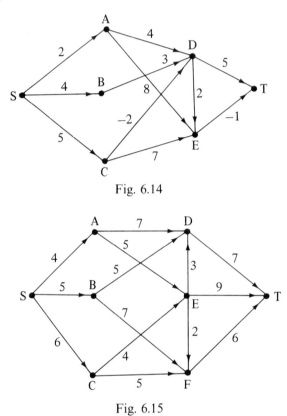

Fig. 6.14

Fig. 6.15

Exercise 2.2   A salesman in the USA flies regularly to five cities L, M, N, P and Q. The fares in dollars for direct flights between the cities are given in the following table.

	L	M	N	P	Q
L	—	100	80	50	20
M	100	—	40	180	50
N	80	40	—	20	50
P	50	180	20	—	110
Q	20	50	50	110	—

Represent this data by a network.

For city L find the cheapest costs between L and the other cities using the shortest path algorithm. Repeat this for the cities M, N, P and Q. Now draw up a table of the cheapest costs between each pair of cities.

6.3 LONGEST PATH ALGORITHM

With a slight modification (and replacing 'least' by 'greatest' where appropriate) the technique for finding the shortest path becomes that for finding the longest. Consider the same network as in section 6.2. This time, the value

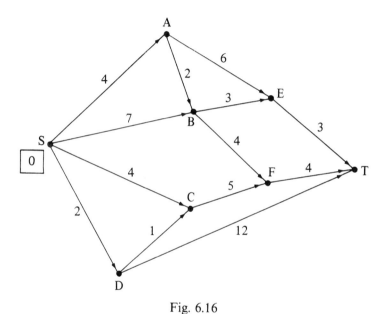

Fig. 6.16

given to S indicates that the greatest distance from S to S is 0. First we consider the vertices reached *only from S directly*; this is the slight modification from the algorithm for the shortest path. There are two such vertices, A and D, and their values are 4 and 2 as shown in Fig. 6.17. Vertices B and C can be reached in two ways. For B we have S-B or S-A-B; and for C we have S-C and S-D-C. So B and C are not included at this stage.

Now we consider the vertices reached only from S, A and D directly. They are B and C. To B, there are two routes, S-A-B and S-B. The length of the path S-A-B is 6 (= value of A + weight on arc AB). The length of SB is 7. We choose the greatest of these (7) and assign to vertex B the value 7. A similar

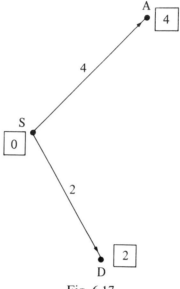

Fig. 6.17

procedure is followed at C, giving the value of C as 4. Next consider the vertices reached directly from S, A, D, B and C. They are E and F, to which we assign the values 10 and 11, respectively. Finally, take the vertices reached directly from S, A, D, B, C, E and F.

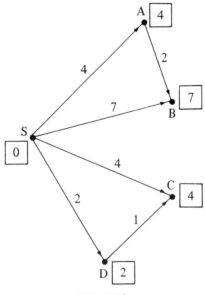

Fig. 6.18

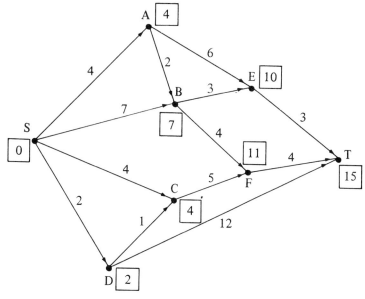

Fig. 6.19

There is only one vertex T for which we assign the value 15. Figure 6.19 gives the final result showing the values of each vertex. The longest path through the network from S to T is S–B–F–T and its length is 15.

Exercise 3.1   Find the longest path from S to T in each of the networks in Exercise 2.1.

Exercise 3.2   Modifying the shortest path algorithm as necessary, find the shortest and longest paths for the network in Fig. 6.20.

Exercise 3.3   A biologist is collecting specimens on a walk from S to T. On the way he has to visit not more than two of the observation points A, B, C, D

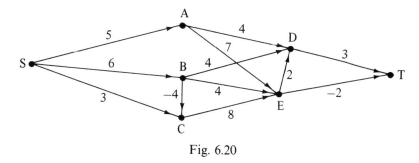

Fig. 6.20

and E. The numbers of specimens he expects to gather on the various stages are known from past experience and are shown in the following table. This includes all the stages which can be managed on foot.

	S	A	B	C	D	E	T
S	—	4	5	6	—	6	—
A	4	—	3	—	8	7	2
B	5	3	—	4	—	—	5
C	6	—	4	—	—	—	8
D	—	8	—	—	—	—	2
E	6	7	—	—	—	—	0
T	—	2	5	8	2	0	—

Which path should he take in order to collect as many specimens as possible?

Exercise 3.4 The weights in the network in Fig. 6.21 represent the expected profits that an itinerant pedlar expects to make on various stages of a journey. Find the route through the network from S to T that maximises his profit.

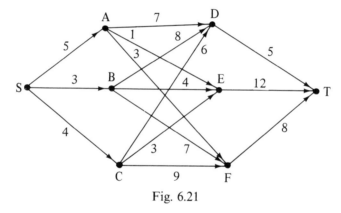

Fig. 6.21

6.4 THE MINIMUM CONNECTOR PROBLEM: THE GREEDY ALGORITHM

In section 6.1 we introduced the minimum connector problem and solved it by a trial and error method. In this and the next section we introduce algorithms for such problems.

The first algorithm that we shall use is called the 'greedy' algorithm. It is called this since it always takes the greediest choice available. We can summarise the algorithm by the following steps.

Step 1 Choose any starting vertex.
Step 2 Join to the nearest vertex.
Step 3 Repeat the procedure, joining up the nearest vertex (not already used) to any vertex already in the solution.
Step 4 End when all vertices have been included.

We will see how this works by first solving the introductory problem in section 6.1 and then using it for the more complicated problem in Exercise 1.2.

Example 1   Find the least amount of cable that is used in connecting each town in Fig. 6.22.

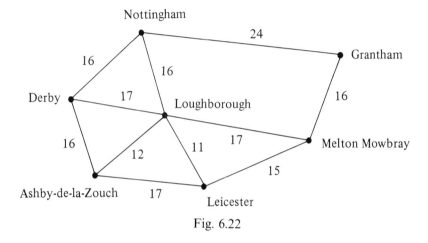

Fig. 6.22

Solution   Following the procedure outlined above, we have:

Step 1 Choose a starting vertex say Leicester (we could start at any vertex).

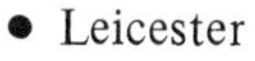

● Leicester

Fig. 6.23

Step 2 Join to the nearest vertex—Loughborough

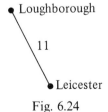

Fig. 6.24

Step 3 Join to the nearest vertex any vertex already in the solution—Loughborough to Ashby de la Zouch.

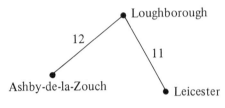

Fig. 6.25

Step 3 Continue–join Leicester to Melton Mowbray (note that each time we are looking for the vertex which is nearest to *any* vertex already in the solution).

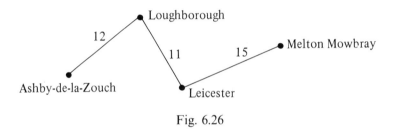

Fig. 6.26

Step 3 We have a choice here, either Melton Mowbray–Grantham or Loughborough–Nottingham or Ashby–Derby.

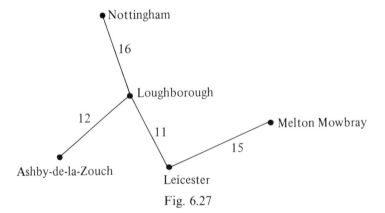

Fig. 6.27

Step 3 Again we have a choice, Nottingham–Derby or Ashby–Derby or Melton Mowbray–Grantham.

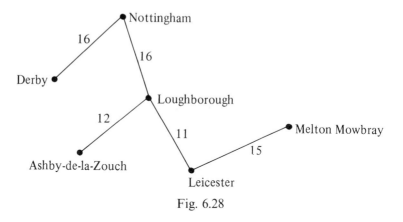

Fig. 6.28

Step 3 No choice now, we join Melton Mowbray–Grantham.

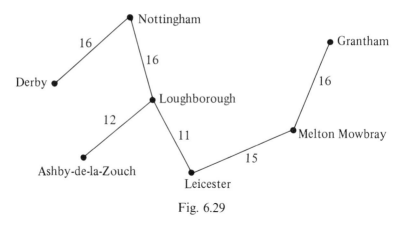

Fig. 6.29

Step 4 Since all vertices have now been considered we **end**.

The total length of cable used is

$$11 + 12 + 15 + 16 + 16 + 16 = 86 \text{ miles}$$

and although the actual layout is *not unique*, the minimum length needed is unique.

Example 2   We will now use the technique to solve Exercise 1.2.

The network in Fig. 6.30 shows the distances in kilometres between cities along main roads. A new national cable TV company wants to connect all

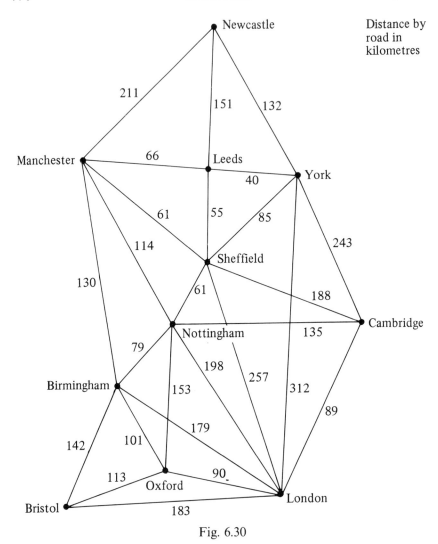

Distance by
road in
kilometres

Fig. 6.30

these cities to London by laying cables alongside main roads. Find the layout
which uses least cable.

Solution We will start at London (connections in the solution will be
indicated by ⌇⌇⌇ when introduced)

Step 1

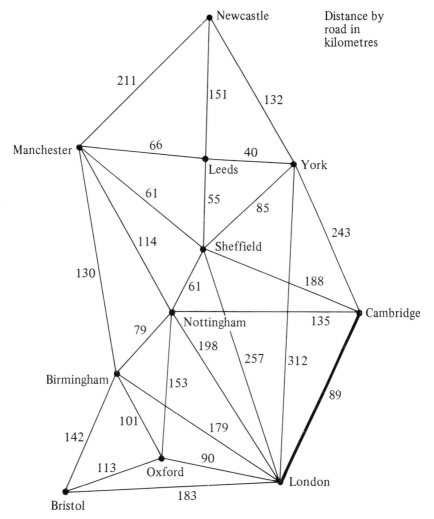

Fig. 6.31

The cable length = 89 km.

Step 2

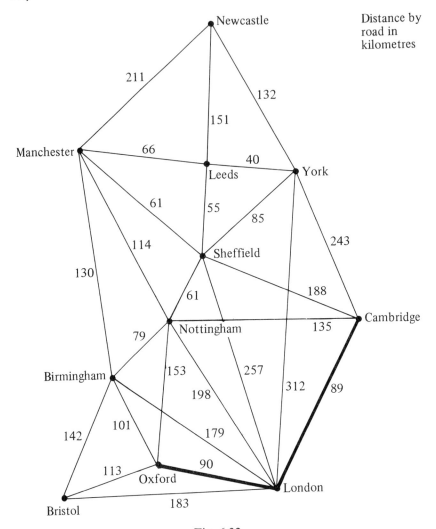

Fig. 6.32

Cable length = 89 + 90 = 179 km.

Step 3

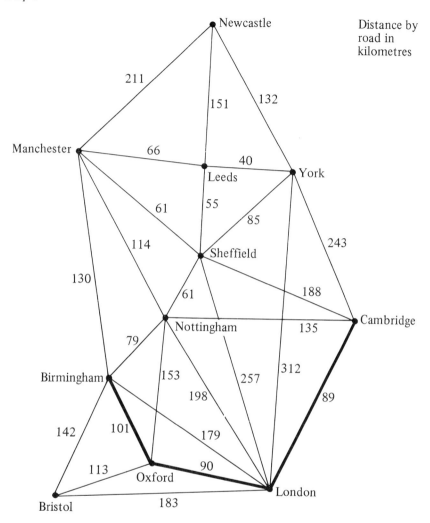

Fig. 6.33

Cable length = 179 + 101 = 280 km.

Step 3

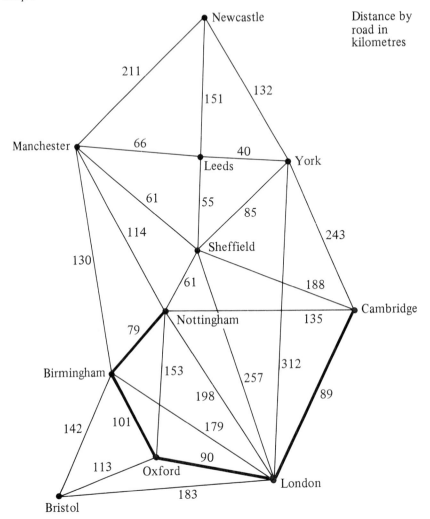

Fig. 6.34

Cable length = 280 + 79 = 359 km.

Step 3

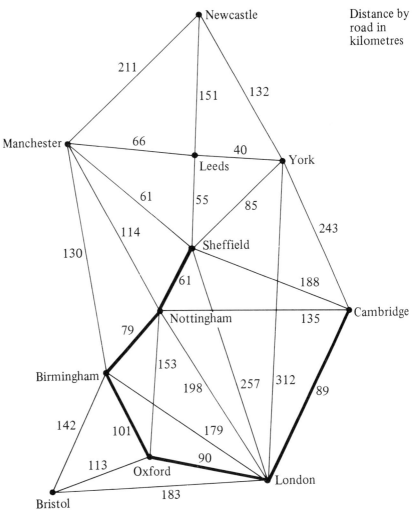

Fig. 6.35

Cable length = 359 + 61 = 420 km.

Step 3

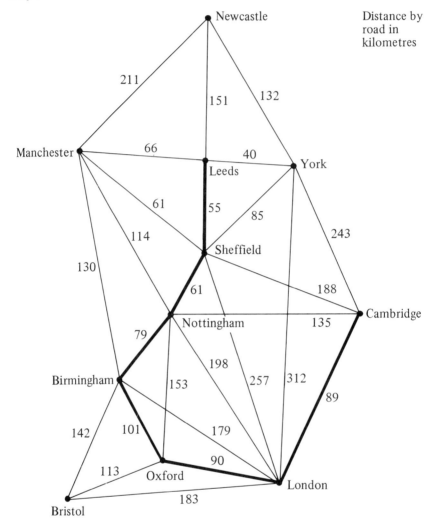

Fig. 6.36

Cable length = 420 + 55 = 475 km.

Step 3

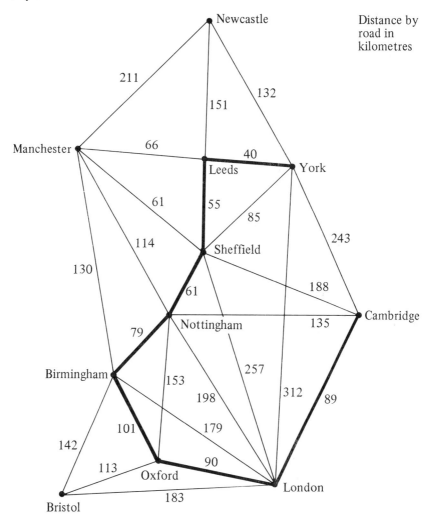

Fig. 6.37

Cable length = 475 + 40 = 515 km.

Step 3

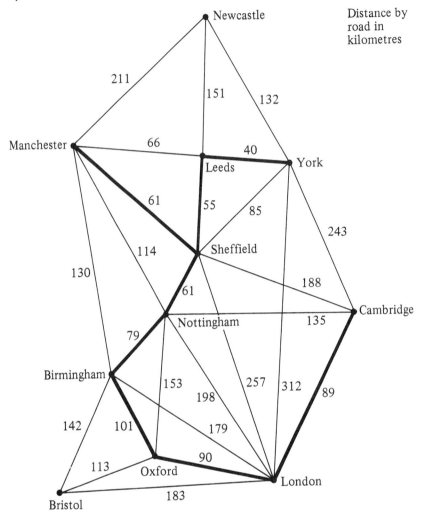

Fig. 6.38

Cable length 515 + 61 = 576 km.

Step 3

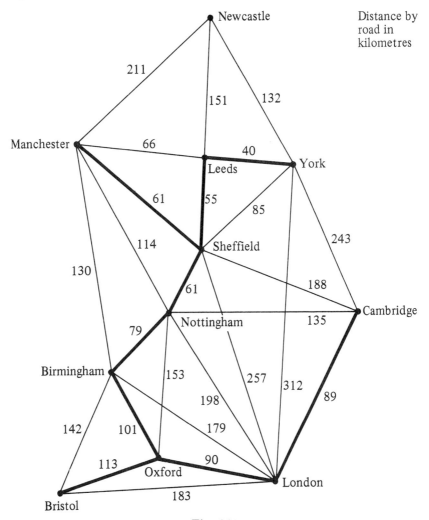

Fig. 6.39

Cable length = 576 + 113 = 689 km.

Step 4

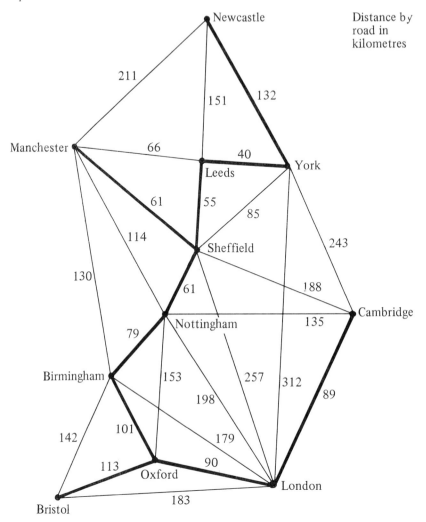

Fig. 6.40

Cable length = 689 + 132 = 821 km.

We have now a connection through the network. The total length of cable needed is 821 kilometres.

Exercise 4.1 Fig. 6.41 shows the distances (in miles) along main roads between nine places in SW England. Use the greedy algorithm to find the layout for a minimum connection using cable alongside the roads.

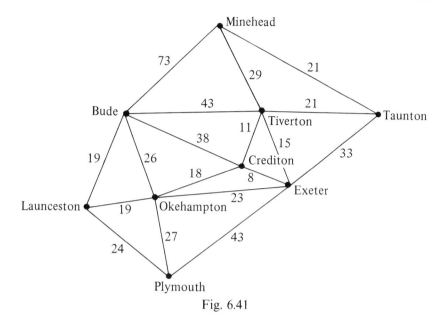

Fig. 6.41

Exercise 4.2   Use the greedy algorithm to find the telephone cable network of minimum length which connects the places shown in Fig. 6.42.

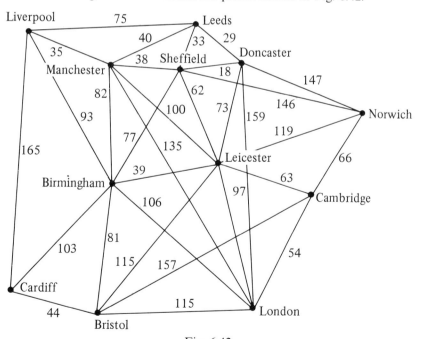

Fig. 6.42

6.5 THE MINIMUM CONNECTOR PROBLEM: PRIM'S ALGORITHM

Although for most problems it is easy to develop the minimum connector on a diagram, for computational purposes it is more useful to describe the method in a tabular format. Consider Example 1 again, we can rewrite the information in a matrix form as shown below.

	Leic.	Lough.	Ashby	MM	Nott.	Gr.	Derby
Leicester	—	11	17	15	—	—	—
Loughborough	11	—	12	17	16	—	17
Ashby	17	12	—	—	—	—	16
Melton Mowbray	15	17	—	—	—	16	—
Nottingham	—	16	—	—	—	24	16
Grantham	—	—	—	16	24	—	—
Derby	—	17	16	—	16	—	—

We first choose a vertex, say Nottingham, delete the Nottingham row and look for the smallest entry in the Nottingham column.

	Leic.	Lough.	Ashby	MM	Nott.	Gr.	Derby
Leicester	—	11	17	15	—	—	—
Loughborough	11	—	12	17	16	—	17
Ashby	17	12	—	—	—	—	16
Melton Mowbray	15	17	—	—	—	16	—
Grantham	—	—	—	16	24	—	—
Derby	—	17	16	—	16	—	—

Nottingham

Loughborough

Fig. 6.43

Now we can choose either Loughborough or Derby; so let us choose Loughborough. Ring the entry and delete the Loughborough row.

	Leic.	Lough.↓	Ashby	MM	Nott.↓	Gr.	Derby
Leicester	—	11	17	15	—	—	—
Ashby	17	12	—	—	—	—	16
Melton Mowbray	15	17	—	—	—	16	—
Grantham	—	—	—	16	24	—	—
Derby	—	17	16	—	16	—	—

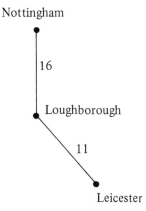

Fig. 6.44

We now look down the Loughborough and Nottingham columns to choose the minimum entry. So we choose Leicester, delete the appropriate row and now look down the three columns for the minimum entry.

	Leic.↓	Lough.↓	Ashby	MM	Nott.↓	Gr.	Derby
Ashby	17	12	—	—	—	—	16
Melton Mowbray	15	17	—	—	—	16	—
Grantham	—	—	—	16	24	—	—.
Derby	—	17	16	—	16	—	—

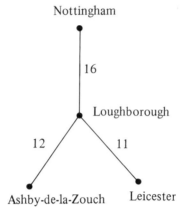

Fig. 6.45

So Ashby–Loughborough comes into the solution, and we now look down the four columns for the minimum entry.

	Leic.	Lough.	Ashby	MM	Nott.	Gr.	Derby
Melton Mowbray	15	17	—	—	—	16	—
Grantham	—	—	—	16	24	—	—
Derby	—	17	16	—	16	—	—

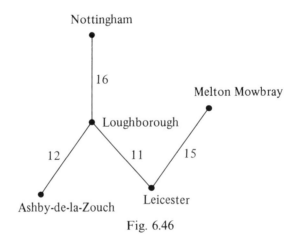

Fig. 6.46

So Leicester–Melton Mowbray comes into the solution.

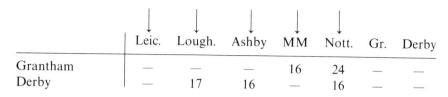

	Leic.	Lough.	Ashby	MM	Nott.	Gr.	Derby
Grantham	—	—	—	16	24	—	—
Derby	—	17	16	—	16	—	—

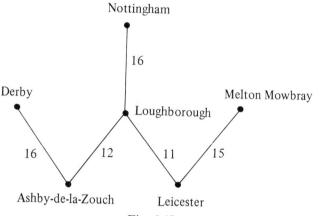

Fig. 6.47

We have a choice here, and we choose Ashby–Derby. Finally we have the table

	Leic.	Lough.	Ashby	MM	Nott.	Gr.	Derby
Grantham	—	—	—	16	24	—	—

and clearly we choose Melton Mowbray–Grantham, giving a final minimum connection of

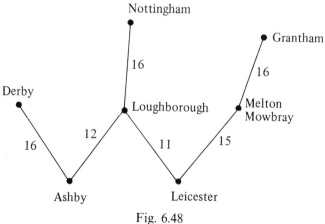

Fig. 6.48

Although this solution is not the same as that found in section 6.4, it does have the same total length of cable, namely 86 miles.

Exercise 5.1   The table below gives the distances (in miles) between five towns.

	A	B	C	D	E
A	—	9	7	5	7
B	9	—	9	9	8
C	7	9	—	7	6
D	5	9	7	—	6
E	7	8	6	6	—

Find the minimum connection between these towns.

Exercise 5.2   Use Prim's algorithm to find the minimum connection between the Irish towns and cities in the table below.

	Athlone	Dublin	Galway	Limerick	Sligo	Wexford
Athlone	—	78	56	73	71	114
Dublin	78	—	132	121	135	96
Galway	56	132	—	64	85	154
Limerick	73	121	64	—	144	116
Sligo	.71	135	85	144	—	185
Wexford	114	96	154	116	185	—

Exercise 5.3   The following table gives the distances (to the nearest 10 kilometres) between six European cities:

	Geneva	Munich	Prague	Strasbourg	Venice	Zurich
Geneva	—	580	950	380	670	280
Munich	580	—	360	380	470	300
Prague	950	360	—	620	780	670
Strasbourg	380	380	620	—	800	230
Venice	670	470	780	800	—	570
Zurich	280	300	670	230	570	—

Solve the minimum connection problem for these cities.

6.6 TRAVELLING SALESMAN PROBLEM (TSP)

We now turn to the third class of problem introduced in section 6.1. As an introduction, suppose that we own a chain of retail computer shops at

> Sheffield
> Aston
> Chapeltown
> Rotherham
> Worksop
> Chesterfield

The road distances between these towns are shown in the network in Fig. 6.49.

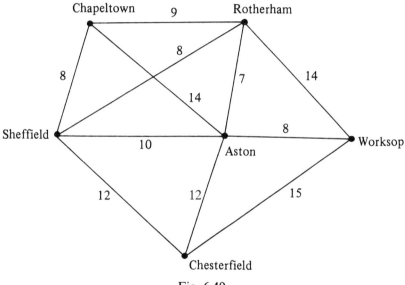

Fig. 6.49

Suppose you live at Sheffield, and each day you have to visit each shop, finally returning to Sheffield. What is the route which has minimum total distance? For example, this route

Sheffield-Chesterfield-Aston-Worksop-Rotherham-Chapeltown-Sheffield

has a total distance of

$$12 + 12 + 8 + 14 + 9 + 8 = 63 \text{ miles,}$$

but can you do better? A little thought should result in the optimum route as

Sheffield-Chesterfield-Worksop-Aston-Rotherham-Chapeltown-Sheffield which has a total distance of

$$12 + 15 + 8 + 7 + 9 + 8 = 59 \text{ miles.}$$

For small-scale problems, it does not take too long to find the best route, but as soon as it gets a little more complicated, the task becomes far more challenging. What we need is a systematic approach, similar to that used for the minimum connector problem. Unfortunately, there is no simple algorithm for this problem. In practical applications it is more usual to use an algorithm that does not guarantee giving the optimal solution but will always achieve a solution close to the best one. One of these approaches is to find upper and lower bounds for the problem, improving these until there is only a small range between the two values. We will see how this is used in the next section.

Exercise 6.1 A bread delivery van delivers each day to the towns shown in Fig. 6.50. Find the route with smallest total distance, which starts at the bakery in Aston, passes through every place at least once and returns to Aston.

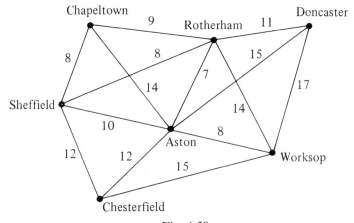

Fig. 6.50

Exercise 6.2 Each day the airfreight lorry at Luton Airport delivers and collects freight at Aylesbury, Milton Keynes, Leighton Buzzard and Bedford, returning to Luton. Find the smallest possible route for the van. (Fig. 6.51)

Exercise 6.3 Figure 6.52 indicates the distances in kilometres between a number of cities in England, using main roads. Design a route starting and finishing at London for a speaking tour for the Prime Minister who wishes to visit all the cities marked.

(i) What is the total length of your chosen route?
(ii) Can you find another route of shorter total length?
(iii) What is the route that has the shortest total length?

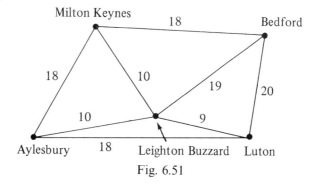

Fig. 6.51

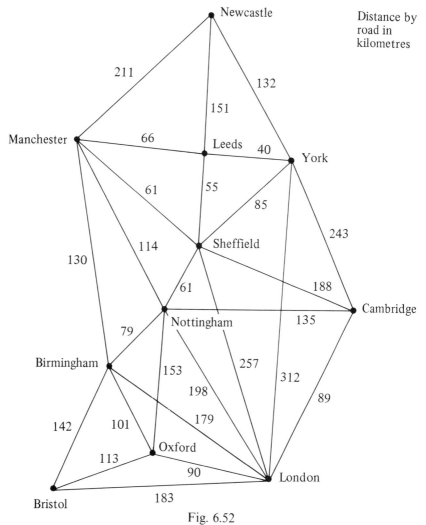

Distance by road in kilometres

Fig. 6.52

6.7 UPPER AND LOWER BOUNDS FOR THE TSP

The solution of Exercise 6.3 is not at all obvious. Even if you feel that you
have got the right answer, you cannot be absolutely sure unless you evaluate
the total length of every possible path. We will show how upper and lower
bounds can be found for this problem.

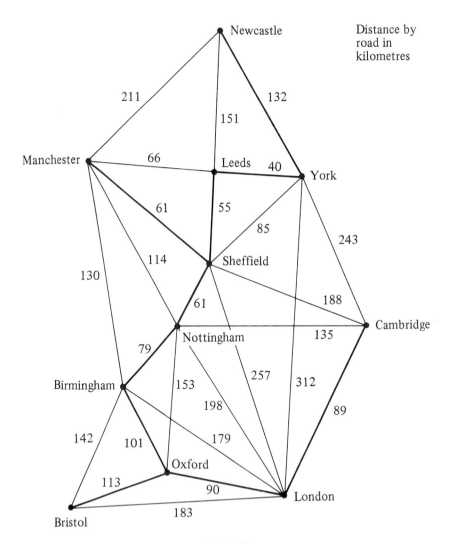

Fig. 6.53

Upper Bound

Whatever solution you found earlier is of course an upper bound to the problem, it might indeed be the actual optimum solution. However, we will use a slightly more formal approach to find an upper bound.

We first solve the corresponding minimum connector problem for the network. This has already been worked through in Example 2 (p. 169) and the result with the minimum connection is shown in Fig. 6.53. This has total length 821 kilometres. Now one very inefficient solution for the TSP is to double this value by going along each arc of the solution in both directions. This is shown in Fig. 6.54. This clearly is a solution to the problem since each

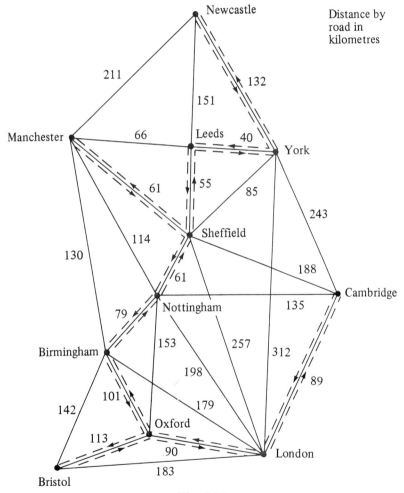

Fig. 6.54

city is visited, but not a very good one, since its total length is 1642 km. However, we can make a number of short cuts. For example

  (i) Cambridge–Sheffield, instead of Cambridge–London–Oxford–Birmingham–Nottingham–Sheffield
 (ii) Sheffield–York, instead of Sheffield–Leeds–York
(iii) Newcastle–Leeds, instead of Newcastle–York–Leeds
 (iv) Leeds–Manchester, instead of Leeds–Sheffield–Manchester.
  (v) Manchester–Nottingham, instead of Manchester–Sheffield–Nottingham
 (vi) Birmingham–Bristol, instead of Birmingham–Oxford–Bristol.

This gives the route shown in Fig. 6.55 which has total length 1249 km.

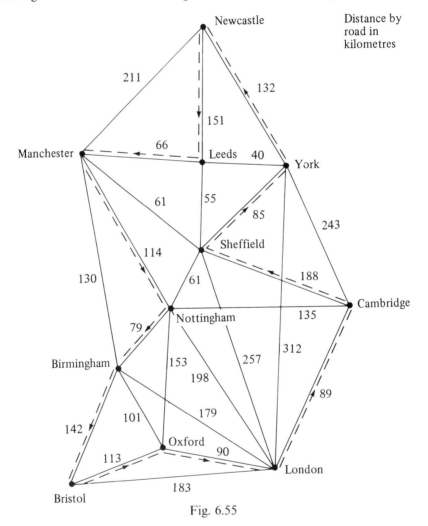

Fig. 6.55

You might well have found a better *upper* bound, but we will stick with this one, and see if we can find a *lower* bound close to this value.

Lower Bound

To find a lower bound, we first delete one of the cities, for example, Newcastle, and delete all routes from this city. This leaves the network shown in Fig. 6.56.

Now if we consider the actual optimum solution to the TSP it will include travelling into Newcastle and back out again. So a lower bound to this part of the solution is given by the sum of the *two least* paths from Newcastle, that is

$$\left.\begin{array}{l} \text{Newcastle--York: 132 km} \\ \text{and} \\ \text{Newcastle--Leeds: 151 km} \end{array}\right\} 132 + 151 = 283 \text{ km}$$

If we now consider the rest of the network, and solve the minimum connection problem for this portion of the network, this will also be a lower

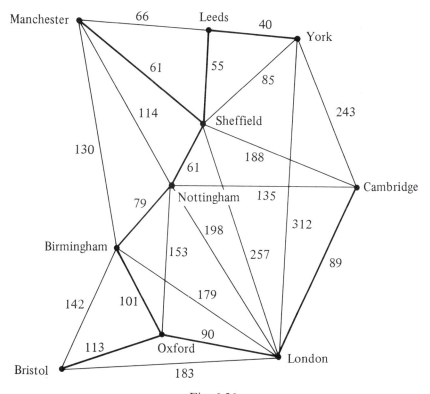

Fig. 6.56

bound for the corresponding part of the TSP solution. This must be so, since the portion of the TSP solution does in fact provide a connection between the cities, not necessarily the minimum connection. So for the example above, the minimum connection, marked on the sketch, gives a total of 689 km.

So we have found lower bounds to the two parts of the TSP solution. Combining these gives a total lower bound of 689 + 283 = 972 km. To find this lower bound we initially deleted Newcastle from the network. Now this choice is arbitrary, we could equally well choose any of the cities. In fact, the table below gives details of the lower bound calculations for deletion of each city.

City deleted	Lower bound for city connection	Lower bound for rest of network	Total lower bound for TSP
Newcastle	283	689	972
Manchester	127	760	887
Leeds	95	811	906
York	125	800	925
Sheffield	116	824	940
Nottingham	140	811	951
Cambridge	224	732	956
Birmingham	180	776	956
Oxford	191	794	985
Bristol	255	708	963
London	179	777	956

So the *best* lower bound (i.e. the largest) has been found by initially deleting Oxford from the network, and has value 985. Unfortunately, it is not obvious (without going through each of the calculations above) which deletion gives the best lower bound until the calculations have been done. So using the maximum lower bound (985 km) and the minimum upper bound, we can deduce that the solution to the TSP, say T, must lie between

$$985 \leq T \leq 1249$$

So there is still quite a wide range of values in which T might lie. In fact the solution to the problem is given by

$$T = 1194 \text{ km}$$

and the actual route is shown in Fig. 6.57.

There has been much research into finding efficient algorithms for solving the TSP, usually these algorithms concentrate on finding, as quickly as

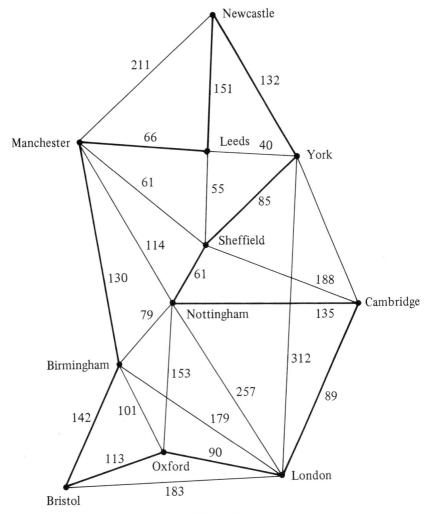

Fig. 6.57

possible, a route which is close to the best solution. For practical applications this is sufficient to provide a basis for the solution.

For example in routing problems, like the one above, having achieved this mathematical solution, management will also have to take into account such factors as:

(i) length of journey time on different roads
(ii) likely delays in certain cities
(iii) when to schedule overnight stops.

So an approximate solution, that gives a route close to the true optimum is usually quite adequate for implementation in the practical situation.

One method that is particularly appropriate to networks that have a physical significance and can be drawn to scale on a map, is to start by moving round a route which takes in all the places on the outside, making it as circular as possible. This can then be progressively refined bringing in places in turn in the most appropriate way. You might like to try out approaches of this type, or design your own technique, and see how well it solves the following exercises.

Exercise 7.1 A petrol tanker has to deliver petrol to garages in Leicester, Ashby de la Zouch, Derby, Grantham and Melton Mowbray. If the tanker depot is situated in Leicester, find

(i) a lower bound for the minimum distance travelled
(ii) an upper bound for the minimum distance travelled

	L	A	D	G	MM
Leicester	—	17	25	28	15
Ashby de la Zouch	17	—	16	40	26
Derby	25	16	—	40	27
Grantham	28	40	40	—	16
Melton Mowbray	15	26	27	16	—

Exercise 7.2 A jogger is planning to do a charity run. She will start and finish at Wigston, and run through Countesthorpe, Blaby, Cosby, Croft and Oadby. Find six lower bounds for the total distance she must run by using the method given in this chapter, and deleting each village in turn.

	W	Cou.	B	Co.	Cr.	O
Wigston	—	3	4	5	7	2
Countesthorpe	3	—	2	3	5	5
Blaby	4	2	—	1	3	5
Cosby	5	3	1	—	2	4
Croft	7	5	3	2	—	5
Oadby	2	5	5	4	5	—

Exercise 7.3   A firm's accountant has to check the accounts at six branches, situated in Durham, Chester-le-Street, Stanley, Newton Aycliffe, Birtley and Ouston.

	D	Ch.	S	NA	B	O
Durham	—	9	11	6	13	11
Chester-le-Street	9	—	8	14	3	4
Stanley	11	8	—	15	6	6
Newton Aycliffe	6	14	15	—	15	14
Birtley	13	3	6	15	—	2
Ouston	11	4	6	14	2	—

What are the best upper and lower bounds you can find for the total distance the accountant will travel?

6.8 CHINESE POSTMAN PROBLEM (ROUTE INSPECTION PROBLEM)

Finally in this chapter we investigate a class of problems having the name the Chinese postman problem.

Suppose that a postman leaves the depot, has to deliver along all the streets in an area and return to the depot. How can the route be planned so as to cover the smallest total distance?

The word Chinese refers to the mathematician who first investigated the problem not to the nationality of the postman!

There are many similar problems of this type. For example, four snow gritting teams have the roads in the town shown in Fig. 6.58 to grit. Find the route for each of the teams which will make the distance they have to travel as small as possible. Problems of this type are solved by inspecting the possible routes and deciding on the best strategy. Such problems are called *route inspection problems*.

We can formulate the general problem as a network and pose the problem:

Find a closed path of minimum total weight which includes every arc at least once.

Consider the route inspection problem for the network in Fig. 6.59. Clearly a lower bound for the total distance travelled is just the sum of the weights which equals 105. This would be the answer if we did not have to go along an arc more than once.

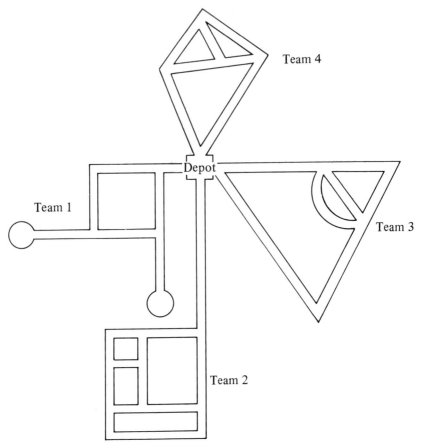

Fig. 6.58

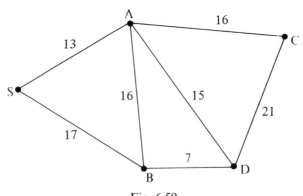

Fig. 6.59

However, consider the path S–B–D–A–B; so far we have travelled along arcs SB, BD, DA and AB only once. But now we have to leave vertex B and to do so requires repeating an arc. Repeating the arc of smallest weight adds the smallest number to the total distance travelled. So suppose that we continue B–D–C–A and back to S along arc AS. The total distance travelled is then 112 and only one arc, fortunately the shortest one, has been repeated. Working through this example suggests that there are two questions to be answered:

1. When is it necessary to repeat an arc?
2. If we do need to repeat an arc which route should we take?

The answer to the first question is quite easy. If we are *not* to repeat any arc then at each vertex there must be an even number of arcs i.e. the degree of each vertex must be even. For example, if we have a vertex with three arcs joining it then we can move into the vertex along AB and out of it along BC; but when we re-enter the vertex along DB there is no way out except by repeating one of the other arcs.

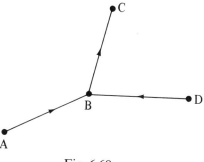

Fig. 6.60

Thus a network with a vertex of odd degree will require at least one arc at that vertex to be repeated. An important consequence of the handshaking theorem (see Chapter 5, section 5.6) is that in any graph the number of vertices of odd degree is even. The proof is quite straightforward; if the number of vertices of odd degree were odd then the sum of all the vertex degrees would be an odd number which contradicts the formula, $\deg v = 2e$ ($2e$ is always even).

To answer the second question we choose to repeat the arcs which lead to the smallest extra distance travelled.

We illustrate the method of solution for 2 and 4 odd vertices by looking at two examples.

Example 1 Solve the route inspection problem for the network in Fig. 6.61 starting and returning to S.

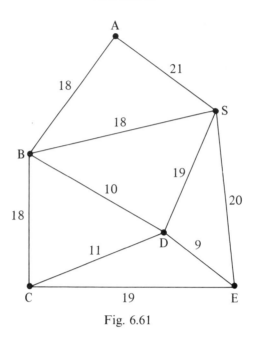

Fig. 6.61

Solution

Step 1 Find the degrees of all the vertices and note any that are odd.

For this network the degrees of the vertices S, A, B, C, D and E are respectively 4, 2, 4, 3, 4, 3. So vertices C and E have odd degree and at least one arc must be repeated. (Note: if all the degrees were even the problem is solved, the shortest distance travelled would be the sum of the weights.)

Step 2 Consider the routes joining the odd vertices in pairs and choose the routes of smallest distance.

For a network with two odd vertices, we choose the route between those vertices of smallest total weight. The arcs making up this route are then repeated. In this example the vertices C and E are odd and the arc CE is the shortest distance between them. The arc CE is repeated giving the route of minimum total weight 182. A possible route which achieves this is shown in Fig. 6.62, the ringed numbers indicating the stages.

Example 2 Consider the map shown in Fig. 6.63 with distances in kilometres. Find the route from London of minimum total distance which traverses each road once.

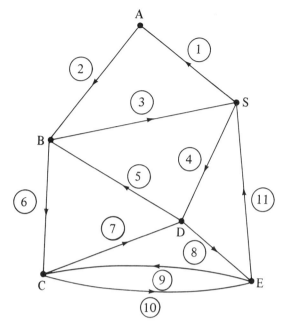

Fig. 6.62

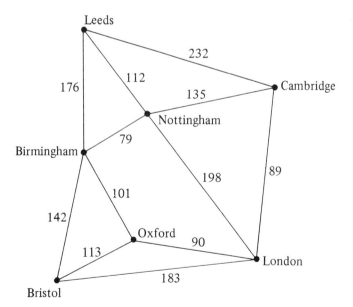

Fig. 6.63

Solution

Step 1 The cities with odd degree are Leeds, Cambridge, Bristol and Oxford (each have degree 3).

Step 2 Join up the cities in pairs; there are three combinations

(i) (Leeds–Cambridge) and (Oxford–Bristol)
(ii) (Leeds–Oxford) and (Cambridge–Bristol)
(iii) (Leeds–Bristol) and (Cambridge–Oxford)

The distances in each case are

(i) $232 + 113 = 345$
(ii) $(176 + 101) + (89 + 183) = 549$
(iii) $(176 + 142) + (89 + 90) = 497$.

Now these distances represent the extra distances to be travelled if we repeat the arcs joining the cities in each case. Clearly we should choose the shortest extra distance. This is 345 km and means repeating the arcs joining Leeds to Cambridge and Oxford to Bristol. A route through the network is shown in Fig. 6.64. The total distance travelled is 1995 km. Note that the actual route taken through the network is not unique.

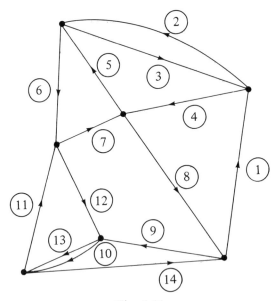

Fig. 6.64

Exercise 8.1 In solving the route inspection problem, for the networks shown in Fig. 6.65, for which problems would we have to repeat an arc?

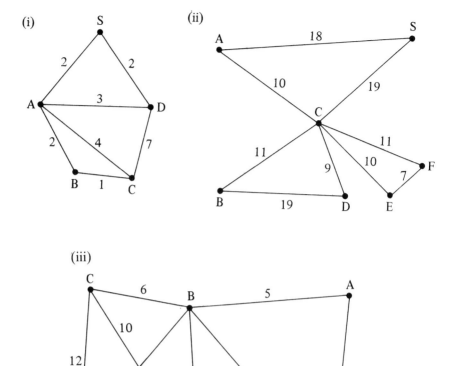

Fig. 6.65

Exercise 8.2   For each network in Exercise 8.1 solve the route inspection problem starting at and returning to S in each case.

6.9   MISCELLANEOUS EXERCISES

M1   Find the shortest path between towns S and T from the road network shown in Fig. 6.66. Distances are in kilometres.

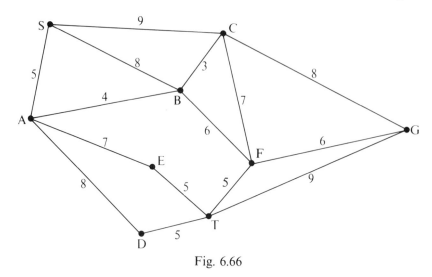

Fig. 6.66

M2 A small firm operates a parcel delivery service between selected cities
and guarantees delivery within 24 hours. The cost in pounds per
kilogramme to send a parcel between these cities is given in the table
below.

	Exeter	London	Oxford	Cambridge	Birmingham
Exeter	—	15	17	29	27
London	15	—	6	6	10
Oxford	17	6	—	7	7
Cambridge	29	6	7	—	10
Birmingham	27	10	7	10	—

Represent this data by a network. Find the cheapest cost between
Exeter and the other cities to send a parcel weighing 1 kg. Use the
shortest path algorithm in order to do this and repeat for the cities
London, Oxford, Cambridge and Birmingham.

M3 A salesman based in London is to make a journey north to Edinburgh.
He intends to do business on the way, but in order to reach Edinburgh
in time to meet an appointment, he cannot afford the time to travel
back on himself. The table indicates the routes he feels able to take in
order to meet his time restrictions and the commission he expects to
make (in £'s × 10) by taking each particular route.

	London	Gloucester	Cambridge	Birmingham	York	Sheffield	Manchester	Carlisle	Newcastle	Edinburgh
London	—	7	4	9	—	—	—	—	—	—
Gloucester	—	—	—	5		9	11	—	—	—
Cambridge	—	—	—	3	9		—	—	—	—
Birmingham	—	—	—	—	4	6	7	—	—	—
York	—	—	—	—	—	—	—	7	6	—
Sheffield	—	—	—	—	—	—	4	4	6	—
Manchester	—	—	—	—	—	—	—	5	—	—
Carlisle	—	—	—	—	—	—	—	—	—	5
Newcastle	—	—	—	—	—	—	—	—	—	8

Draw a network diagram to represent the data in the table. Using the longest path algorithm, find the route(s) which would yield the sales-man the most commission.

M4 An industrial process which begins with a compound A results in a product Z. There are a variety of alternative stages in the production which result in different yields and thus affect the final quantity of product Z. In Fig. 6.67 the weights on the arcs represent yields at the various stages in the process. Find the stages in production which will yield the maximum amount of product Z from compound A.

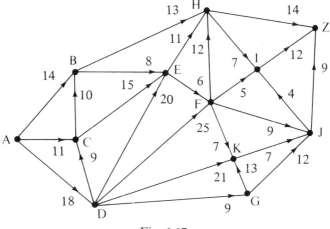

Fig. 6.67

M5 A television company is to lay TV cables so that the towns A, B, C, D
and E are connected. What is the minimum length of cable required?

	A	B	C	D	E
A	—	16	20	20	32
B	16	—	10	17	24
C	20	10	—	15	12
D	20	17	15	—	9
E	32	24	12	9	—

M6 Use (a) the greedy algorithm (b) Prim's algorithm to solve the
minimum connector problem for:

	R	S	T	U	V
R	—	9	7	6	9
S	9	—	4	3	8
T	7	4	—	6	9
U	6	3	6	—	7
V	9	8	9	7	—

M7 A medical supplies representative needs to visit five practices in towns
A, B, C, D and E. The representative lives in C so begins and ends his
journey there. Calculate upper and lower bounds for the distances he
must travel.

	A	B	C	D	E
A	—	7	9	12	10
B	7	—	14	6	3
C	9	14	—	10	15
D	12	6	10	—	6
E	10	3	15	6	—

M8 A weights and measures inspector visits shops in towns V, W, X, Y and
Z to check the accuracy of the scales. If the inspector lives in U which
route would you recommend he uses to minimise the distance travelled,
assuming he starts and finishes at U?

	U	V	W	X	Y	Z
U	—	18	15	3	9	10
V	18	—	12	7	4	12
W	15	12	—	6	9	17
X	3	7	6	—	8	3
Y	9	4	9	8	—	6
Z	10	12	17	3	6	—

M9 A van has to deliver newspapers every morning to village shops at A, C, D, E and F. The van starts and finishes at the printing factory at B. Calculate upper and lower bounds for the distance travelled.

	A	B	C	D	E	F
A	—	12	15	8	7	10
B	12	—	10	6	17	12
C	15	10	—	9	15	8
D	8	6	9	—	16	20
E	7	17	15	16	—	7
F	10	12	8	20	7	—

M10 A county council maintenance department need to inspect roads for serious damage after heavy winter frost. Advise the department on the shortest route which covers all roads and starts and ends at the depot. All distances are in kilometres.

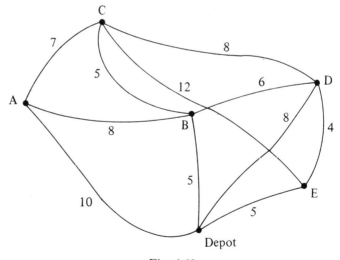

Fig. 6.68

M11 To locate a fault in a pipeline a part of the network must be inspected as illustrated in Fig. 6.69, distances in metres. What is the shortest route which covers every part of the pipeline?

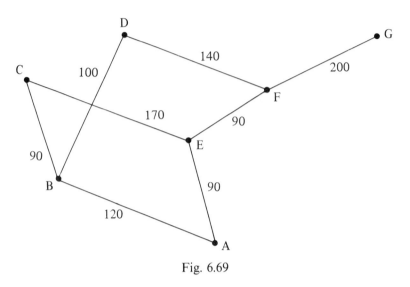

Fig. 6.69

7

RECURRENCE
RELATIONS—1

7.1 THE TOWER OF BRAHMA

In the great temple at Benares, beneath the dome which marks the centre of the world, rests a brass plate in which are fixed three diamond needles, each a cubit high and as thick as the body of a bee. On one of these needles, at the creation, God placed sixty-four discs of pure gold, the largest disc resting on the brass plate, and the others getting smaller and smaller, up to the top one. This is the Tower of Brahma. Day and night unceasingly, the priests transfer the discs from one diamond needle to another according to the fixed and immutable laws of Brahma, which require that the priest on duty must not move more than one disc at a time and that he must place this disc on a needle so that there is no smaller disc below it. When the sixty-four discs shall have been thus transferred from the needle on which at the creation God placed them, to one of the other needles, tower, temple and Brahmins alike will crumble into dust and with a thunderclap the world will vanish.*

If the Brahmins move one disc every second, how long will it be before the world ends? Before trying to answer this we first investigate a simpler problem.

* Copyright Open University. TM361 Course.

The Tower of Hanoi—An investigation

Consider a tower of three rings. The problem is to find the smallest number of moves needed to transfer the discs to another needle. At no time may any disc be placed on top of a smaller one.

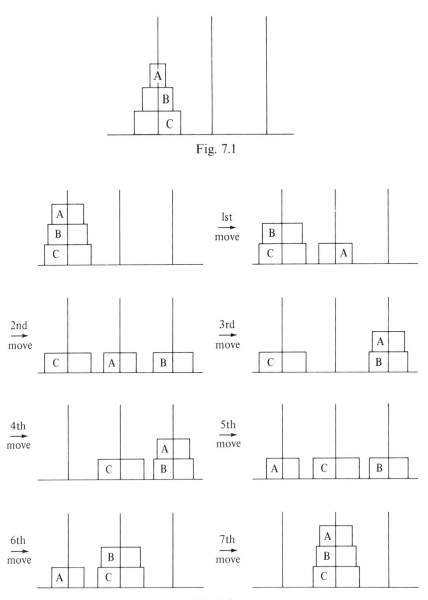

Fig. 7.1

Fig. 7.2

We define the number of moves needed to transfer three discs as U_3. So $U_3 = 7$

(a) Consider a tower of four discs and find U_4.
(b) Consider a tower of five discs and find U_5.
(c) Can you see a connection between U_4 and U_3?

To move your discs you first move the top three discs to another peg, then you move the fourth disc to the third peg, then use the same move as before to move the top three discs on to the fourth. In other words

$$U_4 = U_3 + 1 + U_3$$

$$U_4 = 2U_3 + 1$$

(d) What is the connection between U_5 and U_4?

So what is the connection between U_n and U_{n-1}? It is $U_n = 2U_{n-1} + 1$. Does this tell us how many moves are required to transfer n discs on to another needle? No. So we cannot use it directly to tell us when the world will end! All we know is that

$$U_{64} = 2U_{63} + 1$$

but

$$U_{63} = 2U_{62} + 1.$$

So substituting for U_{63} gives

$$U_{64} = 2(2U_{62} + 1) + 1 \qquad [\, = 2^2 U_{62} + 2 + 1]$$

and so on.

$$U_{64} = 2(2(2U_{61} + 1) + 1) + 1 \qquad [\, = 2^3 U_{61} + 2^2 + 2 + 1]$$
$$= 2(2(2(2U_{60} + 1) + 1) + 1) + 1 \quad [\, = 2^4 U_{60} + 2^3 + 2^2 + 2 + 1]$$
$$\vdots$$
$$= 2(2(2(2 \ldots + 1) + 1) + 1) + 1 \qquad [\, = 2^{63} U_1 + 2^{62} + 2^{61} + \cdots + 2 + 1]$$

Finally,

$$U_{64} = 2^{63} U_1 + 2^{62} + 2^{61} + \cdots + 2 + 1$$

U_1 is the number of moves needed to transfer one disc. So

$$U_1 = 1.$$

$$U_{64} = 2^{63} + 2^{62} + 2^{61} + \cdots + 2 + 1$$

Can we simplify this expression? Rewriting this as

$$U_{64} = 1 + 2 + 2^2 + \cdots + 2^{62} + 2^{63}$$

we see that there is a geometric progression with first term 1 and common
ratio 2 and whose sum is therefore

$$\frac{2^{64} - 1}{2 - 1} = 2^{64} - 1.$$

i.e.

$$U_{64} = 2^{64} - 1.$$

Exercise 1.1   Assuming the priests of Brahma move the discs at the rate of
one disc per second, when will the world end?

7.2 SOLVING PROBLEMS BY ITERATION

The equation

$$U_n = 2U_{n-1} + 1$$

is called a *recurrence relation* (or difference equation). The actual value of U_n,

$$U_n = 2^n - 1$$

is the *solution* of the recurrence relation.

   The process of obtaining the solution from the recurrence relation by the
method of repeated applications, is called *iteration*. For example we can solve
U_n as follows:

$$
\begin{aligned}
U_n &= 2U_{n-1} + 1 \\
    &= 2(2U_{n-2} + 1) + 1 \\
    &= 2(2(2U_{n-3} + 1) + 1) + 1 \\
    &\vdots \\
    &= 2^n U_1 - 1
\end{aligned}
$$

Example 1   James Feather was left £5000 when his mother died. As he is due
to retire in eleven years' time, he is considering investing it until his
retirement, at a fixed rate of 9%. How much will it be worth at the end of that
period?

Solution   Let U_n be the money in the account (in pounds) at the beginning of
the nth year. So

$$U_1 = 5000$$

and

$$U_n = U_{n-1} + U_{n-1} \times \frac{9}{100}$$

$$\uparrow \qquad\qquad \uparrow$$

amount at   interest earned
beginning   during $(n-1)$th
of $(n-1)$th   year
year

So

$$U_n = U_{n-1}\left(1 + \frac{9}{100}\right)$$

$$U_n = U_{n-1} \times 1.09$$

The *general expression* for this recurrence relation is

$$U_n = MU_{n-1}$$

where M is a constant value.

James retires in 11 years time, so we need to calculate the value of the investment at the beginning of the twelfth year.

$$U_{12} = 1.09U_{11} \qquad \text{and } U_{11} = 1.09U_{10}$$
$$= (1.09)^2 U_{10} \qquad \text{and } U_{10} = 1.09U_9$$
$$\vdots$$
$$U_{12} = (1.09)^{11}U_1 \qquad \text{and } U_1 = 5000$$

Thus he will have $£(1.09)^{11} \times 5000$ which is approximately £12 902.

Suppose James can add £250 to his investment at the end of each year. How much will the investment be worth at his retirement in this case? The recurrence relation becomes

$$U_n = U_{n-1} + U_{n-1} \times 0.09 + 250$$
$$U_n = U_{n-1} \times 1.09 + 250$$

The general expression for this recurrence relation is

$$U_n = MU_{n-1} + C$$

where M and C are constants. In this example

$$U_{12} = 1.09U_{11} + 250$$
$$= 1.09(1.09U_{10} + 250) + 250$$
$$= 1.09(1.09(1.090U_9 + 250) + 250) + 250$$
$$\vdots$$
$$= 1.09^{11}U_1 + 250(1.09^{10} + 1.09^9 + \cdots + 1.09 + 1)$$

We have a geometric progression again, with common ratio 1.09

$$U_{12} = 1.09^{11}U_1 + 250\left(\frac{1.09^{11} - 1}{1.09 - 1}\right)$$

$$= 1.09^{11}U_1 + 250\left(\frac{1.09^{11} - 1}{0.09}\right)$$

$$U_{12} = £12\,902 + £4\,390 = \underline{£17\,292}$$

Exercise 2.1   Adam Jones, aged $13\frac{3}{4}$, won £1000 with a Premium bond. On the advice of his parents he decided to invest his money at a fixed rate of compound interest of $7\frac{1}{2}\%$ until his twenty-first birthday. How much would he have by then?

A year after the original investment, Adam withdraws £25 to pay for Christmas presents, and he does this annually until his twenty-first birthday. How much will be in his account on his twenty-first birthday?

Exercise 2.2   Consider a breeding population of white mice which are counted every month. In one month, the number born is twice the population present at the beginning of the month and the number dying is one quarter of the same population. If the breeder starts with 100 mice how many is he likely to have one year later?

If the breeder agrees to supply a pet shop with 100 mice per month starting at the end of the first month how many is he likely to have at the end of the year? If he supplies the shop with 150 mice per month how many is he likely to have at the end of the year? If he wants to end up with 100 mice at the end of the year how many should he sell per month?

7.3 LINEAR FIRST ORDER RECURRENCE RELATIONS

A recurrence relation of the form

$$U_n = MU_{n-1} + C$$

where M and C are constants, is called a *linear recurrence relation*.

$$U_n = MU_{n-1}^2 + C \text{ is not linear.}$$

A recurrence relation is said to be of *Kth order* if the difference between the highest and lowest subscripts is K. So, for example, $U_n = MU_{n-1} + C$ is a *first order* recurrence relation; whereas $U_n = NU_{n-2} + d$ and $U_n = MU_{n-1} + PU_{n-2}$ are second order because the difference between the highest and lowest subscripts is 2 in each case.

(a) The most simple linear first order recurrence relation can be written as

$$U_n = MU_{n-1} \quad \text{and} \quad U_{n-1} = MU_{n-2}$$

so

$$U_n = M(MU_{n-2})$$
$$\vdots$$
$$U_n = M^{n-1}U_1$$

Then

$$\boxed{U_n = M^{n-1}U_1}$$

is the general solution of $U_n = MU_{n-1}$.

(b) The more general first order recurrence relation is

$$U_n = MU_{n-1} + c$$

where M and c are constants. Solving by iteration we have

$$U_n = M(MU_{n-2} + C) + C$$
$$\vdots$$
$$U_n = M^{n-1}U_1 + C(M^{n-2} + M^{n-3} + \cdots + M + 1)$$

If $S_n \equiv M^{n-2} + M^{n-3} + \cdots + M + 1$, then $U_n = M^{n-1}U_1 + C.S_n$.

Consider

$$MS_n - S_n = M(M^{n-2} + M^{n-3} + \cdots + M + 1)$$
$$- (M^{n-2} + M^{n-3} + \cdots + M + 1)$$
$$= M^{n-1} + M^{n-2} + \cdots + M^2 + M - M^{n-2} - \cdots - M^2 - M - 1$$
$$= M^{n-1} - 1$$

So

$$S_n(M - 1) = M^{n-1} - 1$$

If $M \neq 1$,

$$S_n = \frac{M^{n-1} - 1}{M - 1}$$

and

$$U_n = M^{n-1}U_1 + C\left(\frac{M^{n-1} - 1}{M - 1}\right)$$

If $M = 1$,

$$S_n = \underbrace{1 + 1 + 1 + \cdots + 1}_{n - 1 \text{ terms}} = n - 1$$

and
$$U_n = U_1 + C(n-1).$$

The general solution of $U_n = MU_{n-1} + C$ is

$$
\boxed{
\begin{aligned}
U_n &= M^{n-1}U_1 + C\left(\frac{M^{n-1}-1}{M-1}\right) \quad &\text{if } M \neq 1\\
U_n &= U_1 + C(n-1) \quad &\text{if } M = 1
\end{aligned}
}
$$

Example 2 Calculate the quarterly payment on a loan of £2000 for 4 years at a compound interest rate of 14%.

Solution Let U_n = amount owing at the beginning of the nth year. Let p = quarterly payment (in pounds)

$$U_n = U_{n-1} + \underbrace{\frac{14}{100}U_{n-1}}_{\text{interest}} - \underset{\text{1 year's payments}}{4p}$$

$$U_n = 1.14U_{n-1} - 4p.$$

The general solution of this is

$$U_n = 1.14^{n-1}U_1 - 4p\left(\frac{1.14^{n-1}-1}{1.14-1}\right)$$

Since the loan is to be paid off in 4 years, we know that the amount owing at the beginning of the fifth year must be zero.

$$U_1 = 2000$$

therefore

$$U_5 = 1.14^4 \times 2000 - 4p\left(\frac{1.14^4-1}{0.14}\right) = 0$$

$$p = \frac{1.14^4 \times 2000 \times 0.14}{4(1.14^4-1)} = 171.60$$

Therefore the quarterly payment is £171.60

Exercise 3.1 Use the solutions above to find the general solution of each of the following equations.

(i) $U_n = 3U_{n-1}$
(iii) $4 + U_n + 2U_{n-1} = 0$
(v) $U_{n+1} - 2U_n = 3$
(vii) $b_{n+2} - b_{n+1} = 1$

(ii) $U_n - 2U_{n-1} = 1$
(iv) $U_n - U_{n-1} = 2$
(vi) $2t_n + 3t_{n+1} = 4$
(viii) $a_n = a_{n+1} + 1$

Exercise 3.2   Find the general solution of $U_{2n} = 2U_{2n-2}$. If $U_2 = 1$, write out the first six terms of the sequence. What do you find?

Exercise 3.3   Write the recurrence relation $U_{2n+1} = U_{2n-1} - 1$ as a recurrence relation of the form $U_n = \cdots$. If $U_1 = 1$, write out the first six terms of the sequence. What is the general solution of the relation?

Exercise 3.4   Calculate the monthly payment on a loan of £5000 for 5 years at a compound interest rate of $10\frac{1}{4}\%$.

Exercise 3.5   Mr and Mrs Young wish to negotiate a loan of £3500 repayable over 3 years, to buy a new kitchen. A bank offers a flat rate loan (i.e. simple interest) of $9\frac{1}{2}\%$ p.a. A finance company offers a loan at 13.5% p.a. compound interest. By calculating the monthly payments in each case, decide which loan is the better value.

Exercise 3.6   A family buys a new house with a mortgage of £30 000. This has to be paid back over 25 years. The rate of interest is $11\frac{1}{2}\%$ p.a. Let £p be the monthly repayments. Derive a recurrence relation, in terms of p, connecting the amount owed at the beginning of year n, £U_n, with the amount owed at the beginning of the previous year. Solve for U_n. Find p. How much does the family still owe after 10 years?

Exercise 3.7   In a learning experiment, a rat is placed in a starting box at the beginning of a straight runway. Sufficient time is allowed for the rat to run along the runway without dawdling. If he reaches the end of the runway in that time the trial is considered to be a success. When the rat reaches the end of the runway he receives either a reward (food), punishment (a mild electric shock) or nothing. If p_n is the probability of success in the nth trial, then from the experiments, it was found that

$$p_n = p_{n-1} + a(1 - p_{n-1}) - bp_{n-1}$$

where a is the proportion of times success is rewarded and b is the proportion of times success is punished.

(i) When $a = 0.4$ and $b = 0.1$, show that the solution of this relation is $p_n = 0.8 - 0.6 \times (0.5)^{n-1}$ given that $p_1 = 0.2$. What is the probability of success after a very long time?
(ii) When the proportions of reward and punishment are reversed what do you find?
(iii) Investigate the case when $a = b = 0.5$.
(iv) What happens when there is always food at the end of the runway?
(v) What happens when there is no food and the rat gets an electric shock at the end of the runway?

7.4 AN EXTENSION

Example 3 A man is repaying £25 000 at £200 per month. He also decides to pay back £250 at the end of the first year, £500 at the end of the second year, £750 at the end of the third year, and so on. When will he have repaid the £25 000?

Solution   Let U_n = sum owed at the beginning of the nth year.

$$U_2 = U_1 - 2400 - 250$$
$$U_3 = U_2 - 2400 - 250 \times 2$$
$$U_4 = U_3 - 2400 - 250 \times 3$$
$$\vdots$$
$$U_n = U_{n-1} - 2400 - 250(n - 1)$$

The general form of a recurrence relation such as this is

$$U_n = M U_{n-1} + C + f(n)$$

so we cannot use the solution already derived. So we try an iterative approach.

$$U_1 = 25\,000$$
$$U_2 = 25\,000 - 2400 - 250$$
$$U_3 = (25\,000 - 2400 - 250) - 2400 - 500$$
$$= 25\,000 - 2400 \times 2 - 250(1 + 2)$$
$$U_4 = 25\,000 - 2400 \times 3 - 250(1 + 2 + 3)$$

Hence

$$U_n = 25\,000 - (n - 1)2400 - 250 \sum_{r=1}^{n-1} r$$

$$U_n = 25\,000 - (n - 1)2400 - \frac{250n(n - 1)}{2}$$

When he has repaid the £25 000, $U_n = 0$; so that

$$0 = 25\,000 - 2400n + 2400 - 125n^2 + 125n$$
$$125n^2 + 2275n - 27\,400 = 0$$
$$5n^2 + 91n - 1096 = 0$$

However, since n is a positive integer and this equation has no integer solution, we solve the related equation

$$5x^2 + 91x - 1096 = 0$$

where x can take any real value. The positive solution is $x = 8.278$.

This would seem to indicate that the money will be repaid sometime during the eighth year. The additional payment is only paid at the end of each year so we investigate U_8.

$$U_8 = 25\,000 - 7 \times 2400 - 125 \times 8 \times 7$$

$$U_8 = 1200$$

i.e. at the beginning of the eighth year (i.e. after seven years) the amount owing is £1200 which will be paid off in six monthly instalments. Therefore the money will be repaid in exactly $7\frac{1}{2}$ years.

Exercise 4.1   An elderly lady sells her house and goes to live in an old people's home. She invests the money from the house sale and £3000 is paid into her bank account at the beginning of each year. Her living expenses are £2000 in the first year but rise by £200 per year after that. In what year will she first be overdrawn?

Exercise 4.2   A pig farmer has a large rectangular yard containing 52 pigs. He wishes to put up a number of straight fences across the yard to divide it into at least 52 regions. He needs to calculate the minimum number of fences required. In order to do this he needs to find the maximum number of regions produced by a given number of fences.

Let U_n = *maximum* number of regions produced by n fences.

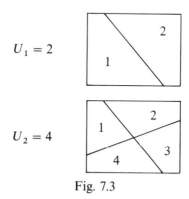

$$U_1 = 2$$

$$U_2 = 4$$

Fig. 7.3

(i) Find, by trial and error, or otherwise, the values of U_n for $n = 3$ and $n = 4$.

(ii) Find a recurrence relation between U_n and U_{n-1}.

(iii) Use the relation to find U_5, U_6,... and hence give the answer to the farmer's problem.

(iv) Solve the relation found in (ii) given that $U_1 = 2$, and hence find the number of regions produced by 20 fences.

7.5 MISCELLANEOUS EXERCISES

M1 Find the general solutions of each of the following equations:

(i) $U_n = \frac{1}{5} U_{n-1}$ (ii) $U_n = 5U_{n-1} + 8$

(iii) $U_n = U_{n-1} - 4$ (iv) $3U_n = 2U_{n-1}$
(v) $2U_n + U_{n-1} = 1$ (vi) $4U_n + 4U_{n-1} = 1$
(vii) $4U_n - 4U_{n-1} = 1$ (viii) $5U_{n+1} = 4U_n$
(ix) $U_{n-1} = 3U_n + 6$ (x) $3U_{n-2} = 3U_{n-1} - 1$

M2 Find the general solution of $U_n = U_{n-1} + 3$. Hence solve the relation for $U_1 = 5$. Find U_{20}.

M3 Solve the following recurrence relations:
   (i) $10U_n = 3U_{n-1}$ and $U_1 = 50$
   (ii) $5U_n + 10U_{n-1} = 33$ and $U_1 = 4.2$
   (iii) $4U_{n+1} = 2U_n + 5$ and $U_1 = \frac{11}{2}$
   (iv) $U_{n-1} = U_{n-2} + 1$ and $U_1 = -1$

M4 (i) If $U_n = 3U_{n-1} + 4$ and $U_1 = 8$ find U_{10}
   (ii) If $2U_n + 4U_{n-1} + 1 = 0$ and $U_1 = \frac{5}{6}$ find U_{12}

M5 (i) If $U_n = 5U_{n-1}$ and $U_6 = 6250$ find U_1
   (ii) If $U_n = 2U_{n-1} + 5$ and $U_7 = 635$ find U_1

M6 If $U_n = U_{n-1} + K$, $U_1 = 3$ and $U_{10} = 93$ find K

M7 If $2U_n = 4U_{n-1} + p$, $U_1 = 1$ and $U_9 = 1021$ find p

M8 (i) £1000 is invested at a fixed rate of 8% p.a., the interest being calculated and added on yearly. How much will the investment be worth after 10 years?
   (ii) If the interest is calculated and added on every six months how much will the investment be worth after 10 years?
   (iii) If the interest is calculated and added on quarterly how much will it be worth after 10 years?

M9 Spode Building Society offers a rate of 9% p.a. calculated every six months. The Gilded Gingerbread Building Society offers a rate of

$10\frac{1}{4}\%$ p.a. calculated annually. In which of the two schemes would you invest a windfall of £500 for 5 years? How much extra would you earn?

M10 Mr and Mrs Bloggitt buy a house and take out a twenty-five year mortgage for £20 000 at 10.5% p.a.

(i) Find the monthly repayments.
(ii) How much do they still owe after 3 years?
(iii) Exactly 3 years after they took out the mortgage the interest rate drops to 9.5%. They elect to continue paying the same monthly payments. How many more years will they need to pay off their mortgage?

M11 A survey is made once every year of the number of seals on Seal Island. During the year the number born is approximately 40% of the population at the beginning of the year and the death-rate is approximately 15% of the same number. At the beginning of the 1985 the population was almost exactly 5000.

(i) Estimate the population in January 1990.
(ii) In what year will the population reach 20 000?
(iii) When the population reaches 20 000 an annual seal cull is organised to restrict the population growth. The cull is set at 2000 seals per year. Estimate the population 5 years later.
(iv) Calculate the size of cull required to reduce the population from 20 000 to around 10 000 in 10 years.
(v) When the population has been reduced to 10 000 calculate the size of the cull required to reduce it to 10 000 each year.

M12 In December 1789 Colonel Fitzwilliam dies leaving his daughter Jemima well provided for. The interest from his estate amounts to £500 a year. In 1790 her living expenses are £300 but they rise by £40 each year. In what year will she need to start living off her capital or reduce her living expenses if her circumstances do not change.

M13 (i) On Amanda Black's first birthday her grandparents invested £100 at a fixed rate of compound interest of 8%. If she left it to accumulate until her eighteenth birthday how much would she have?
(ii) If however, her grandparents add £20 to the investment on her 2nd, 3rd,... 18th birthdays, how much will she have on her eighteenth birthday?
(iii) If, on reflection, they decided to add £5, £10, £15,... on her 2nd, 3rd,... 18th birthdays, how much will she have on her eighteenth birthday?

8

Recurrence Relations—2

8.1 INTRODUCTION

A camp site at Costa Lotta in August charges £p per pitch for two weeks. If the owner increases the price, the demand for the holiday falls and, conversely, a drop in price produces a rise in demand. So he sets his price for the following season according to the change in demand over the previous two years.

If p_r is the price charged and d_r is the demand in year r, he calculates that the connection between them is

$$d_r = 110 - 0.5p_r \qquad (1)$$

In order to set the price the following year he uses the relationship

increase in price = 0.5 (increases in demand over previous two years)

In terms of p and d we write this as

$$p_{r+1} - p_r = 0.5(d_r - d_{r-1}) \qquad (2)$$

Now with these two equations we derive a recurrence relation for p_r and hence predict the price charged and the number of pitches let per fortnight in the August of various years. We have two expressions connecting p and d:

(i) $d_r = 110 - 0.5p_r$

(ii) $p_{r+1} - p_r = 0.5(d_r - d_{r-1})$

So

$$p_{r+1} - p_r = 0.5\,[(110 - 0.5p_r) - (110 - 0.5p_{r-1})]$$
$$= -0.25p_r + 0.25p_{r-1}$$

Hence

$$p_{r+1} = 0.75p_r + 0.25p_{r-1}$$

This is called a *second order recurrence relation* and it is equations of this sort that we discuss in this chapter.

To illustrate its use, suppose further that the camp site owner charges £120 in the tenth year and £100 in the eleventh. How much should he charge in the thirteenth? If p_{10} is 120 and p_{11} is 100 then

$$p_{12} = 0.75 \times 100 + 0.25 \times 120$$
$$= 75 + 30$$
$$= 105$$

and

$$p_{13} = 0.75 \times 105 + 0.25 \times 100$$
$$= 78.75 + 25$$
$$= 103.75$$

Hence the charge should be £103.75p. Further

$$d_{13} = 110 - 0.5 \times p_{13}$$
$$= 110 - 0.5 \times 103.75$$
$$= 110 - 51.875$$
$$= 58.125$$

But d is an estimate for the number of pitches let and must therefore be an integer. So we predict that the owner will charge £103.75 and let around 58 pitches.

Exercise 1.1 Calculate the cost of a pitch and the predicted number of lettings for the 14th, 15th and 18th years. Comment on your results.

Exercise 1.2 In the first year a chalet operator leases 100 chalets at £250 each. In the following year he drops his price to £240 and leases 140 chalets. Assuming cost p and demand d are connected by a relationship of the form $d = A - Bp$, calculate A and B. If $p_{r+1} - p_r = -\frac{3}{4}(d_r - d_{r-1})$ find a recurrence relation for p_r. What will be the cost in the third year and how many chalets are likely to be let?

8.2 GENERAL SECOND ORDER RECURRENCE RELATIONS

The general form for a second order recurrence relation is

$$U_n = SU_{n-1} + tU_{n-2}.$$

Can we find a general solution for equations of this type? Looking at solutions for first order recurrence relations it seems reasonable to try

$$U_n = M^n U_1.$$

Putting this in the recurrence relation above gives

$$M^n U_1 = SM^{n-1}U_1 + tM^{n-2}U_1$$

$$M^{n-2}U_1(M^2 - SM - t) = 0$$

Both $M = 0$ and $U_1 = 0$ give trivial solutions. So for non-trivial solutions we consider $M^2 - SM - t = 0$. This equation for M is called the *auxiliary equation*. The roots are

$$M_1 = \frac{S + \sqrt{S^2 + 4t}}{2} \quad \text{and} \quad M_2 = \frac{S - \sqrt{S^2 + 4t}}{2} \tag{1}$$

Hence $U_n = M_1^n U_1$ is a solution and so is $U_n = M_2^n U_1$. Here we are assuming that $M_1 \neq M_2$, but allowing M_1 and M_2 to be real or complex. We are now going to investigate whether $A(M_1)^n$, for *any* constant A, is also a solution. (We have already looked at the special case when $A = U_1$.) In this case

$$U_n - SU_{n-1} - tU_{n-2} = AM_1^n - ASM_1^{n-1} - AtM_1^{n-2}$$

$$= AM_1^{n-2}[M_1^2 - SM_1 - t]$$

$$= 0$$

since M_1 is a root of $M^2 - SM - t = 0$. So AM_1^n and similarly BM_2^n are both solutions for U_n, for any value of A and B. Now

$$AM_1^n = ASM_1^{n-1} + AtM_1^{n-2}$$

and

$$BM_2^n = BSM_2^{n-1} + BtM_2^{n-2}$$

Adding:

$$(AM_1^n + BM_2^n) = S(AM_1^{n-1} + BM_2^{n-1}) + t(AM_1^{n-2} + BM_2^{n-2})$$

Hence it can be seen that $AM_1^n + BM_2^n$ is also a solution. We conclude:

> $U_n = (AM_1^n + BM_2^n)$ is the general solution
> of the second order recurrence relation
> $U_n = SU_{n-1} + tU_{n-2}.$ $(M_1 \neq M_2)$

But to get this result we assumed that $M_1 \neq M_2$. What happens if $M_1 = M_2$? We then have $U_n = AM_1^n + BM_1^n = (A + B)M_1^n = CM_1^n$ for some constant C. When $M_1 \neq M_2$ the general solution is composed of two different functions of n. When $M_1 = M_2$ we apparently have only one function of n. Is there a second function of n which is a solution in the case of equal roots?

Consider $U_n = DnM_1^n$ (i.e. $n \times DM_1^{n-1}$), where D is some constant. Then $U_n - SU_{n-1} - tU_{n-2}$ becomes

$$DnM_1^n - SD(n-1)M_1^{n-1} - tD(n-2)M_1^{n-2}$$
$$= DM_1^{n-2}[nM_1^2 - S(n-1)M_1 - t(n-2)].$$

We know that M_1 is a root of the auxiliary equation

$$M^2 - SM - t = 0.$$

Since this equation has equal roots we know further from equation (1) that

$$S^2 + 4t = 0 \qquad (2)$$

and so

$$M_1 = \frac{S}{2}. \qquad (3)$$

Now consider the expression

$$nM_1^2 - S(n-1)M_1 - t(n-2)$$

which can be rearranged as

$$n(M_1^2 - SM_1 - t) + SM_1 + 2t = n.0 + SM_1 + 2t$$

$$= \frac{S^2}{2} + 2t \qquad \text{(using equation (3))}$$

$$= \frac{1}{2}(S^2 + 4t) = 0 \qquad \text{(using equation (2))}$$

Hence, if $U_n = DnM_1^n$ then $U_n - SU_{n-1} - tU_{n-2} = 0$, or

$$U_n = SU_{n-1} + tU_{n-2}$$

So, DnM_1^n is also a solution of the recurrence relation for the special case that the auxiliary equation has equal roots. To summarise:

The general solution of $U_n = SU_{n-1} + tU_{n-2}$ is

$$U_n = AM_1^n + BM_2^n, \quad \text{when} \quad M_1 \neq M_2$$

and

$$U_n = (C + Dn)M_1^n, \quad \text{when} \quad M_1 = M_2$$

where A, B, C, D are arbitrary constants dependent on initial conditions.

Note: Fair questions to ask at this stage are:

'Why did we look for a second function which might be a solution?' and 'How do we know there aren't any more solutions, in both cases?'

It is a fact that general solutions to both first order recurrence relations and first order differential equations have just one arbitrary constant. Also, general solutions to both second order recurrence relations and second order differential equations have two arbitrary constants. When $M_1 = M_2$ the solution first obtained was

$$U_n = (A + B)M_1^n$$

which reduces to

$$U_n = CM_1^n$$

This has only one arbitrary constant, so we had to look for another solution. Having found one we then had a general solution with two arbitrary constants and hence all solutions will be of this form. The proof of this is beyond the scope of this book.

Example   Solve the recurrence relation

$$U_n + 4U_{n-2} = 0$$

given that $U_1 = 8i$, $U_2 = -8$.

Solution   The auxiliary equation is $M^2 + 4 = 0$. Solving for M,

$$M = \pm 2i$$

The general solution is

$$U_n = A(2i)^n + B(-2i)^n$$

Now $U_1 = 8i$ so that

$$8i = A2i - B2i$$
$$4 = A - B$$

and $U_2 = -8$ so that

$$-8 = A(2i)^2 + B(-2i)^2$$
$$-8 = -4A - 4B$$
$$2 = A + B$$

Solving for A and B, we have

$$A = 3 \quad \text{and} \quad B = -1.$$

The particular solution is $\underline{U_n = 3(2i)^n - (-2i)^n}$.

Exercise 2.1 Find general solutions for the following recurrence relations:

(i) $U_n = 5U_{n-1} - 6U_{n-2}$ (ii) $U_n - 4U_{n-1} + 4U_{n-2} = 0$

(iii) $U_n - 2U_{n-1} = 3U_{n-2}$ (iv) $U_n + U_{n-1} + U_{n-2} = 0$

(v) $4U_n = 20U_{n-1} - 25U_{n-2}$ (vi) $U_n + 16U_{n-2} = 0$

Exercise 2.2 Find particular solutions to the following that satisfy the given conditions.

(i) $U_n = 4U_{n-1} + 5U_{n-2}$ and $U_1 = 1, U_2 = 14$

(ii) $16U_n + U_{n-2} = 8U_{n-1}$ and $U_1 = 16, U_2 = 2$

(iii) $U_n = 2U_{n-1} - U_{n-2}$ and $U_1 = 3, U_2 = 7$

(iv) $U_n = 2U_{n-1} + U_{n-2}$ and $U_1 = 1 + \sqrt{2}, U_2 = 3 + 2\sqrt{2}$

Exercise 2.3 Solve $U_n + 25U_{n-2} = 0$ given that

(i) $U_1 = 5, U_2 = 50i$ (ii) $U_1 = 5, U_2 = 50.$

Exercise 2.4 Solve $U_n - U_{n-2} = 0$ given $U_1 = 3, U_2 = 7$.

Hence find U_{37} and U_{38}. Could you have found U_{37} and U_{38} quickly without solving the recurrence relation?

Exercise 2.5 Solve $U_n - 2U_{n-1} + 3U_{n-2} = 0$ given that $U_1 = 4, U_2 = -4$.

8.3   APPLICATIONS

8.3.1   A Bee Colony

A male bee, called a drone, has a mother but no father. The queen bee lays fertilised eggs and unfertilised eggs. The fertilised eggs hatch into females, either queens or workers. Drones hatch from unfertilised eggs.

    Let us trace backwards the ancestry of a drone. The drone will have had a mother and the mother will have had both a mother and a father. The family tree would be as shown in Fig. 8.1. Every female had a mother and a father.

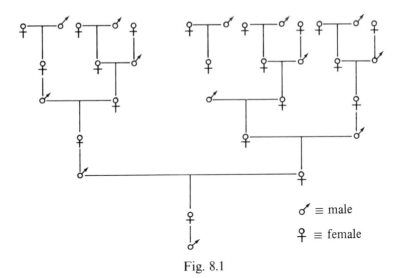

$\sigma' \equiv$ male

$\varphi \equiv$ female

Fig. 8.1

Every male had only a mother. Find the number of bees in the nth generation back.

If U_n = number of ancestral bees in the nth generation back,

$$U_1 = 1 \qquad (1\varphi)$$
$$U_2 = 2 \qquad (1\varphi + 1\sigma')$$
$$U_3 = 3 \qquad (2\varphi + 1\sigma')$$
$$U_4 = 5 \qquad (3\varphi + 2\sigma')$$
$$U_5 = 8 \qquad (5\varphi + 3\sigma')$$

The recurrence relation is a simple one:

$$U_n = U_{n-1} + U_{n-2}.$$

The auxiliary equation is $M^2 - M - 1 = 0$. Solving for M we have two values

$$M_1 = \frac{1 + \sqrt{5}}{2} \quad \text{and} \quad M_2 = \frac{1 - \sqrt{5}}{2}$$

$M_1 \neq M_2$ so that the general solution is

$$U_n = A\left(\frac{1 + \sqrt{5}}{2}\right)^n + B\left(\frac{1 - \sqrt{5}}{2}\right)^n$$

But we know that $U_1 = 1$ and $U_2 = 2$.

$$U_1 = 1 \text{ gives} \quad 1 = A\left(\frac{1 + \sqrt{5}}{2}\right)^1 + B\left(\frac{1 - \sqrt{5}}{2}\right)^1$$

$$2 = A(1 + \sqrt{5}) + B(1 - \sqrt{5}) \tag{1}$$

and

$$U_2 = 2 \text{ gives} \quad 2 = A\left(\frac{1 + \sqrt{5}}{2}\right)^2 + B\left(\frac{1 - \sqrt{5}}{2}\right)^2$$

$$8 = A(1 + \sqrt{5})^2 + B(1 - \sqrt{5})^2 \tag{2}$$

Solving for A and B,

$(1) \times (1 + \sqrt{5})$ gives $2(1 + \sqrt{5}) = A(1 + \sqrt{5})^2 + B(1 - \sqrt{5})(1 + \sqrt{5})$ (3)

Subtracting (2) from (3):

$$2(1 + \sqrt{5}) - 8 = B(1 - \sqrt{5})[1 + \sqrt{5} - (1 - \sqrt{5})]$$

$$-6 + 2\sqrt{5} = B(1 - \sqrt{5})2\sqrt{5} = 2B(\sqrt{5} - 5).$$

Hence

$$B = \frac{\sqrt{5} - 3}{\sqrt{5} - 5} = \frac{5 - \sqrt{5}}{10},$$

and

$$A = \frac{\sqrt{5} + 3}{\sqrt{5} + 5} = \frac{5 + \sqrt{5}}{10}.$$

The number of bees in the nth generation back is given by

$$U_n = \left(\frac{5 + \sqrt{5}}{10}\right)\left(\frac{1 + \sqrt{5}}{2}\right)^n + \left(\frac{5 - \sqrt{5}}{10}\right)\left(\frac{1 - \sqrt{5}}{2}\right)^n$$

8.3.2 Modelling the Economy

A simple model for a nation's economy could be expressed in terms of government expenditure G, investment I, and public expenditure on consumables P. If T is the total national income, then at any time, t,

$$T_t = G_t + I_t + P_t$$

Clearly G, I and P are not independent of each other. We will assume that

(i) The government has a steady programme of expenditure, so $G_t = G$ (G constant).

(ii) The greater the total income in any one year, the more there will be to spend on consumables the next year, so $P_t = AT_{t-1}$ (A constant).

(iii) Any increase in public spending will promote extra investment, so

$$I_t = B(P_t - P_{t-1}) \quad (B \text{ constant})$$

combining these equations we get

$$T_t = G + B(P_t - P_{t-1}) + P_t$$

$$= G + (B+1)AT_{t-1} - BAT_{t-2}$$

This is a second order recurrence relation *with an added constant.*

In order to explore this model of the economy further we need some specific values for the constants A, B and G.

(i) Without loss of generality we can take $G = 1$. All values of P, I and T are thus then expressed as multiples of the unit of government expenditure.

(ii) Suppose half the total income will be spent on consumables in the following year, then

$$P_t = \tfrac{1}{2}T_{t-1} \qquad (A = \tfrac{1}{2})$$

(iii) Suppose investment is at the level of the change in consumer spending, then

$$I_t = P_t - P_{t-1} \qquad (B = 1)$$

We now have

$$T_t = T_{t-1} - \tfrac{1}{2}T_{t-2} + 1.$$

The value of such a model of the economy lies in its ability to predict future events. Taking $T_1 = 1$ and $T_2 = 2$ as initial values of the total income, then

$T_1 = 1$	$T_9 = 1.9375$
$T_2 = 2$	$T_{10} = 2$
$T_3 = 2.5$	$T_{11} = 2.03125$
$T_4 = 2.5$	$T_{12} = 2.03125$
$T_5 = 2.25$	$T_{13} = 2.015625$
$T_6 = 2$	$T_{14} = 2$
$T_7 = 1.875$	$T_{15} = 1.9921875$
$T_8 = 1.875$	etc.

The value of the total income is stabilising fairly rapidly at around 2 units of government expenditure. How dependent is the stability of the economy on the initial values of A and B?

Look at the situation where the government goes for heavy investment. For example, $A = \frac{1}{2}$ and $B = 3$.

$$T_t = 4 \times \tfrac{1}{2} T_{t-1} - 3 \times \tfrac{1}{2} T_{t-2} + 1$$

$$= 2T_{t-1} - 1.5T_{t-2} + 1$$

$$T_1 = 1 \qquad T_3 = 3.5$$

$$T_2 = 2 \qquad T_4 = 5$$

A booming economy—or is it?

$$T_5 = 5.75 \qquad T_7 = 2.375$$

$$T_6 = 5 \qquad T_8 = -1.75$$

The total economy has crashed with the country 1.75 units in the red!

Exercise 3.1 This question concerns the model for the bee colony.

(i) By continuing the sequence, find U_{10}, the number of ancestral bees 10 generations ago.
(ii) Find U_{10}, by rearranging the solution given in the example and then by using the binomial theorem.
(iii) Find U_{10} using the solution and a calculator.

Exercise 3.2 Fibonacci, an Italian merchant, posed the following problem: How many pairs of rabbits will there be after n months, beginning with a single pair, if each month each pair produces a new pair, which itself becomes productive after two months? Assume that the original pair do not breed until the second month and no rabbits die. The table below gives the number of rabbits at the beginning of each month.

Month (n)	1	2	3	4
No. of pairs (U_n)	1	1	2	3

Find a recurrence relation for U_n and hence, by solving it, find the number of rabbits after twenty months.

Exercise 3.3   A gerbil breeder starts with one pair of gerbils. Each pair of gerbils produces 2 pairs of babies at the age of two months and every month thereafter. By extending the family tree for three more generations, find a recurrence relation involving the number of pairs of gerbils at the beginning of each month. Hence, by solving the recurrence relation, find the number of pairs of gerbils (assuming no deaths occur) after 1 year.

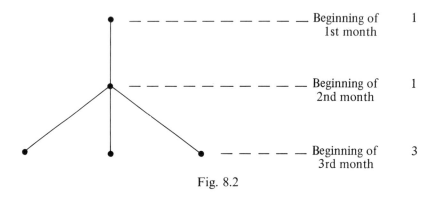

Fig. 8.2

Exercise 3.4   One pair of mice produce two pairs of young per month starting at one month old. Their owner sells pairs to other breeders, after they have bred twice for him. If he starts with one pair of newborn mice find the number of pairs of mice he will have at the beginning of the second, third and fourth months. Hence find a recurrence relation for the number of pairs at the beginning of any month. Using this relation find how many pairs he will have after five months.

If he starts with three pairs of newborn mice, show that the predicted number of pairs at the beginning of the nth month is

$$\frac{\sqrt{3}}{4} [(1 + \sqrt{3})^{n+1} - (1 - \sqrt{3})^{n+1}]$$

Exercise 3.5   In the following questions, use the model of the economy (see section 8.3.2) $T_t = G_t + I_t + P_t$.

(i) If G_t is constant, $P_t = 0.9T_{t-1}$, $I_t = 0.6(P_t - P_{t-1})$, discover whether or not the economy will be stable in the long run, for $T_1 = 1$ and $T_2 = 2$.

(ii) Investigate the stability of the economy if G_t is constant, $P_t = 0.2T_{t-1}$ and $I_t = 6(P_t - P_{t-1})$.

(iii) Explore other values for A and B and investigate which situations lead to a stable economy. Do different values of T_1 and T_2 affect the long term economy?

8.4 MISCELLANEOUS EXERCISES

M1 Find the general solution of each of the following recurrence relations:

(i) $u_n = 6u_{n-2} - u_{n-1}$
(ii) $u_n + 25u_{n-2} = 10u_{n-1}$
(iii) $u_{n+1} = 4u_{n-1}$
(iv) $u_{n+2} + 9u_n = 0$
(v) $u_{n+1} - 2u_n - u_{n-1} = 0$
(vi) $u_{n+4} - 4u_{n+3} + 9u_{n+2} = 0$

M2 Find the particular solutions for $u_{n+1} = 4u_{n-1} + 3u_n$.

(i)   When $u_1 = 13$, $u_2 = 47$.
(ii) When $u_1 = 4$, $u_2 = 16$.
(iii) When $u_0 = 1$, $u_1 = -1$.

M3 Find the particular solution for $u_n + 2u_{n-1} = 2u_{u-2}$,

(i)   When $u_2 = 2 - \sqrt{3}$, $u_3 = -5 - 6\sqrt{3}$.
(ii) When $u_1 = -2$, $u_0 = 2$.
(iii) When $u_2 = -8\sqrt{3}$, $u_1 = 4\sqrt{3}$.

M4 (i)   Find the general solution for $u_{n+2} + 5u_n = 4u_{n+1}$
(ii) Find the particular solution for $u_{n+2} + 5u_n = 4u_{n+1}$ given that $u_1 = -2$ and $u_2 = -8$. Hence find u_3 and u_4
(iii) Find the particular solution for $u_{n+2} + 5u_n = 4u_{n+1}$ given that $u_1 = 6$ and $u_0 = 4$. Use the binomial theorem, or otherwise, to find u_5.

M5 An experiment gives a series of results

$$0, \quad 6, \quad 30, \quad 114, \ldots$$

It is known that they satisfy a recurrence relation of the form

$$u_n + ku_{n-1} + 1u_{n-2} = 0.$$

Find and solve the relation. Hence find the tenth term in the series.

M6 Another experiment gives the results

$$4, \quad 12, \quad 28, \quad 68, \ldots$$

It also satisfies a recurrence relation of the form

$$u_n + ku_{n-1} + 1u_{n-2} = 0.$$

Find and solve the relation. By expanding the solution, find the sixth term of the series of results.

M7 The numbers 1, 3, 4, 7,... are a set of results known to satisfy a recurrence relation of the form

$$u_n = pu_{n-1} + qu_{n-2}.$$

Find p and q and solve the recurrence relation obtained.

M8 A fruitgrower specialises in a rare exotic fruit. The propagation and endurance of the plant which bears the fruit can be modelled by using the following assumptions which the grower has formulated from long experience.

(a) The plants are kept in a large heated greenhouse in which the grower can control the total environment. With care, the grower succeeds in bringing 80% of the plants through the British winter. That is, 80% of the plants alive at the end of one growing season are flourishing at the start of the next. The remaining 20% of the plants which die are the older and weaker plants. There are no losses of plants during the growing season.

(b) The grower takes 10 seeds from each plant during the growing season. These seeds are set in a growing medium and, on average, 24% of the seeds produce healthy plants which can be planted out two years after the start of the season in which the seeds are collected.

Express the problem of finding the number u_r of mature plants in the greenhouse in the growing season r as a recurrence relation. Obtain the general solution of this recurrence relation. Initially, at the beginning of growing season 0, the grower planted 40 new plants. How many of these survived the first winter? Using these two values, obtain an expression for the number of mature plants the grower has in growing season r. Obtain an estimate of the number of plants the grower has in growing season 8 (© Open University).

M9 (i) (a) In a new colony of geese there are 10 pairs of birds, none of which produce eggs in their first year. Each subsequent year, pairs of birds which are in their second and later year produce, on average, 4 eggs (two male and two female). If there are no deaths, show that the recurrence relation which models this population is given by

$$u_{r+1} = u_r + 2u_{r-1} \text{ with } u_0 = 10 \text{ and } u_1 = 10.$$

(b) What is the general solution of this recurrence relation?

(c) What is the particular solution with the above initial conditions?

(d) What is the long term behaviour of this population?

(ii) (a) If 40% of the birds die in their first year, and 30% of the older
      birds die in any one year, what is the new recurrence relation?
   (b) Determine the general solution of this recurrence relation.
   (c) What is the particular solution if $u_0 = 10$ and $u_1 = 10$?
   (d) What is the long-term behaviour of the population?

   (© Open University).

9

Dynamic Programming

9.1 SHORTEST PATH REVISITED

Dynamic programming (DP) was first developed as a management technique by Richard Bellman and others in the 1950s, since when it has been applied in areas such as production planning, stock control, allocation of resources, maintenance and replacement of equipment, investment planning and process design. The general class of problems dealt with by DP involve a sequence of decisions, the object being to optimise time or profit or whatever by taking the correct decision at each stage. We shall consider only the simplest cases, in which the return (time, profit, ...) resulting from every possible decision is known in advance. Even so, this allows us to look at some important problems in quite a realistic way.

The solution of many DP problems is made easier by drawing a directed network, and the easiest problems are about finding the shortest path through such a network from a starting point S to a terminus T. In the network shown in Fig. 9.1, you can imagine that S, A, B, ..., T are towns and that the numbers shown on the connecting arcs are distances in miles. What is the shortest route through the network from S to T ?

We developed an algorithm in Chapter 6.2 to investigate problems of this type. The basic idea of the shortest path algorithm was to work forwards through the network checking each route and choosing the shortest path in stages. The result of applying the algorithm to this problem is a shortest path of 15 miles. An alternative process is to work backwards from the end vertex T and this is the essence of the dynamic programming method that we develop in section 9.2.

236

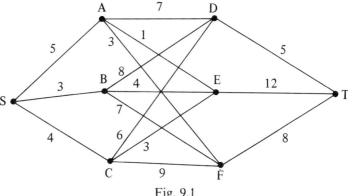

Fig. 9.1

It seems natural in what appears to be a road network to attempt to minimise the sum of arc lengths constituting a route from S to T. However, the networks we shall use will often have no geographical meaning and even when they have, the figures marked on the arcs may not represent distances. Suppose now, for instance, that the numbers in Fig. 9.1 are *expected profits* that an itinerant pedlar allocates to the various stages of a journey. Assuming that he wants to *maximise* total expected profit how should he proceed from S to T?

Work through the following exercises by evaluating the total weights along every possible path from S to T.

Exercise 1.1 If the numbers on the arcs in Fig. 9.2 represent distances, find the shortest distance through these networks from S to T.

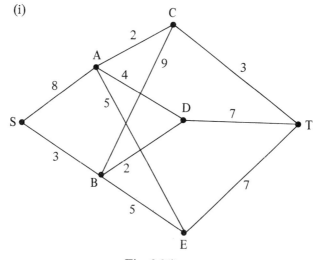

Fig. 9.2(i)

(ii)

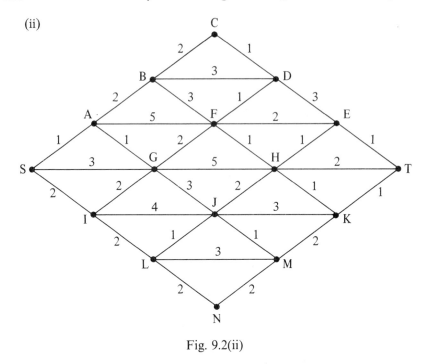

Fig. 9.2(ii)

Exercise 1.2   The network in Fig. 9.3 represents a group of cities through which a carrier is to travel from S to T. The numbers represent his profit in tens of £'s for each possible leg. Find the optimal route of three legs.

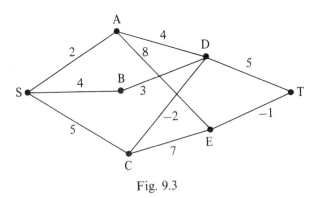

Fig. 9.3

Exercise 1.3   Can you find a route S–T in Fig. 9.4 with a total length as low as 18?

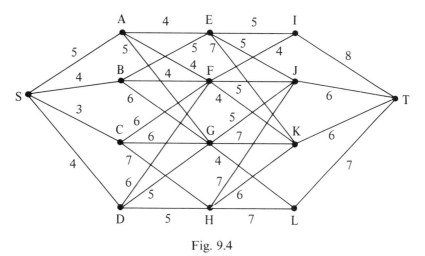

Fig. 9.4

9.2 WORKING BACKWARDS

In solving the exercises in section 9.1 you would have carried out quite a large number of calculations, some of which are not really necessary. If an arc has a large weight relative to the other arcs then it would seem reasonable to avoid the arc in finding the shortest path. Of course, the shortest path algorithm might have reduced the amount of work, but we still have to visit each vertex. In Exercise 1.3 the computation becomes irksome and we can anticipate that matters will get much worse as we elaborate our networks still further. Let us see how bad things get. Suppose we had programmed a computer to solve the first problem in section 9.1 by considering every possible route S–T. How many computations would it need to make? By a computation here we mean

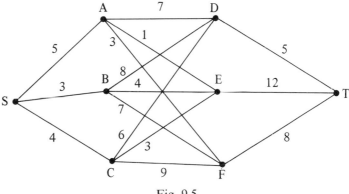

Fig. 9.5

the addition of two numbers or the comparison of two numbers. Well, there are nine possible routes for each of which two additions must be made, giving 18 additions. Finally, to compare the 9 route lengths, 8 comparisons are needed. So the total number of computations is

$$18 + 8 = 26.$$

Now try working out the number of computations needed to answer Exercise 1.3 by the method of exhausting all possible routes.

There are

$$4 \times 3 \times 3 = 36 \text{ paths}$$

each involving three additions, giving

$$36 \times 3 = 108 \text{ additions.}$$

Finally to compare the paths we must make 35 comparisons. So there are

$$108 + 35 = 143 \text{ computations.}$$

You will see that the amount of computation is increasing in an alarming way as the network becomes more complex and the need for some systematic means of cutting it down becomes apparent, even when a computer is being used (see Exercise 2.3).

To see how dynamic programming works we work through the problem in Fig. 9.5 again, *backwards*, starting at T.

Consider the last stage D, E, F to T.

If we are at D, for example, there is only one way to T—along the arc DT with weight 5. So we mark this path, which is optimal from this vertex since there are no other choices, by marking the distance involved with (∗) and note the actual distance to T in a box.

Similarly we label E with ⎡12⎤ and F with ⎡8⎤

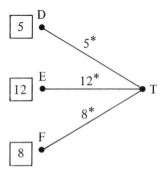

Fig. 9.6

We now move back to the previous stage, starting from A, B, C.

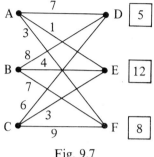

Fig. 9.7

At A there are three possible paths:

$$ADT = 7 + 5 = 12$$
$$AET = 1 + 12 = 13$$
$$AFT = 3 + 8 = 11 \leftarrow \text{best route}$$

So we mark the 3 on the arc AF to show that this is on the optimal route from A to T, and note the distance $\boxed{11}$ next to the vertex A.

Similarly for the vertex B, there are three possible paths:

$$BDT = 8 + 5 \ = 13 \leftarrow \text{best route}$$
$$BET = 4 + 12 = 16$$
$$BFT = 7 + 8 \ = 15$$

and so we mark the 8 on arc BD and mark B with $\boxed{13}$. Similarly for C; we then have the diagram shown in Fig. 9.8. So finally to S. There are three choices:

$$S\text{--}A\text{--}T = 5 + 11 = 16$$
$$S\text{--}B\text{--}T = 3 + 13 = 16$$
$$S\text{--}C\text{--}T = 4 + 11 = 15 \leftarrow \text{best route}$$

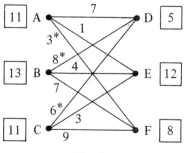

Fig. 9.8

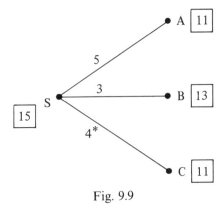

Fig. 9.9

So we mark S with $\boxed{15}$ and mark the 4 on arc SC. We now have the final diagram showing that the shortest distance from S to T is 15 and the path is given by tracing a route from S to T along the distances marked with an asterisk in Fig. 9.10. At first sight this might seem a tedious way of solving the

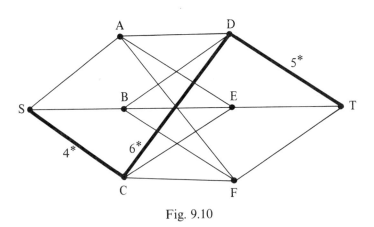

Fig. 9.10

problem, but if we check the number of computations we will see that we have made a saving. For at A, B and C we made 9 additions and at S we made 3 additions—a total of 12 instead of the 18 additions made in looking at every possible route. As the networks get more complicated the amount of saving becomes even more significant.

Exercise 2.1 Find the shortest path through the networks from S to T, starting at T and working backwards.

(i)

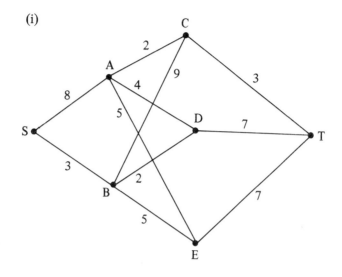

(ii)

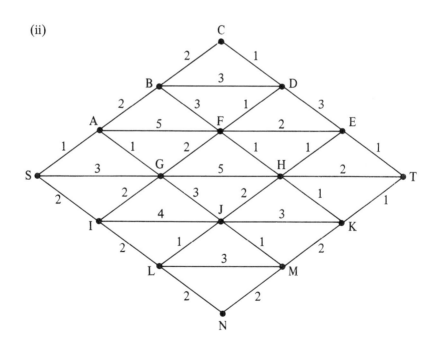

(iii)

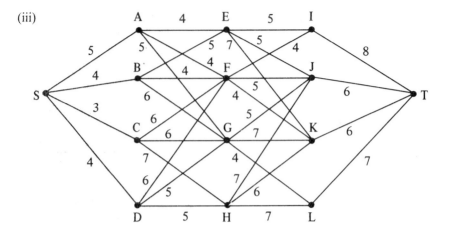

9.3   THE VALUE ITERATION METHOD

The 'backwards' approach starting at T and working through the network towards S to find the optimal path, is usually written out in tabular form. We often do not need to draw a network diagram.

Before introducing it we free ourselves from the geographical viewpoint and use terms which we can apply in all the situations we shall consider. We define the following dynamic programming terminology:

State   a vertex in a network.

Action   a (directed) arc from one state to the next.

Stage   transition from one state to the next; the route from the initial state to the final state is accomplished in a sequence of moves, each move being a stage.

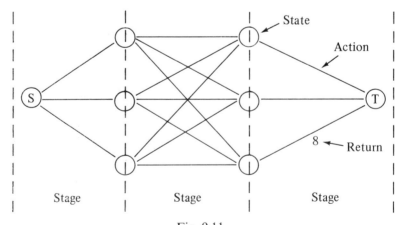

Fig. 9.11

Return   the weight ('pay-off') associated with an action, shown by a number
on the action arc.
Value   the sum of the returns given by a squence of actions.

The *optimal plan* in a DP problem then usually consists of maximising or
minimising the value of a sequence of actions taking us through all the stages.

The method of solution is called *the value iteration method* and we illustrate
the tabular layout by working through the first problem in section 9.1 again.

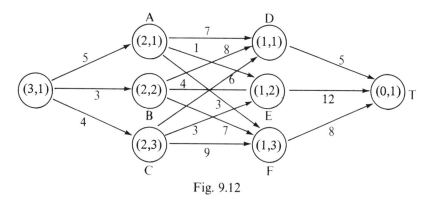

Fig. 9.12

In this figure the ordered pairs of numbers at each vertex show respectively
the number of stages still to be completed and the numbers allocated to the
state. Where there is a choice of actions they are numbered 1, 2, 3 ... taking
the corresponding arcs in order as we move down the diagram. Thus from
state (2, 1) (i.e. vertex A)

> action A–D is denoted by 1
> action A–E is denoted by 2
> action A–F is denoted by 3

We proceed backwards from the end vertex T (0, 1). At T there is nothing to
decide. With one stage to go, we can be at states D, E or F and we form the
table

Stage	State	Action	Value
1	1	1	$\underline{5}$
	2	1	$\underline{12}$
	3	1	$\underline{8}$

To illustrate what is going on in the table we include the relevant diagram from section 9.2. The 'possibles' for an optimal plan are underlined—these correspond to the boxed numbers in the diagram. At stage 2 there are three possible actions from each state to states in stage 1. The table continues

Stage	State	Action	Value
2	1	1	$7 + 5 = 12$
		2	$1 + 12 = 13$
		3	$3 + 8 = \underline{11}$
	2	1	$8 + 5 = \underline{13}$
		2	$4 + 12 = 16$
		3	$7 + 8 = 15$
	3	1	$6 + 5 = \underline{11}$
		2	$3 + 12 = 15$
		3	$9 + 8 = 17$

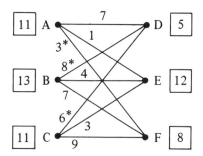

The underlined numbers indicate the shortest distances from the state to T. For example, from state $(2, 1)$ (i.e. A) to $(0, 1)$ (i.e. T) the shortest route is along action 3 (A–F) and then F–T. Now we proceed from stage 3.

There is one state $(3, 1)$ and three possible actions. Now, in the same way as we only considered the boxed numbers in the diagram, here we only need consider the underlined values at stage 2 thus reducing the number of computations.

Stage	State	Action	Value
3	1	1	$5 + 11 = 16$
		2	$3 + 13 = 16$
		3	$4 + 11 = \underline{15}$

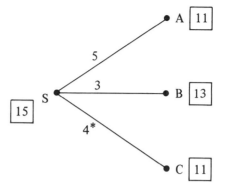

This final stage tells us that the smallest value through the network is 15.

We do not usually present the diagrams; the solution would take the form of the complete table like this:

Stage	State	Action	Value
1	1	<u>1</u>	<u>5</u>
	2	1	<u>12</u>
	3	1	<u>8</u>
2	1	1	$7 + 5 = 12$
		2	$1 + 12 = 13$
		<u>3</u>	$3 + 8 = \underline{11}$
	2	<u>1</u>	$8 + 5 = \underline{13}$
		2	$4 + 12 = 16$
		3	$7 + 8 = 15$
	3	<u>1</u>	$6 + 5 = \underline{11}$
		2	$3 + 12 = 15$
		3	$9 + 8 = 17$
3	1	1	$5 + 11 = 16$
		2	$3 + 13 = 16$
		<u>3</u>	$4 + 11 = \underline{15}$

The optimal plan is seen to be:

> in stage 3, action 3
> in stage 2, action 1
> in stage 1, action 1

and the value of the plan is 15.

By looking down the right-hand column in the table you will see that there are 12 additions and 8 comparisons—a total of 20 computations. The previous total for checking every possible route has been reduced by 6.

Exercise 3.1 (i) Answer Exercise 1.3 by value iteration. (ii) How many computations are needed in your method?

Exercise 3.2 Suppose a shortest path problem has n stages, r states at the end of every stage (except the last) and k actions per state in every stage (except the first and last). (Thus in the case of the last question $n = 4$, $r = 4$ and $k = 3$.) Find the number of computations needed in its solution (i) if the values of all possible plans are found and compared, (ii) by the value iteration method.

Exercise 3.3 Use the value iteration method to find the shortest and longest paths from S to T in these networks.

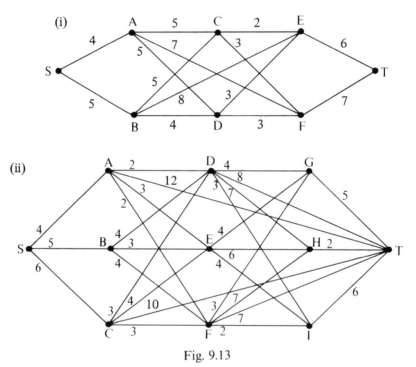

Fig. 9.13

Note: In part (i) S should be labelled (4, 1) even though S–B–E–T is only a three-stage journey. The first ('stage') coordinate in such cases is taken as the *maximum* number of stages to complete.

Exercise 3.4   Water supply for a new town can be provided by adding extra capacity to some sections of an existing network of pipes. The cost in thousands of £'s of adding the necessary capacity to each section is shown in Fig. 9.14. Find the cheapest way to arrange for the new supply if it must all come from either Reservoir 1 or Reservoir 2.

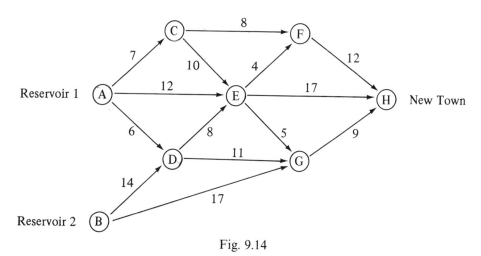

Fig. 9.14

Note: A and B should be labelled (4, 1) and (4, 2).

Exercise 3.5   A company has a warehouse in which it can store a certain commodity. At the beginning of each year the warehouse is either full or empty. If it is full the company chooses one of the following actions.

1. No action. Warehouse is full at start of next year.
2. Sell the contents and purchase fresh stock. Again, warehouse is full at start of next year.
3. Sell the contents and buy nothing. Warehouse is left empty.

If the warehouse is empty at the start of the year the company can either

1. Buy nothing.
2. Buy sufficient to fill the warehouse.

A forecast of the buying and selling prices for the commodity for the next five years has been prepared and is as follows.

Year	1	2	3	4	5
Buying price (£ hundreds)	9	11	13	12	13
Selling price (£ hundreds)	10	11	11	15	13

If the warehouse is kept full for a year with no stock movement there is a charge of £100. Find the optimal plan for the company over the five-year period. Assume that the warehouse is full initially and that it is to be full at the end of the planning period.

Exercise 3.6 A market salesman decides that in a four-week period he will concentrate on country fairs, spending a week in each country town and travelling from one directly to another. He starts and finishes at home and estimates that he ought to allow 40p per mile for his travel. Table 9.1 shows when the fairs are held, Table 9.2 shows the expected profit at each fair and Table 9.3 shows mileages.

Table 9.1

Week	1	2	3	4
Location of fair	A, B, C	D, E	F, G, H	I, J

Table 9.2 Expected profit in £s

A—200	F—150
B—300	G—200
C—250	H—200
D—150	I—200
E—250	J—150

Table 9.3   Mileage chart

	A	B	C	D	E	F	G	H	I	J
Home	25	160	90						105	5
A				55	80					
B				120	180					
C				100	70					
D						75	90	80		
E						60	45	15		
F									75	90
G									105	60
H									30	85

Find the plan which maximises his expected profit.

9.4   VARIATIONS ON THE SHORTEST PATH THEME

As noted in section 9.1, the optimal plan may not always be the 'shortest path'; sometimes the best 'path' is the longest. To appreciate the importance of still other possibilities, consider the problem in Fig. 9.15.

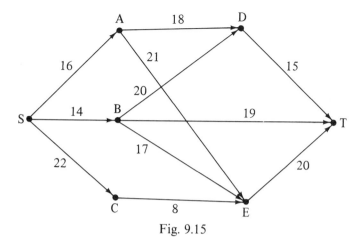

Fig. 9.15

The vertices in this network represent airports and the figures on the arcs distances in hundreds of kilometres. Freight is to be transported from S to T and we wish to maximise the payload. This in turn involves minimising the fuel to be carried on any leg of the journey. Hence we want a route the longest leg of which is as short as possible. When the object is to *minimise the maximum return* the problem is said to be of the *minmax* type. Try solving the problem. You should find that the best route is S–A–D–T. You will have guessed what comes next; where there is a minmax there is bound to be a *maxmin*! In problems of the maxmin kind we wish to maximise the minimum return. Examples include optimising the throughput of a production line where production rate depends upon the slowest stage.

Example 1   A construction company is planning to build three new buildings, A, B and C, at a rate of one per year. The order in which they are built is a matter of choice. Construction costs are rising each year and as each building is erected, it causes access problems for future work. The company estimates the costs as in this table.

	Cost (£ thousands)		
Already built	A	B	C
Nothing	50	40	30
A	—	45	40
B	65	—	45
C	55	50	—
A and B	—	—	55
A and C	—	60	—
B and C	70	—	—

For tax purposes it is best to arrange the sequence so that the least annual cost is as large as possible. In what order should the buildings be constructed?

Solution   The network diagram is shown in Fig. 9.16. The tabular solution for the maxmin problem is laid out similarly to that of the shortest path problem but at each stage we choose the largest of the minimum values.

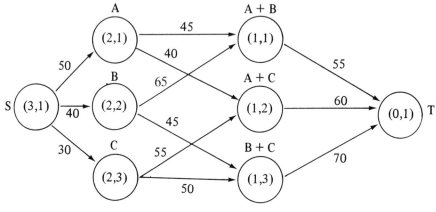

Fig. 9.16

Stage	State	Action	Value
1	1	1	55
	2	1	60
	3	1	70
2	1	1	min (45,55) = 45
		2	min (40,60) = 40
	2	1	min (65,55) = 55
		2	min (45,70) = 45
	3	1	min (55,60) = 55
		2	min (50,70) = 50
3	1	1	min (50,45) = 45
		2	min (40,55) = 40
		3	min (30,55) = 30

Optimal plan: A, B, C should be built in that order.

Exercise 4.1 For each of the networks shown in Fig. 9.17 find the maxmin and minmax plans and their values.

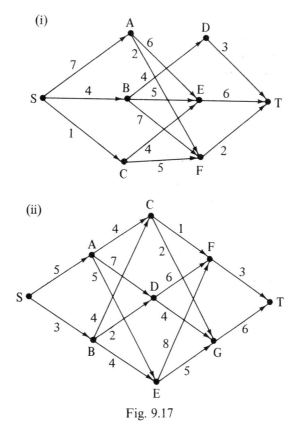

(i)

(ii)

Fig. 9.17

Exercise 4.2 Figure 9.18 shows an airline network, the numbers representing distances in kilometres. Find the route to be taken from S to T by (i) heavy freight aircraft, when fuel carried is to be minimised, (ii) light freight aircraft, when total distance is to be minimized.

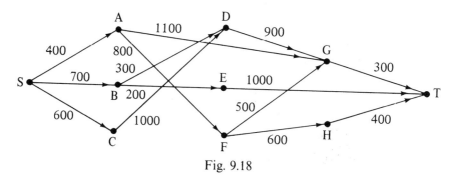

Fig. 9.18

Exercise 4.3 Solve the building problem (Example 1 of this section) in the cases when (i) total cost is to be minimised, (ii) maximum annual cost is to be minimised.

Exercise 4.4 A charity decides to support three African villages by giving all it raises each year to just one of them at a time. Over a three-year period all the villages are to receive aid. The council of the charity determines that the best policy is to maximise the minimum return on its outlay. The benefits resulting from the various donations are estimated to be as shown in this table. (They are on a 6-point scale.)

Year already aided	1	2			3		
	Nil	A	B	C	A + B	A + C	B + C
To be aided A	5	—	2	6	—	—	3
B	4	1	—	4	—	2	—
C	3	5	5	—	5	—	—

Find the policy to be adopted.

9.5 SOME APPLICATIONS

The remainder of this chapter will be used to introduce important classes of problems which may be attacked by DP. In each case the problem can be reduced to a network; whether to draw this is a matter of personal choice.

9.5.1 Production Planning

An electronics firm assembles a particular model of computer. It plans production for 5 months ahead working in units of one complete month. On 31 January the following table shows the orders for delivery at the end of each month named.

Month	Feb.	Mar.	Apr.	May	Jun.
No. of computers	1	2	5	3	2

The firm can make up to four computers in any month and can additionally hold up to three computers in stock. If computers are made in a particular month there is an overhead cost (for heating, cleaning and preparation of the work area) of £500 and for each computer made a construction cost of £1200. For computers held in stock the cost is £100 per month for each computer.

How should production be planned so as to minimise total costs? Assume that no stock is held before or after the period in question and that all orders are met.

You may find it useful to draw a network but here the solution will be found directly by forming a table. The usual words will be used and interpreted as follows.

> Stage —a month (e.g. stage 3 means 3 months to go)
> State —stock level at a particular stage
> Action —no. of computers to be made in next stage
> Return—cost of action (in £ hundreds)

We note that the construction costs for the 13 computers will have to be met irrespective of the plan chosen, so these will not be included in the return or value, which will simply cover overheads and storage. The table needs quite careful study; in case of difficulty the note following it will be useful.

Stage	State	Action	Value	Demand
1	0	$\underline{0}$	$\underline{2}$	2
		$\underline{1}$	$\underline{6}$	
		$\underline{2}$	$\underline{5}$	
2	0	3	$5 + 5 = \underline{10}$	3
		4	$5 + 6 = 11$	
	1	2	$6 + 5 = 11$	
		3	$6 + 6 = 12$	
		$\underline{4}$	$6 + 2 = \underline{8}$	
	2	1	$7 + 5 = 12$	
		2	$7 + 6 = 13$	
		$\underline{3}$	$7 + 2 = \underline{9}$	
	3	$\underline{0}$	$3 + 5 = \underline{8}$	
		1	$8 + 6 = 14$	
		2	$8 + 2 = 10$	
3	1	$\underline{4}$	$6 + 10 = \underline{16}$	5
	2	3	$7 + 10 = 17$	
		$\underline{4}$	$7 + 8 = \underline{15}$	
	3	2	$8 + 10 = 18$	
		$\underline{3}$	$8 + 8 = \underline{16}$	
		4	$8 + 9 = 17$	

(Continued)

Stage	State	Action	Value	Demand
4	0	3	$5 + 16 = 21$	2
		4	$5 + 15 = \underline{20}$	
	1	2	$6 + 16 = 22$	
		3	$6 + 15 = \underline{21}$	
		4	$6 + 16 = 22$	
	2	1	$7 + 16 = 23$	
		2	$7 + 15 = \underline{22}$	
		3	$7 + 16 = 23$	
	3	0	$3 + 16 = \underline{19}$	
		1	$8 + 15 = 23$	
		2	$8 + 16 = 24$	
5	0	1	$5 + 20 = 25$	1
		2	$5 + 21 = 26$	
		3	$5 + 22 = 27$	
		4	$5 + 19 = \underline{24}$	

The optimal plan is shown in a table.

Month	Feb.	Mar.	Apr.	May	Jun.
Action	4	0	4	3	2
Return	5	3	6	5	5

Total production cost is: $13 \times £1200 + £2400 = £18\,000$.

Note: As an example of the method used to form the table consider the case of Stage 2, State 1. Since one computer is in stock, to satisfy the current month's (May) requirement at least two more must be made. The total requirement to the end of the run (planning horizon) is $3 + 2 = 5$, so not more than four must be made (which is the maximum possible in any case). If 2 are made then none will be left for stock in the following month; so we consider together action 2 in May and State 0 in June. The cost for May is £100 for storage and £500 for overheads, a total return of 6. Adding this to June's value we obtain our May value of $6 + 5 = 11$, and so on.

9.5.2 Allocation

A dairy manufacturer can make cheese, butter and yoghurt. He can process up to 4 units of milk and he calculates that the profits from the various possible allocations of the milk are as shown in the table below.

No. of units of milk	1	2	3	4
Cheese	8	18	22	24
Butter	3	6	9	12
Yoghurt	6	7	8	10

Maximise his profit, assuming that only whole units of milk are to be used.

We shall give these meanings to our usual terms.
Stage —a product: cheese—1, butter—2, yoghurt—3
State —number of units of milk available
Action—number of units of milk allocated to a product
Value —cumulative profit

This time a network is drawn although you could possibly well manage without. As usual Stage 1 is the *final* stage and we trace our way through the network backwards.

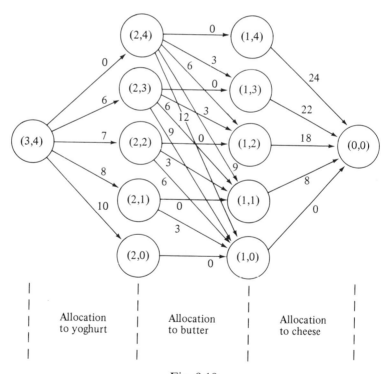

Fig. 9.19

Tabular solution:

Stage	State	Action	Value
1	0	$\underline{0}$	$\underline{0}$
	1	$\underline{1}$	$\underline{8}$
	2	$\underline{2}$	$\underline{18}$
	3	$\underline{3}$	$\underline{22}$
	4	$\underline{4}$	$\underline{24}$
2	0	$\underline{0}$	$0 + 0 = \underline{0}$
	1	$\underline{0}$	$0 + 8 = \underline{8}$
		1	$3 + 0 = 3$
	2	$\underline{0}$	$0 + 18 = \underline{18}$
		1	$3 + \ \ 8 = 11$
		2	$6 + \ \ 0 = \ \ 6$
	3	$\underline{0}$	$0 + 22 = \underline{22}$
		1	$3 + 18 = 21$
		2	$6 + \ \ 8 = 14$
		3	$9 + \ \ 0 = \ \ 9$
	4	0	$0 + 24 = 24$
		$\underline{1}$	$3 + 22 = \underline{25}$
		2	$6 + 18 = 24$
		3	$9 + \ \ 8 = 17$
		4	$12 + \ \ 0 = 12$
3	4	0	$0 + 25 = 25$
		$\underline{1}$	$6 + 22 = \underline{28}$
		2	$7 + 18 = 25$
		3	$8 + \ \ 8 = 16$
		4	$10 + \ \ 0 = 10$

The optimal allocation is of 1 unit to yoghurt and 3 units to cheese.

9.5.3 Capital Investment

When evaluating a plan involving financial returns over a considerable time
(say two years or more) we should consider factors affecting the value of
those returns in the future. A complete analysis of these factors is complicated, including in particular three considerations.

(i) If the money was simply invested in a bank it would earn interest.
(ii) At present, money depreciates in value as time passes.
(iii) There is a risk that firms with which you deal will be unable to settle their debts.

A thorough planning model might include these considerations separately but it is often sufficient to lump them together under the general observation: £1 in your pocket now is worth more than £1 in a year's time. Assuming a rate of appreciation (or depreciation, depending on how you look at it) r,

$$£1 \text{ now is worth } £(1 + r) \text{ in a year's time}$$
$$\text{or } £(1 + r)^2 \text{ in two years time}$$
$$\text{or } £(1 + r)^n \text{ in } n \text{ years time.}$$

So the *present value* of $£(1 + r)^n$ to be received in n years is £1. To put it another way, the present value of $£x$ to be received in n years is

$$£ \frac{x}{(1 + r)^n},$$

Letting $d = 1/(1 + r)$ we may write this as $£d^n x$. In this case d is called the discount factor.

Example   A firm has to decide whether to expand and, if so, how. Given the information in the network in Fig. 9.20, find its optimal plan for the three-year period. Returns are in £ thousands; take $r = 33\frac{1}{3}\%$.

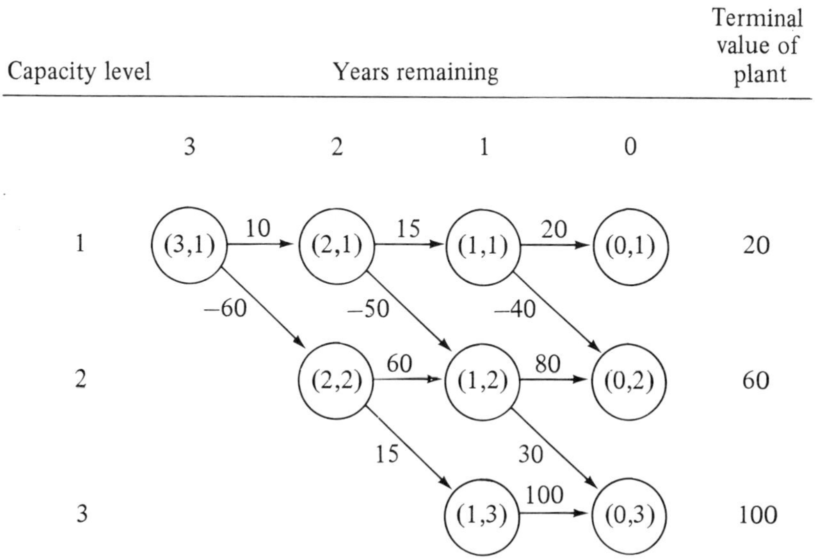

Capacity level	Years remaining				Terminal value of plant
	3	2	1	0	
1	(3,1) →10	(2,1) →15	(1,1) →20	(0,1)	20
	−60	−50	−40		
2		(2,2) →60	(1,2) →80	(0,2)	60
		15	30		
3			(1,3) →100	(0,3)	100

Fig. 9.20

Solution   The discount factor $d = 1/(1 + r) = 0.75$.

Tabular solution:

Stage	State	Action	Value
1	1	1	$20 + 0.75 \times 20 = \underline{35}$
		2	$-40 + 0.75 \times 60 = 5$
	2	1	$80 + 0.75 \times 60 = \underline{125}$
		2	$30 + 0.75 \times 100 = 105$
	3	1	$100 + 0.75 \times 100 = \underline{175}$
2	1	1	$15 + 0.75 \times 35 = 41.25$
		2	$-50 + 0.75 \times 125 = \underline{43.75}$
	2	1	$60 + 0.75 \times 125 = \underline{153.75}$
		2	$15 + 0.75 \times 175 = 146.25$
3	1	1	$10 + 0.75 \times 43.75 = 42.8$
		2	$-60 + 0.75 \times 153.75 = \underline{55.3}$

Extract the optimal plan:

Stage	State	Action	Value
1	2	1	125
2	2	1	153.75
3	2	2	55.3

The optimal plan involves expansion at the end of the first year only.
Note: in this solution the discount factor has been applied to the terminal value of the plant. A detailed knowledge of the particular case would be needed to judge whether this was sound.

Exercise 5.1   A firm produces aluminium castings of three types. There are four tons of aluminium available. The returns (in £ hundreds) resulting from allocation to the various types of casting are shown in the table below.

Allocation of Al (tons)	Type of casting		
	1	2	3
1	10	6	8
2	17	17	11
3	19	—	—

If allocations are restricted to the levels shown find the plan which maximises the total return.

Exercise 5.2   A building job has to be completed in 20 days. The work is in three phases: preparation, erection and finishing; which are to be undertaken in that order. The cost of each stage depends on the time taken for that stage as shown in the table below.

Time for stage (days)	Costs (£ thousands)		
	Preparation	Erection	Finishing
4	18	11	20
8	17	8	15
12	8	7	9
16	6	5	8

If the work is to be allocated in four-day lots, find the plan which minimises the cost and determine that cost.

Exercise 5.3   A specialist coach-builder converts standard cars into de luxe models. He has orders for delivery at the ends of the months shown according to the table below.

Month	Mar.	Apr.	May	Jun.	Jul.	Aug.
No. of cars	2	4	10	6	4	2

There is no stock at the beginning of March and he plans to have no stock after the August delivery. If work is done in any month there is an overhead cost of £20 per car per month. To fulfil the orders and minimise his costs what should be his plan

(i) if he can only undertake six conversions per month and only stock six cars,

(ii) if there is no constraint on the number of cars in stock but he can only manage six conversions.

Exercise 5.4   A trader in electrical goods transports them in boxes in his estate car which has a usable capacity of 140 cubic feet. He sells four models, whose volumes are as follows.

(A) 10 ft^3 (B) 30 ft^3 (C) 40 ft^3 (D) 60 ft^3

The expected profits (in £) yielded by various levels of stock are shown in the table overleaf.

		Model		
Stock level	A	B	C	D
1	2	12	16	24
2	4	18	28	40
3	6	26	38	50
4	8	30	44	—
5	10	32	—	—

To maximise his profit find his plan

(i) if he has a free hand on what he carries,
(ii) if he is obliged to carry at least one of each model.

Exercise 5.5   A farmer has a contract to supply a fixed number of pigs at the end of each month for the period May to September. The selling price in £ depends on the month and the weight of the pigs as shown in the table below.

	Weight (kg)				
Month	40	45	50	55	60
May	40	60	80	—	—
Jun.	32	40	56	80	96
Jul.	16	24	40	56	80
Aug.	8	16	32	56	80
Sep.	0	8	32	56	88

At the beginning of May all the pigs weigh 40 kg. Thereafter they may be fed in three ways. Diet A maintains the weight of the pig without increase, diet B increases its weight by 5 kg a month and diet C increases its weight by 10 kg a month. All the pigs are to be fed on the same diet throughout each month. The cost of each diet varies with the weight of the pig at the beginning of the month as shown in the table below.

Weight	Diet		
(kg)	A	B	C
40	4	8	20
45	12	16	28
50	20	24	28
55	32	36	—
60	40	—	—

Find the best plan and the return under that plan.

Exercise 5.6   Solve the expansion problem (Example, section 9.5.3) in the case when the discount factor is not applied to the terminal value of the plant (i.e. the given terminal values can be realised at stage 0, immediately).

Exercise 5.7   Solve Exercise 4.3 assuming that all future prices (buying and selling) are to be discounted at 25% p.a.

Exercise 5.8   A travel firm specialises in ski holidays. At present they offer only a resort in France but they are considering adding next year a resort in Italy and in the following year one in Austria. Their planning horizon is three years and they estimate the profits in £ thousands on the various possible plans as shown in Fig. 9.21. They estimate that the value to the firm of 'goodwill' at the end of the three years will be £50 000 if they offer only one resort but £60 000 if they offer two and £70 000 if they offer three.

Years to horizon

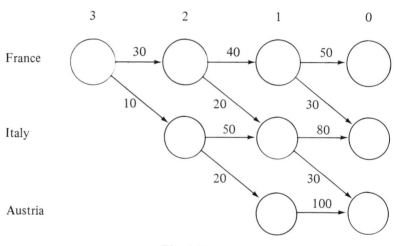

Fig. 9.21

Find their optimal plan assuming a discount rate of $33\frac{1}{3}\%$ p.a.

(i) if the 'goodwill' figure is ignored,
(ii) if the 'goodwill' figure is included. (Assume that it is realisable immediately at the end of the three-year period.)

9.6   MISCELLANEOUS EXERCISES

M1   For the network shown find (a) the shortest path, (b) the longest path, (c) the minmax path, (d) the maxmin path.

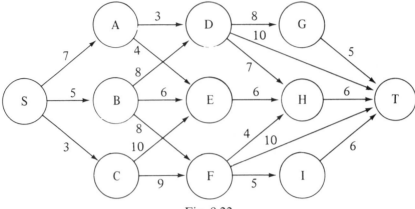

Fig. 9.22

M2 In the board game 'Jungle Explorer' players start from the port of San Miguel and try to reach the secret treasure house of the Incas before anyone else. Moves are made by shaking a die and any route may be taken at a junction. The network below represents the routes on the board; the first figure on each arc indicates the number of squares between junctions and the figure in brackets shows the number of 'hazard' squares.

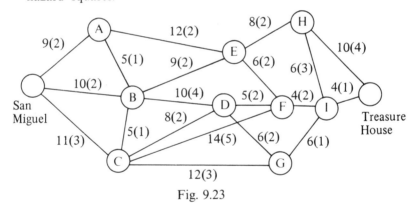

Fig. 9.23

(a) Find the shortest route from San Miguel to the Treasure House.
(b) By how many squares is it shorter than the next shortest route?
(c) Which route contains the fewest 'hazard' squares?

M3 A boat builder specialises in a particular design. He has promised delivery at the ends of months as shown

Month	Feb.	Mar.	Apr.	May	June
No. of boats	1	3	4	4	3

There is no stock at the beginning of February and he plans to be without stock at the end of June. When work is done in any month the workshop overheads increase by £100. Stockholding costs £30 per boat per month. He cannot make more than four boats in a month and the total number of boats in store and being built cannot exceed five. If he builds more than two boats in a month he must hire labour at a cost of £320.

(a) What should be his plan to fulfil his orders while minimising costs?

(b) If during February he receives another order for a boat for delivery at the end of March what change should he make to his plan?

M4 A newsagent has the problem of deciding whether to expand. He decides on a four-year planning horizon and considers the possibility of owning up to three shops, the other two to be acquired one after the other, at intervals of one or two years. He estimates the returns (in £ thousands) to be shown in Fig. 9.24.

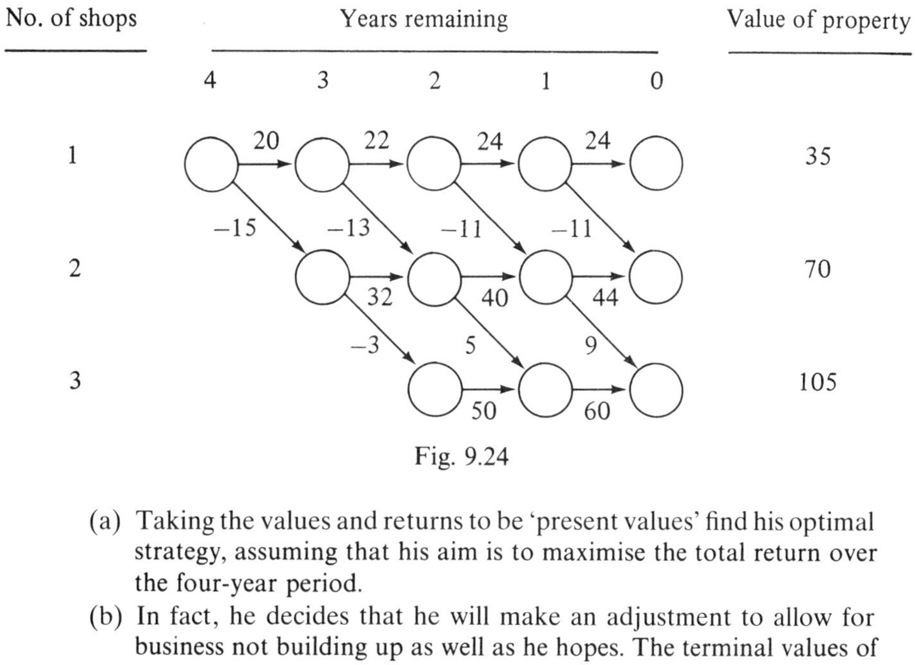

Fig. 9.24

(a) Taking the values and returns to be 'present values' find his optimal strategy, assuming that his aim is to maximise the total return over the four-year period.

(b) In fact, he decides that he will make an adjustment to allow for business not building up as well as he hopes. The terminal values of the shops will stay as they are (£35 000 each at present values) but an annual discount factor of 0.8 will be applied to all the returns in the diagram.

(i) Is this a reasonable adjustment to make?

(ii) Will the adjustment result in a change of strategy?

10

Network Flows

10.1 INTRODUCTION

Flow through a network can represent many physical problems, for instance, water flowing through a pipework system, traffic flowing along the motorway network, or people walking along corridors. This chapter studies the problem of calculating the maximum possible flow through a network from one end to the other. Two methods for finding the maximum flow are examined:

(i) The maximum flow–minimum cut theorem.
(ii) The labelling procedure.

Both methods determine the maximum flow, but the labelling procedure also finds the route of maximum flow.

We begin by extending the notation used in Chapter 6 on Networks. Figure 10.1 illustrates a network. S, A, B, C, D, T, are *vertices* (or nodes). AC is an *arc* (or edge) directed from A to C whose maximum *capacity* is 14. By this we mean that the actual flow must lie between $0 \leqslant p \leqslant 14$. The arrows indicate a direction of 'flow' along the arcs.

We do not allow backwards flows along such arcs. We call the start of the network, the *source*, and the finish, the *sink*, and these are usually labelled S and T, respectively. An arc is *saturated* if the actual flow in the arc is equal to the capacity of the arc, i.e. flow, $p = 14$, in arc AC, means that AC is saturated.

Figure 10.2 illustrates a network in which no direction of flow is indicated on arcs AB and BT. These arcs are called *undirected arcs*, along which flow is allowed in either direction.

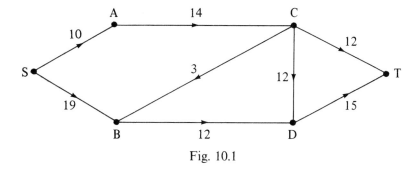

Fig. 10.1

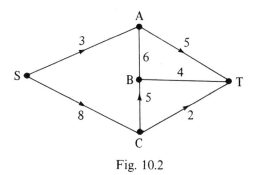

Fig. 10.2

Figure 10.2 could therefore be represented as Fig. 10.3 below. We wish to find the maximum flow from S to T. Can you find it by inspection? It should not take you too long to convince yourself that the maximum possible flow from S to T is 22 units.

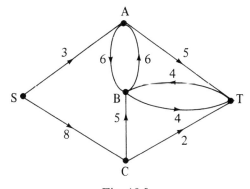

Fig. 10.3

Now try this network—find the maximum flow from S to T.

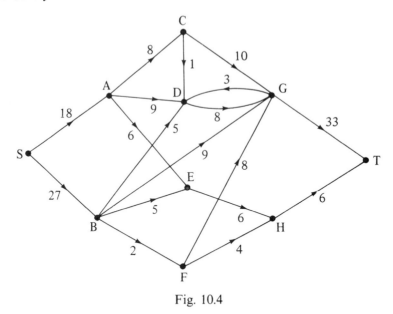

Fig. 10.4

It is not quite so easy to find the maximum flow by inspection, and if the network becomes any more complicated it would become even more difficult. In section 10.2 we look at our first systematic method of approach.

Exercise 1.1 A, B, C, D and E are towns. The maximum traffic flows, in hundreds of cars per hour, are:

A to B: 3
B to C: 7
C to E: 6
A to D: 5
D to E: 2

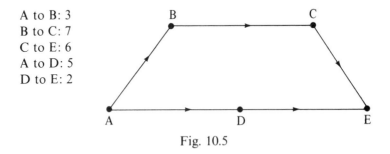

Fig. 10.5

(i) Find the maximum possible traffic flow from A to E.
(ii) A new road is built which can carry 400 cars per hour from D to C. What is now the maximum flow from A to E?

Exercise 1.2 A, B, C, D, E and F are towns connected by a railway network.

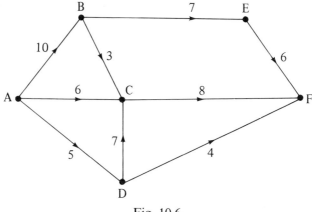

Fig. 10.6

The figures give the maximum possible volume of freight (in thousands of tons per week) that can be carried on each part of the railway line.

(i) What is the maximum volume of freight that can be carried from A to F?
(ii) If the capacity from E to F is increased from 6 to 10, calculate the new maximum volume of freight that can be carried from A to F.

Exercise 1.3 Flights connect the airports at London, Madrid, Paris, Oslo and Vienna. The figures represent the maximum number of passengers, in hundreds, that can be carried in a fixed time.

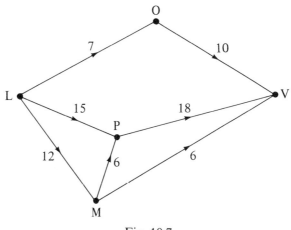

Fig. 10.7

(i) Find the maximum number of pasengers that can be carried between London and Vienna.
(ii) Mark a route of the maximum flow.

10.2   THE MAXIMUM FLOW–MINIMUM CUT THEOREM

As the numbers of vertices and arcs increase, the problem of finding the maximum flow becomes more difficult and a better method than 'inspection' is needed. To this end, we define a *cut*. A cut is a line dividing the network into two parts, X and Y; X containing S and Y containing T. A typical cut is illustrated here

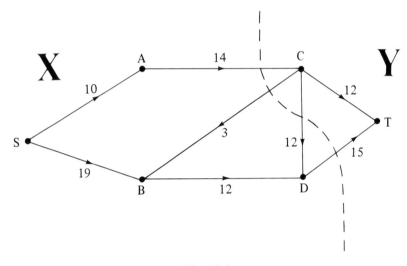

Fig. 10.8

Restricting attention only to the arcs which a cut intersects, the *capacity* of a cut is the sum of the capacities of the arcs directed from vertices in X to vertices in Y. The capacity of the cut here is

$$\text{Capacity of cut} = 14 + 15 = 29$$

Note that the arcs CB and CD are directed from Y to X. The capcity of a cut is the maximum flow, *from X to Y*, which can cross the cut. So, the capacity of any cut gives an upper bound on the maximum flow from S to T.

We can deduce that

$$\text{maximum flow} \leqslant \text{value of any cut}$$

and if we take the cut which has minimum value, then we have

$$\boxed{\text{maximum flow} \leqslant \text{value of minimum cut}}$$

Although we will not prove it here, we can go one step further, and the *maximum flow/minimum cut theorem* states that

> maximum flow = value of minimum cut

We can use this result to find the maximum flow in the following way:

Find the value of *every* possible cut;
the *maximum* possible flow corresponds to the cut of *minimum* value.

Example 1 Find the maximum flow through the network

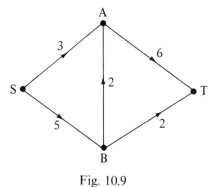

Fig. 10.9

Solution There are four possible cuts, C_1, C_2, C_3 and C_4.

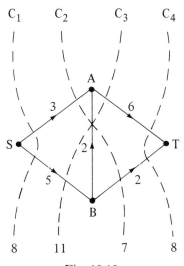

Fig. 10.10

The capacities are respectively 8, 7, 11, 8 and so the maximum flow is 7. This is achieved by 4 units along SB and 3 units along SA. We can now apply this method to our first two networks. For the first network

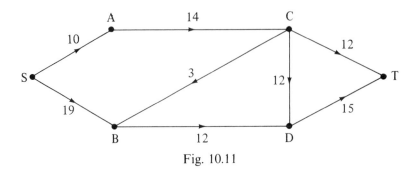

Fig. 10.11

Table 10.1 describes each cut and its capacity.

Table 10.1

Arcs in cut	Vertices in X	Vertices in Y	Capacity of cut
SA, SB	S	A, B, C, D, T	10 + 19 = 29
AC, SB	S, A	B, C, D, T	14 + 19 = 33
SA, BC, BD	S, B	A, C, D, T	10 + 0 + 12 = 22 **minimum cut**
AC, BC, BD	S, A, B	C, D, T	14 + 0 + 12 = 26
AC, BC, DC, DT	S, A, B, D	C, T	14 + 0 + 0 + 15 = 29
CT, CD, BD	S, A, B, C	D, T	12 + 12 + 12 = 36
CT, CD, BC, SB	S, A, C	B, D, T	12 + 12 + 3 + 19 = 46
SA, BC, CD, DT	S, B, D	A, C, T	10 + 0 + 0 + 15 = 25
CT, DT	S, A, B, C, D	T	12 + 15 = 27

Since 22 is the value of the minimum cut, this must be the value of the maximum flow. This flow is shown in Fig. 10.12 on the next page. Note that the arcs SA and BD are saturated.

We have seen that there are two drawbacks to the maximum flow–minimum cut theorem:

(i) The theorem does not immediately provide the route of maximum flow which is often important.
(ii) As the number of vertices and arcs increase so does the number of possible cuts.

Of course, if we can spot a cut of minimum capacity in a network then we can immediately deduce the value of a maximum flow. In many examples the

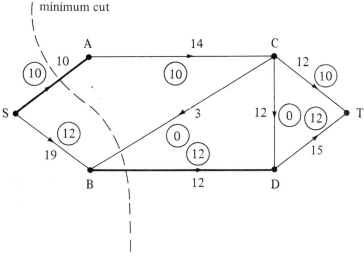

Fig. 10.12

minimum cut can be found quite easily by inspection. However, a slightly different approach for networks that are not too large is to spot a maximum possible flow and find a cut that has the same value. If we can, then we have indeed found the maximum flow. Consider the network:

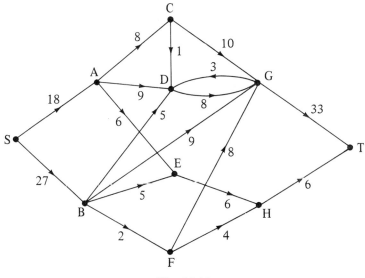

Fig. 10.13

There are a very large number of cuts. For this example, a flow of 33 units is shown, in circles, on the network. We have also indicated the arcs that are saturated, as this gives a clue to finding the cut of minimum value.

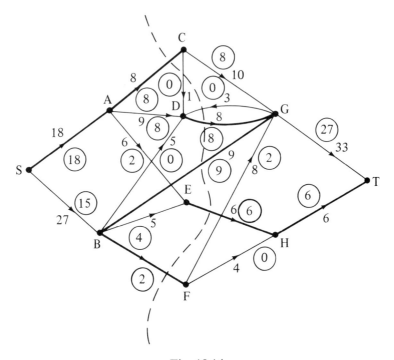

Fig. 10.14

The value of the cut = 8 + 0 + 0 + 8 + 9 + 6 + 2 = 33 and it only passes through saturated arcs (AC, DG, BG, EH, BF) and backwards arcs with zero flow (GD, CD). So we have a feasible flow of 33 units and a cut of value 33. By our theorem we can immediately deduce that the flow is a maximum. However, for finding network flows through large and complicated networks, finding a minimum cut by inspection is impracticable. In such problems we use a more systematic approach such as the labelling procedure introduced in section 10.3.

Exercise 2.1 Determine the capacities of the cuts shown.

(i)

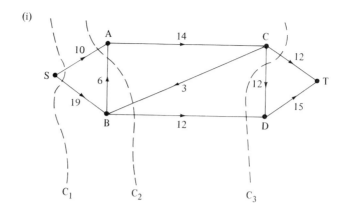

(ii)

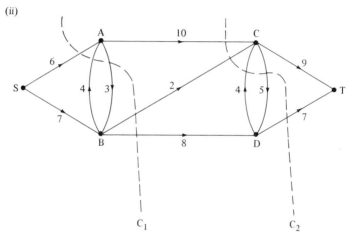

(iii)

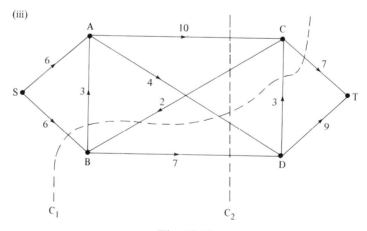

Fig. 10.15

Exercise 2.2 By calculating the capacities of all the cuts, find the maximum flow in the networks in Fig. 10.16.

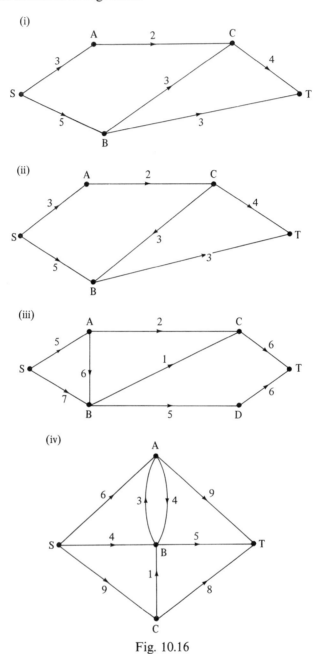

Fig. 10.16

Exercise 2.3 Find the maximum flow through the networks in Fig. 10.17 and mark on a diagram a route which gives this maximum flow.

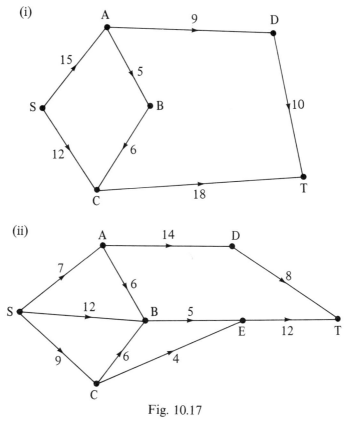

Fig. 10.17

Exercise 2.4 (i) In the following basic network, find a flow value of k from S to T, and a cut with capacity k, for the same value of k.

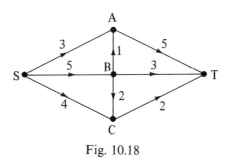

Fig. 10.18

(ii) Is the flow in (i) a maximum flow? (Give a reason for your answer.)

Exercise 2.5 Verify that the max-flow/min-cut theorem holds for the network in Fig. 10.19

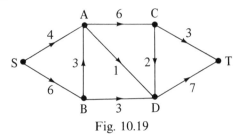

Fig. 10.19

Exercise 2.6 By finding a maximum flow and a minimum cut in each case, verify the max-flow/min-cut theorem for each of the networks in Fig. 10.20.

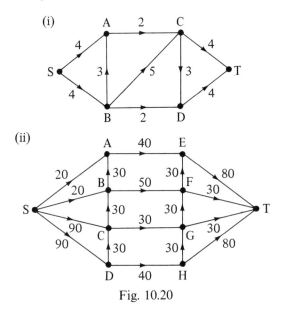

Fig. 10.20

Exercise 2.7 For the network below, find the minimum cuts, and verify the max-flow/min-cut theorem.

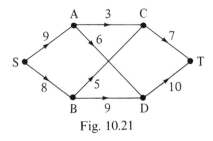

Fig. 10.21

10.3 THE LABELLING PROCEDURE

This is a systematic way of finding both the maximum flow and its route through the network. It is explained with reference to the following network.

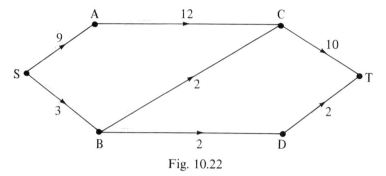

Fig. 10.22

We look for *any* route from S to T, say SBCT and note the capacities.

SB	capacity 3
BC	capacity 2
CT	capacity 10

By looking at the capacities we see that the maximum possible flow along this route is 2. It is the minimum of the capacities of the arcs which comprise the route. Suppose a flow of 2 exists along SBCT. Then the *excess* capacity along SB is 1, along BC it is 0, and along CT it is 8. This is shown as

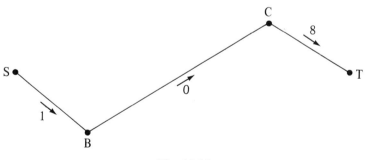

Fig. 10.23

Since a flow of 2 along SBCT may not be correct, we need a device which enables that flow to be reduced.

The flow along SB may be reduced by 2, so we imagine a capacity of 2 from B to S. Thus, should we wish at some stage in the calculation of the maximum flow, to reduce the flow along SB, we do this by considering a flow from B to S. BC and CT are treated similarly.

The full network, with excess capacities and artificial backward capacities along SBCT is shown in Fig. 10.24.

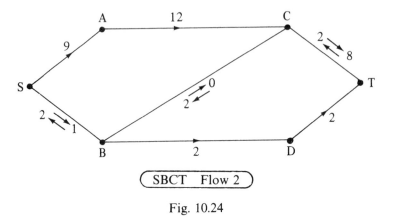

Fig. 10.24

The process is repeated. Considering route SACT

SA   capacity   9
AC   capacity 12
CT   capacity   8

the maximum flow for this route is 8. Writing in the excess capacities and artificial backward capacities the network is now

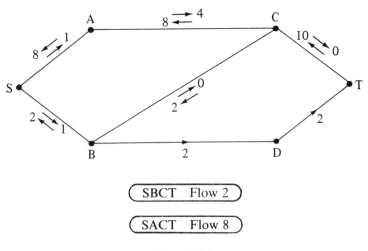

Fig. 10.25

Treating the path SBDT in a similar way, the maximum flow being 1 yields

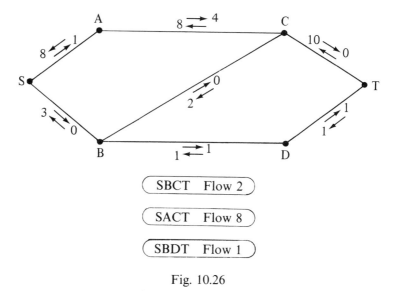

Fig. 10.26

There is now only 1 possible route to increase the flow; SACBDT. We are using the artificial capacity of 2 along CB to effectively reduce the flow along BC. The maximum flow along the route is 1. The network is now

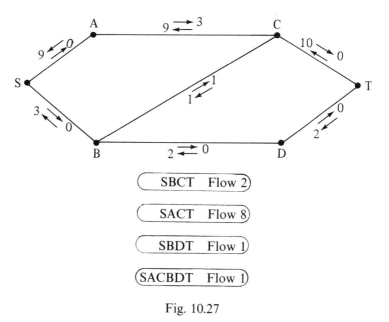

Fig. 10.27

Since all arcs into T are saturated then it is impossible to increase the flow. Hence the maximum flow has been found and the route of maximum flow is illustrated in Fig. 10.28.

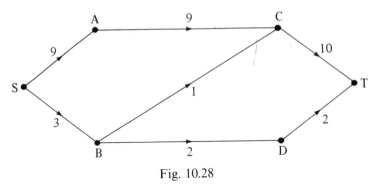

Fig. 10.28

Note that at any vertex, except S and T, the sum of the flows into the vertex equals the sum of the flows out of the vertex, that is there is no 'build-up' at a vertex.

Exercise 3.1   Use the labelling procedure to determine the maximum flow and its route through the networks in Exercises 2.2 and 2.3.

Exercise 3.2   Find the maximum flow, using the labelling procedure, for the networks in Fig. 10.29.

(i)

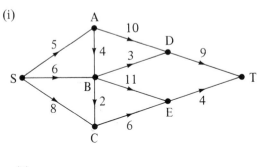

(ii)

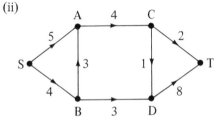

Fig. 10.29(i) and (ii)

(iii)

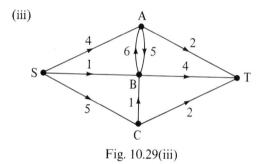

Fig. 10.29(iii)

Exercise 3.3   Find a maximum flow in the following network, by using the labelling procedure:

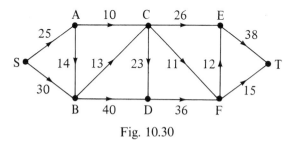

Fig. 10.30

10.4   NETWORKS WITH MANY SOURCES AND SINKS

Sometimes a network has many sources and/or sinks as illustrated in Figure 10.31.

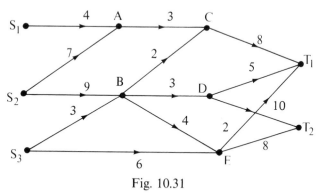

Fig. 10.31

In these cases, a 'supersource', S, and 'supersink', T are introduced as shown in Fig. 10.32. Since no more than 4 units can leave S_1, the capacity of the arc SS_1 is put at 4. Similarly no more than 16 units can leave S_2 so arc SS_2 is assigned a capacity of 16. The capacities of the terminal arcs, T_1T and T_2T, are likewise calculated. As T_1 cannot have more than 15 units entering it, the

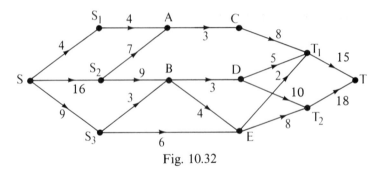

Fig. 10.32

capacity of T_1T is 15. The flow through the network can now be calculated using the labelling procedure.

Example 2 Find the maximum flow through the network in Fig. 10.33.

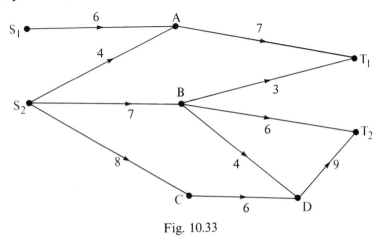

Fig. 10.33

Solution The supersource and supersink are added to the network.

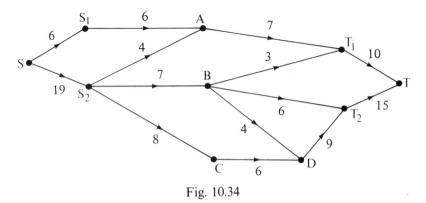

Fig. 10.34

The labelling procedure is now applied to this network, resulting in a maximum flow of 20, the route is detailed in Fig. 10.35 below.

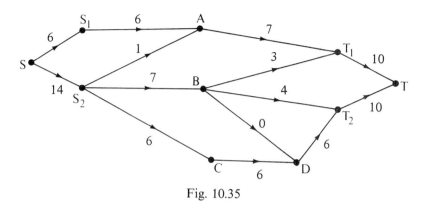

Fig. 10.35

The maximum flow in the original network is found by simply removing the supersource and supersink to give the solution.

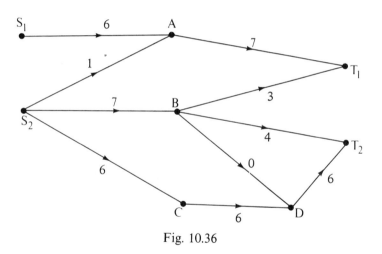

Fig. 10.36

If a cut is defined as a line dividing the network into two parts, X containing the sources, and Y containing the sinks, then the maximum flow–minimum cut theorem still holds. Can you find a minimum cut?

Exercise 4.1   Determine the maximum flow and its route for the following networks shown in Fig. 10.37. Verify that the maximum flow–minimum cut theorem holds

(i)

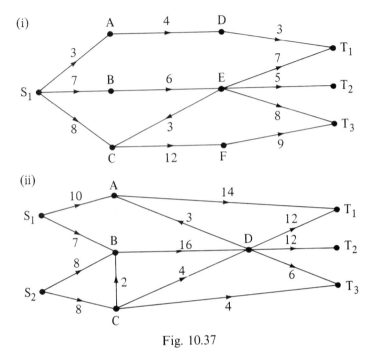

(ii)

Fig. 10.37

Exercise 4.2 Find a maximum flow in the following network:

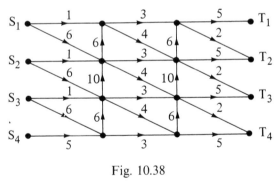

Fig. 10.38

Exercise 4.3 Figure 10.39 represents a network with two sourcs S_1 and S_2 and two sinks T_1 and T_2:

(i) What is the value of a maximum flow from S_1 to T_1?
(ii) What is the value of a maximum flow from S_2 to T_2?
(iii) What is the maximum total amount of the commodity that can be sent simultaneously from S_1 to T_1 and from S_2 to T_2 without exceeding any of the capacities?

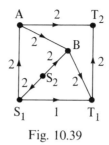

Fig. 10.39

10.5   NETWORKS WITH VERTEX RESTRICTIONS

Just as an arc has a maximum capacity, sometimes a vertex also has capacity restrictions placed on it.

Figure 10.40 shows part of a network. The maximum flow possible through *vertex* B is 6.

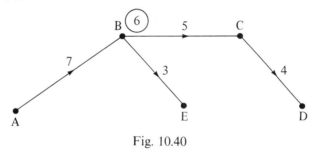

Fig. 10.40

Networks with vertex restrictions are easily transformed into networks without vertex restrictions. In the above example, vertex B would be replaced by two vertices, B_1 and B_2 and an arc $B_1 B_2$ with a capacity of 6.

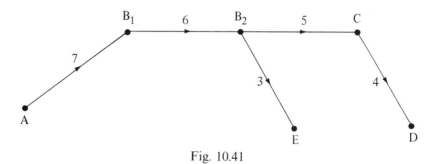

Fig. 10.41

All arcs directed into B in the original network are directed into B_1; all arcs directed out of B in the original are directed out of B_2. Maximum flow through the net network is found (using inspection or the labelling procedure) and then the flow through the original network is readily obtained. The following example illustrates the method:

Example 3   Find the maximum flow through the network.

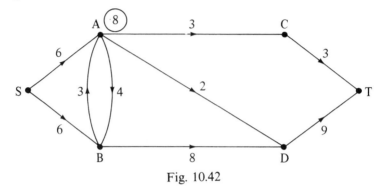

Fig. 10.42

Solution   There is a capacity restriction of 8 on vertex A. The network, without vertex restrictions is given by

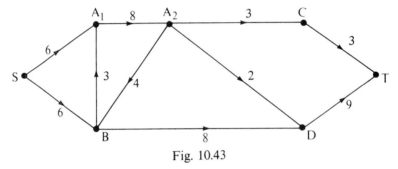

Fig. 10.43

Note that the arcs SA and BA are now the arcs SA_1 and BA_1 (i.e. into A_1) while the arcs directed out of A, that is AC, AD, AB, are now A_2C, A_2D and A_2B. Application of the labelling procedure, produces a maximum flow

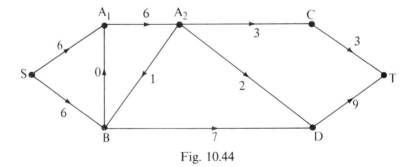

Fig. 10.44

Maximum flow = 12

The flow in the original network is

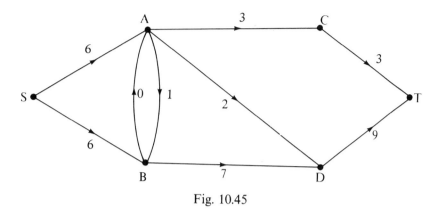

Fig. 10.45

Exercise 5.1   Determine the maximum flow in the networks shown in Fig. 10.46.

(i)

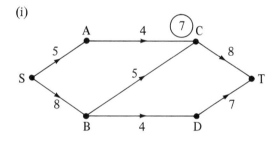

(ii)

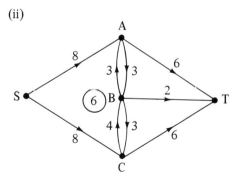

Fig. 10.46(i) and (ii)

(iii)

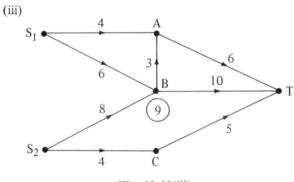

Fig. 10.46(iii)

Exercise 5.2   Use the labelling procedure to find the maximum flow in the networks in Fig. 10.47.

(i)

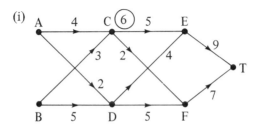

(ii)

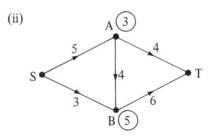

(iii)

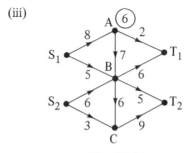

Fig. 10.47

10.6 NETWORKS WITH LOWER AND UPPER CAPACITIES

Arcs in networks can have lower as well as upper capacities. The networks we have dealt with so far can be thought of as having a lower capacity of 0 on the arcs. Figure 10.48 shows a network with lower and upper capacities on each arc. The first number is the lower capacity, the second number is the upper capacity.

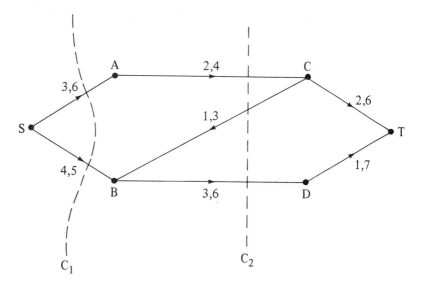

Fig. 10.48

The maximum flow–minimum cut theorem can be applied to such a network, provided the definition of the capacity of a cut is modified. Restricting attention only to the arcs which a cut intersects then

Capacity of cut = sum of upper capacities of arcs directed from X to Y
                   − sum of lower capacities of arcs directed from Y to X

For example, in the network shown above

the capacity of cut C_1 is $6 + 5 = 11$
the capacity of cut C_2 is $4 − 1 + 6 = 9$.

Note that for cut C_2, the arc CB is directed from the sink side, Y, to the source side, X, resulting in the lower capcity of 1 being subtracted in the calculation.

The labelling procedure can also be applied to networks with upper and lower capacities. *A feasible flow* through the network (i.e. one satisfying *all* the capacity restrictions) must first be found. Having found a feasible flow, then flow-augmenting paths are sought and the labelling procedure applied in the usual way. If the flow in an arc is reduced, then it must not be reduced to less than the minimum capacity of the arc.

Example 4 Find a feasible flow through the network. Hence, using the labelling procedure determine the maximum flow.

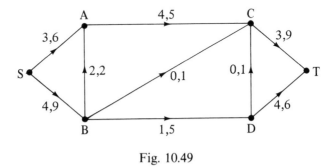

Fig. 10.49

Solution   A feasible flow is

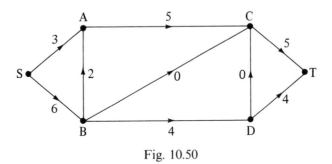

Fig. 10.50

All the capacity restrictions are satisfied.

Consider arc SB. The actual flow is 6, the upper capacity is 9, leaving an excess capacity of 3. The lower capacity is 4, so the flow of 6 could be reduced by 2, giving rise to the backward arrow marked 2. Similarly for arc BD. An actual flow of 4 leaves an excess capacity of 1; a lower capacity of 1 means that the flow can be reduced by 3. All arcs are treated in this way.

Writing the excess forward capacities and artificial backward capacities, the network becomes

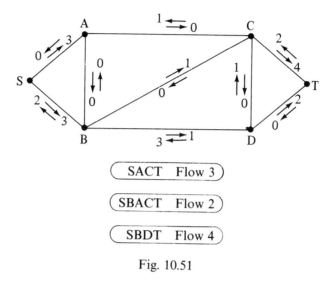

Fig. 10.51

Flow-augmenting paths are SBDT (flow can be increased by 1) and SBCT (flow can be increased by 1). This results in

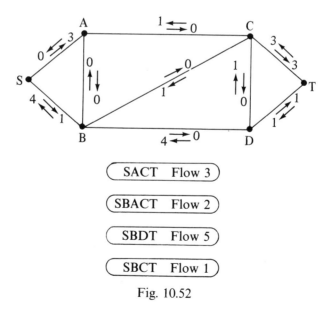

Fig. 10.52

There are no other flow-augmenting paths. The maximum flow through the network is 11,

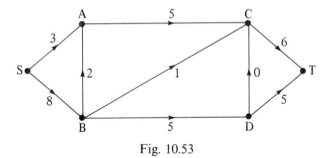

Fig. 10.53

The minimum cut is

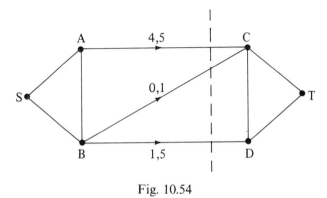

Fig. 10.54

Example 5 Find a feasible flow through the network shown. Use the labelling procedure to determine the maximum flow and verify the maximum flow–minimum cut theorem.

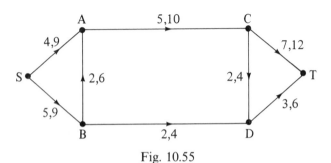

Fig. 10.55

Solution   A feasible flow is

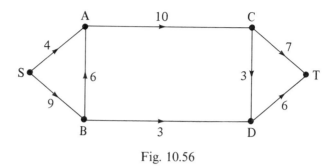

Fig. 10.56

Writing in the excess forward capacities, and the artificial backward capacities, the network is

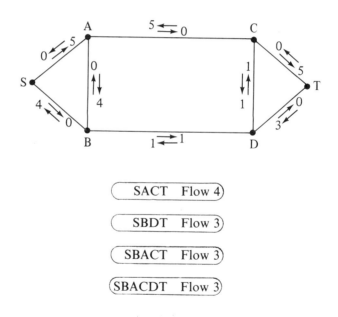

SACT   Flow 4

SBDT   Flow 3

SBACT   Flow 3

SBACDT   Flow 3

Fig. 10.57

It is now possible to identify a flow-augmenting path; SABDCT. It is possible to have a flow of 1 along this route. The flow of 6 from B to A is actually being reduced by 1 to 5, and the flow from C to D is also being reduced by 1 from 3 to 2. The network is now

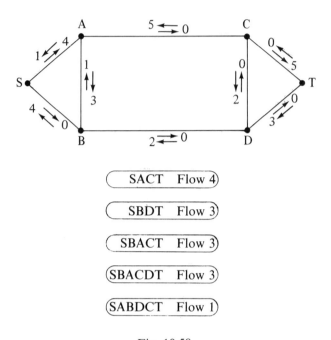

Fig. 10.58

There are no other flow augmenting paths. The maximum flow is 14, given by

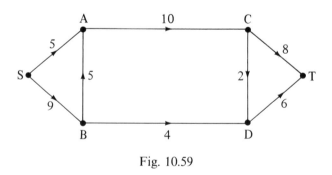

Fig. 10.59

The minimum cut is shown in Fig. 10.60.

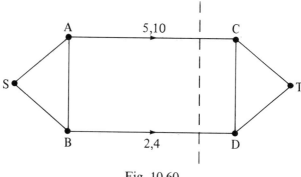

Fig. 10.60

Exercise 6.1 Can a feasible flow be found through the following networks with upper and lower capacities? If so, give an example of a feasible flow.

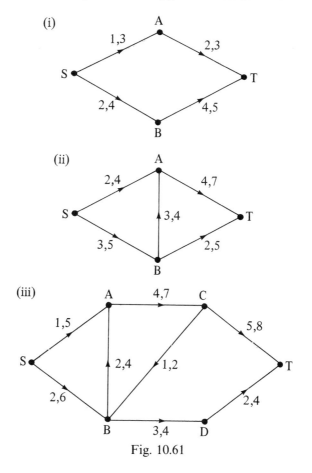

Fig. 10.61

Exercise 6.2 Determine the maximum flow for the feasible networks in
Exercise 6.1 by using the maximum flow–minimum cut theorem.

Exercise 6.3 Show by inspection that the following networks are feasible.
Use the labelling procedure to determine the route of maximum flow. Sketch
the minimum cut.

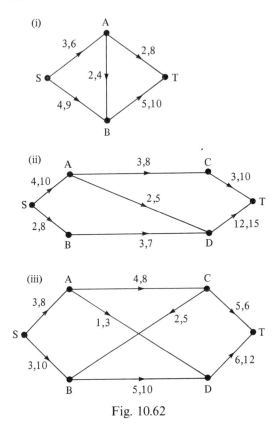

Fig. 10.62

Exercise 6.4 Consider the following network with lower and upper capacities

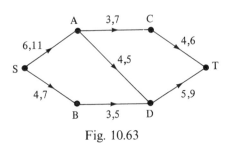

Fig. 10.63

(i) (a) Find a flow in this network.
    (b) By considering 'flow-augmenting paths', find a maximum flow in this network.
(ii) Does there exist a flow in each of the following networks?

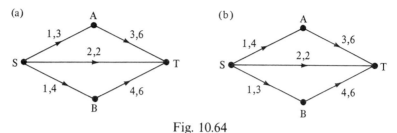

Fig. 10.64

Exercise 6.5 Find a flow in the following network with lower and upper capacities.

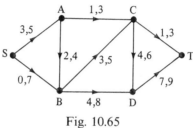

Fig. 10.65

Exercise 6.6 Verify the generalised max-flow/min-cut theorem for each of the following networks.

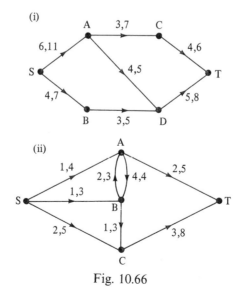

Fig. 10.66

Exercise 6.7   Consider the following network with lower and upper capacities

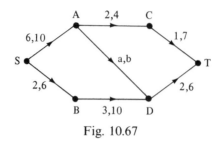

Fig. 10.67

For each of the following values of a and b, decide whether or not the network is feasible

(i) $a = 2, b = 6$
(ii) $a = 4, b = 8$

10.7   MISCELLANEOUS EXERCISES

M1 The towns and cities Edinburgh, Glasgow, Perth, Aberdeen, Fort William and Inverness are connected by telephone cables. The maximum number of calls that each cable can carry is given in hundreds in the table below, for example Edinburgh–Glasgow (9) means Edinburgh is connected to Glasgow and the maximum number of calls carried is 900.

Edinburgh–Glasgow	(9)
Edinburgh–Perth	(7)
Perth–Aberdeen	(3)
Perth–Inverness	(5)
Perth–Fort William	(3)
Glasgow–Fort William	(4)
Fort William–Inverness	(10)
Aberdeen–Inverness	(6)
Glasgow–Perth	(6)

With the aid of the map (Fig. 10.68), draw a network to show this information and work out the maximum number of calls that can pass between Edinburgh and Inverness. On the network mark a possible route to achieve this maximum flow.

Fig. 10.68

M2 Consider the network in Fig. 10.69.

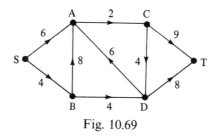

Fig. 10.69

Calculate the capacity of each of the following cuts.

(i) (AC, BD, DA)
(ii) (BA, BD, SA)
(iii) (AC, CD, DT)
(iv) (AC, BA, DA, SB)

M3 In the basic network in Fig. 10.70 the flows on some of the arcs are not specified. What are these missing flows?

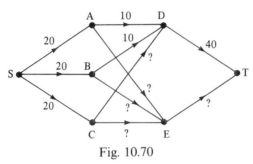

Fig. 10.70

M4 Find a flow with value 20 in the network in Fig. 10.71.

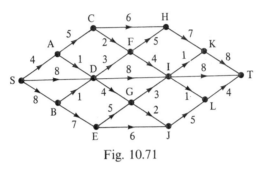

Fig. 10.71

M5 Consider the following network in which each arc is labelled with its capacity

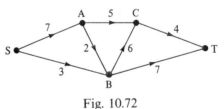

Fig. 10.72

     (i) Find a flow of value 9 from S to T, and draw a diagram showing the flow in each arc.
     (ii) Find a cut of capacity 9.
     (iii) What is the value of a maximum flow? (Give a brief reason for your answer.)

M6 The following network has eight cuts. Draw up a table (similar to Table 10.1, p. 272) listing these cuts, the vertices in X and Y, and the capacity of each cut. Which are the minimum cuts?

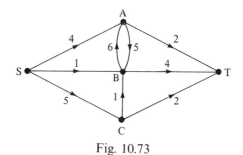

Fig. 10.73

M7 Consider the network in Fig. 10.74.

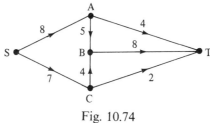

Fig. 10.74

Draw up a table listing all the cuts, and the capacity of each cut. Which are the minimum cuts?

M8 Check that the max-flow/min-cut theorem holds for the networks in Fig. 10.75.

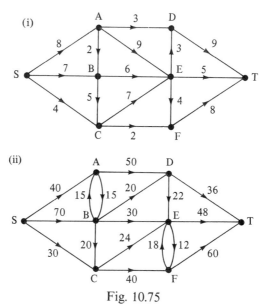

Fig. 10.75

M9 Is the network in Fig. 10.76 with lower and upper capacities feasible? If so, find a maximum flow.

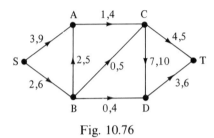

Fig. 10.76

M10 Consider the network in Fig. 10.77 with lower and upper capacities.

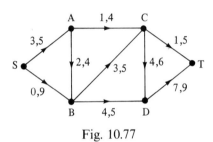

Fig. 10.77

(i) Find by inspection a feasible flow in the network.
(ii) Check that the generalised max-flow/min-cut theorem holds for this network.

M11 Check that the network in Fig. 10.78 with lower and upper capacities is feasible. Find a maximum flow from S to T, and check that the max-flow/min-cut theorem holds for this network.

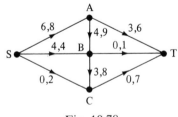

Fig. 10.78

11

Assignment

11.1 INTRODUCTION

We begin with a typical problem of the type considered in this chapter.

A store has four specialist departments. These are the Electrical, Furniture, Food and Hardware Departments. Each department needs someone to manage it and there are four employees called Anne, Barry, Carol and David who have the experience to be given a managerial role.

However, the experience varies from person to person. Ann could manage the Electrical or Furniture Departments. Barry has never worked in the Furniture Department but has considerable experience in each of the other departments. Similarly, Carol has experience of three departments but has no experience of the Hardware Department. David is very practical and has considerable experience of the Electrical and Hardware Departments.

How should the Store Manager allocate managerial responsibilities?

Problems of this type, called *matching problems*, can be expressed in the mathematical form of a bipartite graph introduced in Chapter 5. The table below shows the information in the problem statement and next to it a graphical representation of the same data.

Employees	Department		Employees		Department
Anne	Electrical, Furniture		Anne		Electrical
Barry	Electrical, Food, Hardware		Barry		Furniture
Carol	Electrical, Furniture, Food		Carol		Food
David	Electrical, Hardware		David		Hardware

In the bipartite graph we represent the employees by black vertices and the departments that need managing by white vertices. We joint a black vertex to a white vertex if the corresponding employee is suitable to manage that department.

We can show the assignment of an employee to a department by using heavy arcs. For example, in the bipartite graph below we have assigned Anne to the Furniture Department and David to the hardware Department.

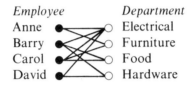

The pairing of some or all of the employees with a department is called a *matching*. The problem of assigning one employee to manage each department is equivalent to trying to find a matching containing four arcs in the bipartite graph. In this problem one matching is shown below.

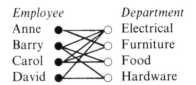

So one solution to this problem is to assign Anne to the Electrical Department, Barry to the Food Department, Carol to the Furniture Department and David to the Hardware Department. There are three other possible solutions.

(i) Anne —Furniture   (ii) Anne —Furniture   (iii) Anne —Furniture
      Barry —Electrical   Barry —Food   Barry —Hardware
      Carol —Food   Carol —Electrical   Carol —Food
      David—Hardware   David—Hardware   David—Electrical

In other problems it is not always possible to find such a matching. The following example illustrates such a problem.

Example Four tasks are to be assigned to four workers as shown in the following table.

Workers	Tasks
Alan	Painting, sanding
David	Painting, sanding, joinery, glazing
John	Painting, sanding
William	Sanding

Can all four workers be assigned to different tasks for which they are qualified?

Solution   We begin by drawing the bipartite graph.

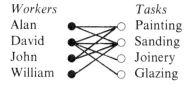

Workers   *Tasks*
Alan   Painting
David   Sanding
John   Joinery
William   Glazing

Clearly in this problem both joinery and glazing cannot be done by different workers, as only David is qualified to do these tasks. A matching cannot be found in this graph, and the four workers cannot be assigned to different tasks.

In the example above we can only match three arcs; one possible way is shown below:

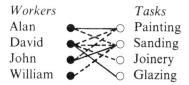

Workers   *Tasks*
Alan   Painting
David   Sanding
John   Joinery
William   Glazing

This is called a *maximum matching*. It is a matching using the largest possible number of arcs. The following exercises are examples of matching problems.

Exercise 1.1   The Prime Minister wishes to make some changes to the Cabinet. The four MP's June, Kay, Sir Len Hughes and Michael all deserve a place in the Cabinet. Due to the reshuffle the posts available are Foreign Secretary, Chancellor of the Exchequer, Home Secretary and Minister of Education. The Prime Minister believes that June would be best in either the Foreign or Home Office. Kay would also make a good Foreign Secretary but she would also make a good Chancellor of the Exchequer. Sir Len is being considered for both the Education Department and the Treasury. Michael does not have the experience to be Foreign Secretary or Chancellor; however, he could do well at either the Home Office or the Education Department. How many options has the Prime Minister got in allocating Ministerial responsibilities?

Exercise 1.2   A small firm which makes window frames, doors, etc. employs four men, Fred, George, Harry and Ian. The jobs to be done by these employees fall into the four broad categories—operating machinery, joiner/ fitter, driver and glazer. Fred is good at operating machinery and is a skilled joiner/fitter. George is a driver who can also operate machinery. Harry is a very useful employee as the only job he is not qualified to do is operate machinery. Ian, who lost his driving licence recently, is not a qualified joiner/fitter nor glazier. How should the Production Manager allocate the work?

Exercise 1.3   A small company, which has yachts for charter, has applications from four separate groups of people who wish to hire a yacht for one week commencing 1st August. Mr and Mrs Hills want a 6-berth yacht as do Mr and Mrs Watson. Mr and Mrs Colins are taking their two children for their first yachting holiday. The fourth party consists of eight members of a rugby club. Can the company satisfy all four applications if they have two 4-berth, one 6-berth and one 8-berth?

Exercise 1.4   In a major reorganisation of a large garden a man has to decide on the positioning of various kinds of plants within five fixed plots of land. He categorizes his plants into the five groups—flowers and shrubs, root crops, peas and beans, brassicas and finally herbs. Because of restrictions associated with the size of plots, the previous crop, light and shade and so on, the various categories can only be assigned to plots acording to the following table.

Flowers and shrubs		B, C
Root crops		A, C, E
Peas and beans	can be planted on	B, D
Brassicas		C, E
Herbs		A, E

Can the plants be accommodated on the plots within these restrictions?

11.2   AN ALGORITHM FOR FINDING MAXIMUM MATCHING

A deputy head has to timetable 5 classes for a double period. The teachers available are Mrs Adams, Miss Brown, Mr Clark, Mrs Duncan and Mr Evans. The subjects to be taught are (1) English, (2) Mathematics, (3) Geography, (4) Science and (5) History. The following table shows which teacher can teach each subject.

Adams (A)		1, 3, 5
Brown (B)		2, 4
Clark (C)	can teach	3, 5
Duncan (D)		2, 3
Evans (E)		1, 5

Can the deputy head timetable the classes?

The following algorithm gives a method of increasing, if possible, the number of arcs in a matching. In this example a matching of 4 arcs is increased to a matching of 5 arcs.

Step 1 Draw a bipartite graph to represent the information.

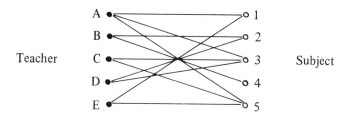

Start with any matching M. Here we have the matching A–5, B–2, D–3, E–1.

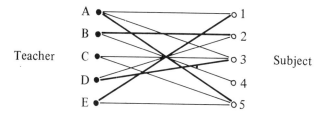

Label all the left-vertices which do not belong to this matching M with an asterisk (*). In the above, C is the only teacher vertex not belonging to the matching.

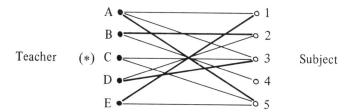

Now we follow the two steps 2 and 3 alternatively until no further labelling is possible:

Step 2 Choose a newly labelled left-vertex, *a* say, and label with *a* all the unlabelled right-vertices joined to *a* by an arc **not in** M. Repeat this for all newly labelled left-vertices.

Step 3 Choose a newly labelled right-vertex, *k* say, and label with *k* all the unlabelled left-vertices joined to *k* by an arc **in M**. Repeat this for all newly labelled right-vertices. Return to step 2.

So for the matching of Teacher/Subjects we have:

Step 2 Start with a labelled teacher vertex, in this case C. Label all the unlabelled subject vertices connected to C by an arc *not in M*. Vertices 3 and 5 are labelled with C.

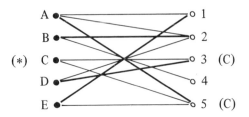

Step 3 Choose a newly labelled subject vertex (3 or 5). Pick out arcs *in M* which join subject vertex 3 to an unlabelled teacher vertex. D–3 is such an arc, so label D with 3. Similarly for the subject vertex 5. A–5 is in the matching M so we label A with 5.

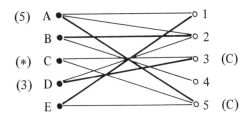

Now repeat steps 2 and 3 again.

Step 2 A and D are newly labelled vertices. Pick out arcs from A and D *not in M* which go to unlabelled subject vertices. A–1 and D–2 are such arcs. Label 1 with A and 2 with D.

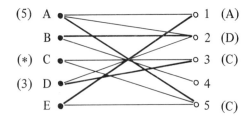

Step 3 1 and 2 are newly labelled vertices. Pick out arcs from 1 and 2 *in M* which go to unlabelled teacher vertices. E–1 and B–2 are such arcs. Label E with 1 and B with 2.

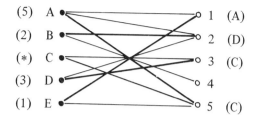

Repeating step 2 again results in labelling vertex 4 with B.

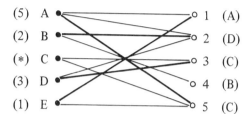

No further labelling is now possible. So we move on to step 4.

Step 4 Look for a labelled right-vertex which does not belong to the matching M. If no such vertex exists the current matching M has the maximum possible number of arcs. If there *is* such a vertex we say that *breakthrough has occurred*. In this case subject vertex 4 is labelled and does not belong to the current matching. Starting at this vertex find a path by proceeding to the vertex indicated by its label, i.e. 4–B. From B go to the vertex indicated by its label and so on until a vertex labelled by an asterisk (*) is reached. The path (P) 4–B–2–D–3–C is called the *alternating path*.

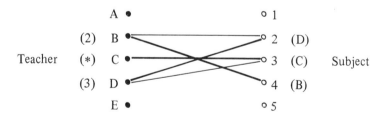

Step 5 The new matching consists of:
  (i) Arcs of the current matching which are not in the alternating path (P), i.e. A–5, E–1.
  (ii) Arcs of the alternating path (P) which are not in the current matching i.e. B–4, D–2, C–3.

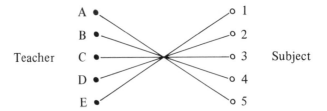

Since each teacher can be allocated to a subject this is obviously a maximum matching but not necessarily a unique solution.

Exercise 2.1 A hotel employs Ann, Barbara, Chris, Diana and Sally to act as receptionist and book-keeper, clean rooms, wash up, prepare meals and serve behind the bar.

Ann, who has no qualifications, can clean the rooms or wash the dishes in the kitchen. Barbara is a good cook and is prepared to wash the dishes and clean the rooms. Chris is an attractive barmaid. Diana, who is well qualified, refuses to work in the kitchen. Sally has a C & G qualification in cooking which is the only job she is prepared to do. How should the hotel manager assign the jobs?

Exercise 2.2 A company based in the north-east of England has a sales force of five people to sell its products in that area. Having examined where existing and potential customers operate, the sales manager divides the area into five parts, one for each sales person. The areas are Tyneside, Teesside, Durham, Northumberland and North Yorkshire. In consideration of where his sales force live, their knowledge and circumstances, they can be allocated to areas as indicated by the following table.

Use the algorithm described earlier to find how the sales manager should assign the sales areas to his sales staff.

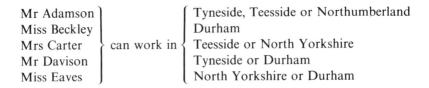

Exercise 2.3 After reorganisation of the Schools' Inspectorate, a Local Authority has six inspectors to take responsibility for English, Foreign Languages, CDT, Mathematics, Music and Science. The following table shows which inspectors have the expertise and experience for each subject area. Use the algorithm to find how the Chief Education Officer should

assign the subject area to the inspectors. In how many ways can the inspectors be assigned their responsibilities?

Mr Godson		Languages and CDT
Ms Johnson		Languages and CDT
Mrs Pegg	has the expertise	Music
Mr Watson	and experience for	English and Maths
Mrs Royston		Music and Science
Mr Coulston		CDT, Maths and Science

Exercise 2.4 A school has an annual sports day. Each form has to provide a team of six pupils each of which may only be entered for one event. The six events are 100 m, 400 m and 1500 m races, the javelin and long and high jumps. A fifth form has six pupils who are capable of taking part in various events as shown in the table. Which events should be assigned to which pupils? How many variations has the Team Captain got?

Ann		100 m, 1500 m
Bob		Long jump
Cynthia	can take part in	100 m
Doreen		400 m, high jump and long jump
Edward		400 m, 100 m
Frank		High jump, javelin

Exercise 2.5 A car hire firm has six cars available and has been approached by six possible clients who express preferences according to their requirements. The cars available are a Metro, Maestro, Fiesta, Sierra, Montego and Rover. The table indicates the preference of each prospective hirer. Can the hire company satisfy the requirements of all the clients? If not, use the given algorithm to obtain the maximum matching.

Mr Robinson		Metro, Maestro or Fiesta
Mr Sands		Metro or Sierra
Mr Taylor		Sierra
Miss Unwin	would like to hire a	Metro
Mrs Vardy		Maestro, Montego or Rover
Ms Williams		Rover

Exercise 2.6 Seven primary schools wish to take some pupils to the local Safari Park. As the schools are all in the same area, they all approach The Safe Coach Co. Ltd, which has seven coaches, to book a coach for the day's

visit. The coach company has a 15-seater mini-bus, a 40-seater coach, four 50-seater coaches and a 60-seater coach. The number of pupils from each school who wish to go on the visit is:

> 50 from St Joseph's
> 48 from Mill Lane
> 45 from Hill Top
> 53 from Rowley
> 60 from Park Road
> 12 from The Avenue
> 55 from The Grove

How should the coach company allocate its coaches? Use the algorithm to make sure you have a maximum matching. If all the schools cannot be catered for, which schools are going to be disappointed?

11.3 THE ALLOCATION ALGORITHM

In the previous section we were interested in finding a matching with the maximum number of arcs in a bipartite graph. As seen from the previous exercises, there are often many solutions to the maximum matching problem. In a practical situation, there is usually one solution which is, however, more desirable than others, that is, there is an optimal solution. Consider the following problem:

Four supermarkets, W, X, Y and Z, are supplied from four warehouses, A, B, C, and D. The cost (in pounds) of supplying one lorry-load of good from each warehouse to each supermarket is tabulated below

	W	X	Y	Z
A	3	7	6	2
B	4	3	5	8
C	5	4	6	5
D	6	7	3	7

We wish to allocate a warehouse to each supermarket so that the total cost is minimised. We could list all possible matchings and calculate the cost of each. This would involve 24 calculations. With n warehouses and n supermarkets there will be $n!$ calculations. The *allocation algorithm* gives a method of finding the minimum cost matching.

In finding a solution only *relative* costs are important. To simplify the matrix we can add or subtract any number from all the elements of a row or column. As the elements of the matrix represent costs then they should not become negative. If the minimum number in a row (or column) is subtracted from each element in that row (or column), then this will always produce a 'zero' element. Using the example, subtracting 2 from the numbers in row A, 3 from row B, 4 from row C and 3 from row D, gives:

	W	X	Y	Z
A	1	5	4	0
B	1	0	2	5
C	1	0	2	1
D	3	4	0	4

The process is repeated using columns. This then gives

	W	X	Y	Z
A	0	5	4	0
B	0	0	2	5
C	0	0	2	1
D	2	4	0	4

We now draw a bipartite graph. The vertices are A, B, C, D and W, X, Y, Z. The arcs are the zero cost edges in the new cost matrix.

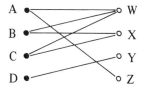

There are two maximum matchings.

These maximum matchings are minimum cost solutions to the problem. The costs involved are

	(i)		(ii)	
	AZ	2	AZ	2
	BW	4	BX	3
	CX	4	CW	5
	DY	3	DY	3
		13		13

Sometimes the problem is not so easily solved. If a matching involving all the vertices of the bipartite graph cannot be found then the full allocation algorithm must be applied. This is illustrated in the following example. The unit costs in the warehouse–supermarket problem are now

	W	X	Y	Z
A	3	7	6	2
B	4	6	5	3
C	5	7	6	3
D	6	4	3	7

The cost matrix is simplified, as before, by subtracting minimum values from rows,

	W	X	Y	Z
A	1	5	4	0
B	1	3	2	0
C	2	4	3	0
D	3	1	0	4

and then by subtracting values from columns. This is the current cost matrix.

	W	X	Y	Z
A	0	4	4	0
B	0	2	2	0
C	1	3	3	0
D	2	0	0	4

The corresponding bipartite graph is

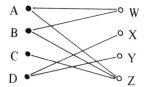

In this case it is impossible to find a matching with 4 arcs (try it and see). A maximum matching has 3 arcs and there are many such matchings. They are listed below.

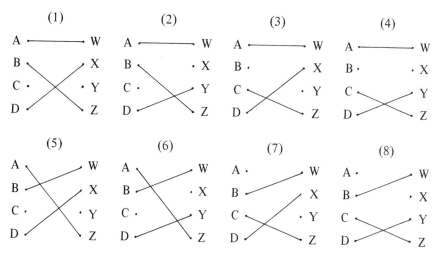

Remember that the cost of all these matchings is zero since every arc belongs to the bipartite graph. We now examine each matching in turn and note the current cost of 'joining' the two remaining vertices. For example, if in (1) C and Y are joined, then from the current cost matrix, this cost 3. The rest are tabulated below.

	(1)	(2)	(3)	(4)	(5)	(6)	(7)	(8)
Arc	CY	CX	BY	BX	CY	CX	AY	AX
Cost	3	3	2	2	3	3	4	4

The lowest cost is 2, given in (3) and (4). So the best solutions are

AW   AW
BY   BX
CZ and CZ
DX   DY

Both have a current cost of 2. The cost of both solutions, using the original cost matrix is

$$3 + 5 + 3 + 4 = 15.$$

Example   Before a new house is occupied workers go to the house to (a) sweep out the rooms (b) clean the windows (c) check the central heating is working (d) check the electrics are working. Time and motion men check the times spent on these jobs by four workmen A, B, C, and D. The times in minutes are

	Job			
Workman	Sweep	Clean windows	Check CH	Check electrics
A	12	24	12	14
B	14	27	10	16
C	16	23	13	15
D	14	22	11	17

Which man should the site manager allocate to which job in order to minimise the total time spent in each house?

Solution   The matrix is simplified to:

	Job			
Workman	Sweep	Windows	Check CH	Electrics
A	0	12	0	2
B	4	17	0	6
C	3	10	0	2
D	3	11	0	6

and then to

	Job			
Workman	Sweep	Windows	Check CH	Electrics
A	0	2	0	0
B	4	7	0	4
C	3	0	0	0
D	3	1	0	4

The corresponding bipartite graph is

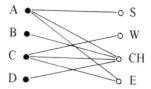

The maximum matchings have 3 arcs, and the 6 possible cases are listed below:

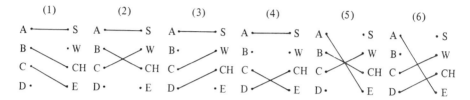

As before the cost of the 'missing' arc in each matching is noted.

	(1)	(2)	(3)	(4)	(5)	(6)
Arc	D–W	D–E	B–E	B–W	D–S	B–S
Cost	1	4	4	7	3	4

The minimum cost is 1, so the solution (which is unique) is A–S, B–CH, C–E, D–W. The actual cost is 12 + 10 + 15 + 22 = 59. It is interesting to note that the following gives a simple method of determining the number of arcs in the maximum matchings. Cover up the zeros of the current cost matrix using the *minimum* number of lines.

	S	W	CH	E
--A--	--0----	2----	0----	0
B	4	7	0	4
--C--	--3----	0----	0----	0
D	3	1	0	4

The minimum number of lines required to cover all the zero elements is the number of arcs in a maximum matching. (In this example it is 3.)

The costs of the 'missing' arcs are simply the actual uncovered elements

$$(4, 7, 4, 3, 1, 4).$$

Exercise 3.1　A company has contracts with three different haulage firms to transport its products to three different locations. The cost of delivery per ton varies with size and type of load coupled with the distance between the haulage company and the destination.

　The table gives the cost, in £s, charged per ton by each firm to deliver to the given locations. For commercial reasons it is desirable to give work to each haulage company. Which haulage company should deliver to each destination?

	Haulage company		
Destination	Road Rollers	Safe Goods	Tidy Move
Dorton	14	12	11
Exford	14	16	13
Fording	18	17	13

Exercise 3.2　A school has to enter four pupils in an athletics competition. The competition consists of the four track events: 100 m, 400 m, 800 m and 1500 m. The rules permit a pupil to enter only one event and the winning team is the one whose total time for the four events is least. Barlaston High School has trials to decide who should run in each event. The times, in seconds, taken by each pupil for each event are given in the table below. In order to obtain the best result in the competition, who should be recommended for each event?

	Event			
Pupil	100 m	400 m	800 m	1500 m
Ann	12	63	145	380
Barbara	14	61	147	360
Carolyn	13	62	150	370
Donna	14	64	143	350

Exercise 3.3　A builder owns three areas of land on which he wishes to build. The local council insist that each area of land has a different type of building, and, once the type of building has been chosen, each building on that area of land must be of the same design. The profit made by the builder depends on the land and the type of building. The profit, in £s, is given on the next page. What should be the builder's strategy in order to maximise his profit?

	Land		
Building	High Farm	George Farm	Tidy Farm
Bungalow	45 000	40 000	35 000
Detached house	45 000	50 000	40 000
Semi-detached house	40 000	40 000	20 000

Exercise 3.4   A firm has four employees and they are to be employed to do the four jobs—turning, milling, welding and cutting. Due to their varying experience some can do certain jobs better than others and this affects the cost of each job. The costs, in £s, are given below. Harry has no experience of welding, hence the question mark in the table. How should the production manager assign the jobs in order to minimise the cost?

	Job			
Workman	Turning	Milling	Welding	Cutting
George	15	15	20	12
Harry	18	19	?	11
Ian	16	15	20	13
John	19	18	21	13

11.4   THE HUNGARIAN ALGORITHM

Consider the following example:

Example   A medley relay swimming team consists of Alan, Brian, Colin and David, and they are required to swim backstroke, breaststroke, butterfly and crawl. The times taken, in seconds, by each boy to complete 100 m using each stroke is given by the following table:

	Stroke			
Swimmer	Back	Breast	Butterfly	Crawl
Alan	67	70	73	61
Brian	69	70	75	63
Colin	63	68	74	62
David	65	69	76	65

Which stroke should each boy swim in order to complete the relay of 100 m at each stroke in the shortest time? How long do you expect the relay to take?

Solution   The cost matrix is simplified to

	Ba	Br	Bu	Cr
A	6	9	12	0
B	6	7	12	0
C	1	6	12	0
D	0	4	11	0

and then to

	Ba	Br	Bu	Cr
A	6	5	1	0
B	6	3	1	0
C	1	2	1	0
D	0	0	0	0

This is the current cost matrix. The corresponding bipartite graph is:

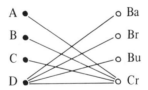

Note that in the current cost matrix, only two lines are needed to cover all the zeros. There are 9 maximum matchings, having 2 arcs. The 9 maximum matchings are:

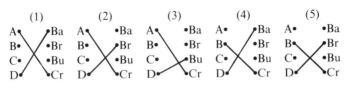

The 'unused' vertices in each matching can, in this case, be joined in two ways for each matching. For example in matching (1) we could join B–Br, C–Bu or B–Bu, C–Br. These possibilities and their costs are listed below.

	Arcs	Cost		Arcs	Cost
(1)	B–Br, C–Bu	$3 + 1 = 4$	(2)	B–Ba, C–Bu	$6 + 1 = 7$
	B–Bu, C–Br	$1 + 2 = 3$		B–Bu, C–Ba	$1 + 1 = 2$
(3)	B–Ba, C–Br	$6 + 2 = 8$	(4)	A–Br, C–Bu	$5 + 1 = 6$
	B–Br, C–Ba	$3 + 1 = 4$		A–Bu, C–Br	$1 + 2 = 3$
(5)	A–Ba, C–Bu	$6 + 1 = 7$	(6)	A–Ba, C–Br	$6 + 2 = 8$
	A–Bu, C–Ba	$1 + 1 = 2$		A–Br, C–Ba	$5 + 1 = 6$
(7)	A–Br, B–Bu	$5 + 1 = 6$	(8)	A–Ba, B–Bu	$6 + 1 = 7$
	A–Bu, B–Br	$1 + 3 = 4$		A–Bu, B–Ba	$1 + 6 = 7$
(9)	A–Ba, B–Br	$6 + 3 = 9$			
	A–Br, B–Ba	$5 + 6 = 11$			

The minimum time solutions are:

(2) with B–Bu, C–Ba and (5) with A–Bu, C–Ba.

The solutions are:

$$
\begin{array}{ccc}
\text{A–Cr} & & \text{A–Bu} \\
\text{B–Bu} & \text{and} & \text{B–Cr} \\
\text{C–Ba} & & \text{C–Ba} \\
\text{D–Br} & & \text{D–Br}
\end{array}
$$

The actual times for these solutions are $61 + 75 + 63 + 69 = \underline{268}$ seconds.

The Hungarian Algorithm

The previous example is somewhat long and unwieldy. Although the method does finally yield the solution, it would be convenient to have a more tractable method. For this reason the Hungarian algorithm is introduced. To illustrate and explain this algorithm the previous example is used again.

Step 1   Form the revised cost matrix exactly as before.

	Ba	Br	Bu	Cr
A	6	5	1	0
B	6	3	1	0
C	1	2	1	0
D	0	0	0	0

Step 2   Cover the zero elements with the minimum number of lines. If this minimum number equals the number of rows, then it is possible to obtain a maximum matching, using all vertices, immediately. Otherwise continue to step 3.

	Ba	Br	Bu	Cr
A	6	5	1	0
B	6	3	1	0
C	1	2	1	0
--D--	---0---	---0---	---0---	---0--

Step 3   Note the minimum uncovered element; in this case it is 1. As mentioned earlier, the optimum allocation depends only on relative costs, so we can add or subtract a number to a row or column.

(i) The minimum uncovered element is added to the rows and columns which are covered (i.e. row 4 and column 4). Adding 1 to row 4 produces

	Ba	Br	Bu	Cr
A	6	5	1	0
B	6	3	1	0
C	1	2	1	0
D	1	1	1	1

Adding 1 to column 4 produces

	Ba	Br	Bu	Cr
A	6	5	1	1
B	6	3	1	1
C	1	2	1	1
D	1	1	1	2

(ii) The minimum uncovered element is now subtracted from the entire matrix. This produces the revised cost matrix:

	Ba	Br	Bu	Cr
A	5	4	0	0
B	5	2	0	0
C	0	1	0	0
D	0	0	0	1

Note that the net effect of applying both these steps is:

(a) All uncovered elements are reduced by 1. This must produce additional zero elements.

(b) Elements covered by one line are unaffected.

(c) Elements covered by two lines are increased by 1.

Step 2 is repeated.

	Ba	Br	Bu	Cr
A	5	4	0	0
B	5	2	0	0
--C--	--0----	--1----	--0----	--0--
--D--	--0----	--0----	--0----	--1--

In this case four lines are required to cover all the zeros and so a maximum matching with four arcs can be found. The bipartite graph is

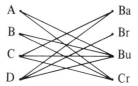

There are two matchings with four edges. They are:

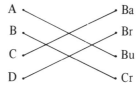

and

This is the solution as found previously.

Exercise 4.1   Members of a walking club decide to check four footpaths to see that they are still open. Some walkers find it easier to cover some paths than others due to both the location and terrain. The Club Secretary estimates how long, including travelling time to the path, it would take each walker to check each path. His estimates, in hours, are:

Walker	Path			
	A	B	C	D
Keith	4.2	7.4	9.4	1.9
Lorraine	4.0	7.7	8.9	2.2
Mary	4.3	6.9	8.4	2.0
Nigel	3.9	7.0	9.0	2.3

How should the secretary assign the walks so that the total time taken is a minimum?

Exercise 4.2 A department store wishes to place four different advertisements in the local newspapers, freesheets and magazines. The cost of placing an advertisement depends on its size and the periodical in which it is placed. These costs, in £s, are given in the table below. What recommendation would you make to the store manager?

Periodical	Advertisement type			
	A	B	C	D
The Echo	110	95	140	80
The Advertiser	105	82	145	80
Freesheet	125	78	140	75
Central News	115	90	135	85

Exercise 4.3 A small haulage company is seeking local garages to maintain and repair their vehicles. Inspection of their records reveals that there are five jobs which occur fairly regularly, and so they ask the garages to quote prices for each of these tasks. The table below gives the quotation from each garage for each job.

Task	Garage				
	A	B	C	D	E
Servicing	90	86	105	95	93
Exhaust replacement	210	195	200	215	205
Tyre replacement	75	74	77	73	80
Renew brake-shoes	85	97	80	95	82
Sign writing	100	105	95	100	*

The * indicates that garage E is not prepared to quote for sign writing. For commercial reasons the haulage company wishes to patronise all five garages. Which garages should do which jobs so that the total estimated cost is a minimum?

11.5 MISCELLANEOUS EXERCISES

M1 A group of teachers get together to write materials for use in the teaching of mathematics. Initially they decide to divide the project into 4 areas; investigations, problem solving, mathematical techniques and general worksheets. The four teachers concerned have different backgrounds which mean that Mr Philips would make a good job of writing material for both the investigations and problem solving areas. Miss Watson enjoys both investigations and mathematical techniques. Mrs Briggs is a good mathematician who would produce good material for studying mathematical techniques. Mr Alan is used to producing problem solving material. General worksheets could be written well by both Mrs Biggs and Mr Philips. Who should be given the various writing jobs?

M2 A manufacturing company has recently appointed Ms Forsyth as General Manager. After some consideration she decides to reorganise the general administration into four departments. After interviewing some of the staff she is left with Mr Williams, Miss Edwards, Mrs Scott and Mr Franks to manage the Sales, Accounts, Production and Person-nel Departments. Further interviews reveal that Mr Williams could look after both the Sales and Production Departments, Miss Edwards would do well in the Personnel Department but could also manage the Sales Department. Mrs Scott would not make a suitable Head of Production Department but could manage any of the other departments. Mr Franks knows both the customers and the salesmen well and is also a qualified accountant, hence he could do well in both the Sales and Accounts Departments. How should Ms Forsyth allocate the departments to the staff?

M3 In solving a word puzzle Jill find she is left with the words ACRID, ANVIL, BEGIN, BOXED and BROIL to fit into five positions on a grid. Position 1 needs to begin with the letter A and position 3 needs a word ending in L. BEGIN and BROIL will both fit in position 5 and ACRID and BOXED both fit in position 2. Position 4 needs a word with an R in the middle. Can Jill fit the words into the five positions or has she made a mistake earlier in the solution? If she can fit the words into the grid, in which positions should they be placed?

M4 Eccleshire has four advisory teachers for mathematics each of whom is to be responsible for the development of the teaching of mathematics in a group of schools. In order to make best use of the advisers' time, it is decided to keep their travelling to a minimum. The table below gives the estimated weekly mileage of each adviser when assigned a particular group of schools. How should the schools be allocated to the advisers in order to make best use of the advisers' time?

Adviser	Group A	Group B	Group C	Group D
Eric	48	64	72	76
Fleur	56	62	73	72
Grace	52	62	75	74
Harry	56	65	71	70

M5 High Rise Building Co. Ltd is a large firm of builders which subcontracts work out to smaller firms of builders. These firms are asked to quote for each of four jobs even though each only has the resources to do one of them. The table below gives the quotes, in £s, for each job. Who should be given each job in order to minimise the cost? J. Little and Son does not employ a plasterer, hence the reason for no quotation from this firm for plastering.

Firms	Electrics	Plumbing	Decorating	Plastering
Home Improvements Ltd	750	600	900	700
J. Little and Son	900	550	1100	?
House Repairs Ltd	800	650	950	750
T. Cowboy and Sons Ltd	850	600	1000	650
W. Hills and Co. Ltd	950	700	1050	700

M6 A large manufacturing company has five electricity generators which can supply electricity to each of its five plants. The quantity of electricity which can be supplied to each plant depends both on the generators and the network of wires in the factory. The number of units which can be supplied in each case is given in the table below and the flow of electricity can be controlled by isolation switches. If each generator can only supply one plant at a time, how should the generators be allocated to the plants in order to maximise the amount of available electricity?

	Plant				
Generator	A	B	C	D	E
P	23	13	33	18	33
Q	38	23	0	28	28
R	28	33	23	18	23
S	18	28	48	13	48
T	43	38	23	13	23

12

The Transportation Problem

12.1 INTRODUCTION

In this chapter we discuss a variation of the basic assignment problem of Chapter 11.

Consider the following problem.

Warehouses A_1, A_2 and A_3 each have a stock of goods which have to be supplied to supermarkets b_1, b_2, b_3 and b_4. The demand from each supermarket and the amount in each warehouse is known. The cost of supplying a single item from each warehouse to each factory is also known. A typical example is shown below, with the costs of supply given in matrix form.

			Demand			
			⑤	③	⑤	②
			b_1	b_2	b_3	b_4
	⑤	A_1	15	14	17	16
Supply	④	A_2	10	13	11	10
	⑥	A_3	15	12	13	13

The problem is to determine which warehouse should supply which supermarkets, so that all supply and demand constraints are satisfied, and the total cost is minimised.

This is an example of *the transportation problem*. It is more complicated than an assignment problem because we need to specify the amount of flow along each arc and also because a single supply vertex (warehouse in this case) may send goods to more than one demand vertex (supermarket).

The method of solution begins in the same way as for the assigment problem. As with the allocation problem the solution depends on *relative* costs, so the matrix may be simplified by subtracting the smallest value in each row and column from the other entries.

Subtracting from rows, the matrix is simplified to

		Demand			
		⑤	③	⑤	②
		b_1	b_2	b_3	b_4
	⑤ A_1	1	0	3	2
Supply	④ A_2	0	3	1	0
	⑥ A_3	3	0	1	1

Subtracting from the columns, the matrix is simplified to

		Demand			
		⑤	③	⑤	②
		b_1	b_2	b_3	b_4
	⑤ A_1	1	0	2	2
Supply	④ A_2	0	3	0	0
	⑥ A_3	3	0	0	1

A bipartite graph of 'zero' arcs is

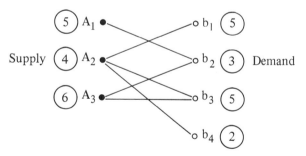

Fig. 12.1

Using the bipartite graph we see that the following are possible supply routes. (There are numerous other possible initial supply situations.)

(a) 2 units from A_1 to b_2
(b) 4 units from A_2 to b_1
(c) 5 units from A_3 to b_3
(d) 1 unit from A_3 to b_2

This leaves the following situation

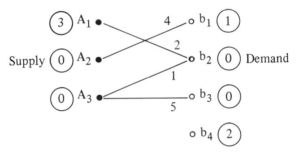

Fig. 12.2

So that warehouse A_1 has three items in stock and supermarkets b_1 and b_4 require goods. However, A_1 cannot supply b_1 and b_4 using this graphical representation.

The algorithm for the transportation problem is described in the next section.

Exercise 1.1   By 'trial and error' find a possible method of supplying each warehouse with the correct number of goods. For your solution work out the total cost.

12.2   THE TRANSPORTATION ALGORITHM

The algorithm for the transportation problem is an extension of the Hungarian algorithm outlined in Chapter 11 for the assignment problem. It uses the bipartite graph for the flow from supply to demand vertices.

We illustrate each part of the algorithm by solving the example in section 12.1. This is summarised by the following table.

		Demand			
		⑤	③	⑤	②
		b_1	b_2	b_3	b_4
	⑤ A_1	15	14	17	16
Supply	④ A_2	10	13	11	10
	⑥ A_3	15	12	13	13

Part 1   Constructing the Initial Bipartite Graph

Step 1   Simplify the cost matrix by subtracting the smallest value in each row and column from the other entries.
Step 2   Form a bipartite graph whose arcs have zero cost.

This is the 'zero cost' bipartite graph and the total cost of transporting from the supply to demand vertices is zero. So this is a least cost solution but it may be that not all the demand is satisfied. We then adjust the graph in stages to satisfy the demand. At each stage we have a least-cost flow cycle. For our example we already have from the introduction

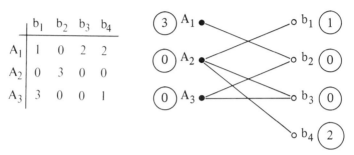

	b_1	b_2	b_3	b_4
A_1	1	0	2	2
A_2	0	3	0	0
A_3	3	0	0	1

Fig. 12.3

Part 2   Labelling the Vertices

Step 3. Note the supply vertices which still have goods left.
Step 4 From the bipartite graph note any demand vertx which is connected to these supply vertices.
Step 5 Note the supply vertices which are actually supplying the demand vertices noted in step 4.
Step 6 Repeat steps 4 and 5 until

either

(a) a demand vertex whose demand is not satisfied is noted. If such a vertex is noted we say that *breakthrough has occurred*. This means that it will be possible to find a new flow pattern which sends more goods than in the original situation (Part 4)

or

(b) no more labelling is possible. In this case we modify the bipartite graph (Part 3).

Consider then Part 2 applied to this example.

Step 3 A_1 has goods left and we label it with (*).
Step 4 From the graph, demand vertex b_2 is noted and labelled with A_1.

The bipartite graph with these labels on is shown in Fig. 12.4.

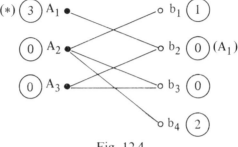

Fig. 12.4

Step 5   The supply vertices supplying b_2 are A_1 and A_3. We label A_3 with (b_2). A_1 is already labelled with (*).

Step 6   Repeat steps 4 and 5.

b_3 is connected to A_3 so we label b_3 with (A_3). (b_2 is also connected to A_3 but we have already noted this.) The vertex supplying b_3 is A_3 and this is already labelled. So we have the labelled bipartite graph shown in Fig. 12.5.

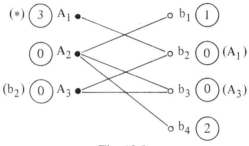

Fig. 12.5

Repeating steps 4 and 5 again will *not* introduce any more vertices. The vertices b_1 and b_4 whose demands are unsatisfied will not be labelled and so breakthrough has not occurred. Thus it is definitely not possible to augment the number of goods being supplied in the original situation.

At this stage it is necessary to revise the cost matrix in order to find the next cheapest route. From the application of the algorithm, the supply vertices noted are A_1 and A_3, and the demand vertices *not* noted are b_1 and b_4. Now A_1 is the only vertex with goods still available. However, when reorganising the allocation of goods we need to consider A_1 and A_3. Roughly speaking, A_1 and A_3 are connected (via b_2). When supplying goods from A_1 this may also indirectly involve A_3. In this example, vertices b_1 and b_4 both require goods, but as we shall see in the next example it is sometimes necessary to also consider vertices whose demand is satisfied.

So we move on to the next part of the algorithm.

Part 3   Modifying the Bipartite Graph

If breakthrough has not occurred revise the cost matrix in the following way:

Step 7   (i) Note the supply vertices labelled.
           (ii) Note the demand vertices not labelled.
           (iii) Find the lowest current cost, c say, on any arc that starts at a labelled supply vertex and ends at an unlabelled demand vertex.

Step 8   (i) Subtract c from each row containing the labelled vertices
           (ii) Form a new matrix and bipartite graph in the usual way
           (iii) Return to Part 2.

Consider Part 3 of the algorithm applied to the bipartite graph shown above:

Step 7   (i) Supply vertices A_1 and A_3 are labelled after Part 2
           (ii) Demand vertices not labelled are b_1 and b_4
           (iii) The costs of the following routes are noted:

$$\left. \begin{array}{ll} A_1 b_1 & \text{cost } 1 \\ A_1 b_4 & \text{cost } 2 \\ A_3 b_1 & \text{cost } 3 \\ A_3 b_4 & \text{cost } 1 \end{array} \right\} \text{minimum value} = 1$$

To introduce new zeros into the cost matrix, and hence new routes into the bipartite graph, the minimum value is subtracted from rows A_1 and A_3.

		Demand			
		① b_1	⓪ b_2	⓪ b_3	② b_4
③	A_1	0	-1	1	1
Supply ⓪	A_2	0	3	0	0
⓪	A_3	2	-1	-1	0

It is permissible to do this since it is only relative costs which are important. To rid the cost matrix of negative values, 1 is added to columns b_2 and b_3.

		Demand			
		① b_1	⓪ b_2	⓪ b_3	② b_4
③	A_1	0	0	2	1
Supply ⓪	A_2	0	4	1	0
⓪	A_3	2	0	0	0

The corresponding bipartite graph is then:

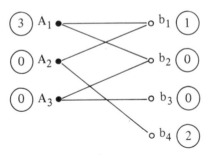

Fig. 12.6

Clearly it is possible to satisfy b_1 by supplying 1 unit from A_1. The situation in full is now:

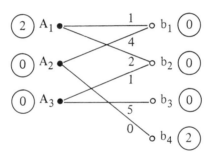

Fig. 12.7

To see if the number of goods supplied can be increased we repeat Part 2 of the algorithm.

Step 3 A_1 can still supply goods and is labelled (*)
Step 4 b_1 and b_2 are connected to A_1 and labelled (A_1)
Step 5 A_1, A_2 and A_3 are actually supplying b_1 and b_2; so label A_2 with (b_1) and label A_3 with (b_2). (We need to label a vertex only once.)
Step 6 Repeating steps 4 and 5, we label b_3 with (A_3) and b_4 with (A_2).

Now breakthrough has occurred since b_4 has been reached. The labelled bipartite graph is shown in Fig. 12.8.

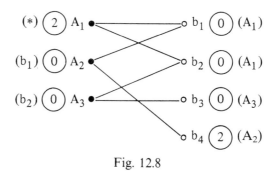

Fig. 12.8

Now we move on to Part 4 of the algorithm.

Part 4   Modifying the Flow Pattern

Step 9   Start with the breakthrough vertex and work through the graph backwards until a supply vertex labelled (*) is reached.
Amend the flow along each arc to take up the spare supply capacity.
If all the demand is satisfied the solution has been found.
If not then return to Part 2 of the algorithm.

For our example, working through the graph backwards from b_4 to A_1 we have

$$b_4 \text{ is connected to } A_2$$
$$A_2 \text{ is connected to } b_1$$
$$b_1 \text{ is connected to } A_1$$

Thus we have found a route from the supply vertex with goods to the demand vertex requiring goods.

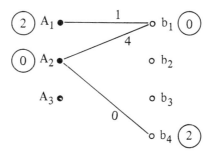

Fig. 12.9

Since breakthrough has occurred the number of goods supplied can be increased.

$$A_1 \text{ supplies an extra 2 units to } b_1$$
$$A_2 \text{ supplies 2 units to } b_1$$
$$A_2 \text{ supplies 2 units to } b_4$$

Thus we now have:

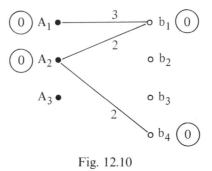

Fig. 12.10

We can see that even though A_2 had already supplied all its goods, it was still important in finding a way of increasing the number of goods supplied. The full solution is thus:

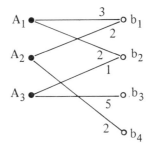

Fig. 12.11

The cost is:

$$3(15) + 2(14) + 2(10) + 2(10) + 1(12) + 5(13)$$
$$= 45 + 28 + 20 + 20 + 12 + 65$$
$$= \underline{190}$$

As a further illustration of the algorithm consider another example.

Example A warehouse and factory problem is summarised in the matrix below:

		Warehouse			
		⑥	⑤	⑤	④
		b_1	b_2	b_3	b_4
	⑨ A_1	6	4	3	6
Factory	⑦ A_2	8	6	2	5
	④ A_3	3	4	7	5

How should the goods be supplied to the warehouses so that the transport cost is a minimum?

Solution   **Part 1** of the algorithm produces an initial bipartite graph. The cost matrix is simplified, by subtracting minimum values from rows:

	⑥	⑤	⑤	④
	b_1	b_2	b_3	b_4
⑨ A_1	3	1	0	3
⑦ A_2	6	4	0	3
④ A_3	0	1	4	2

and then subtracting from the columns:

	⑥	⑤	⑤	④
	b_1	b_2	b_3	b_4
⑨ A_1	3	0	0	1
⑦ A_2	6	3	0	1
④ A_3	0	0	4	0

The initial bipartite graph is:

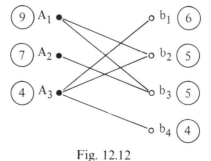

Fig. 12.12

A possible initial supply of goods is:

$$A_1 b_2 \quad 5 \text{ units}$$
$$A_1 b_3 \quad 4 \text{ units}$$
$$A_2 b_3 \quad 1 \text{ unit}$$
$$A_3 b_4 \quad 4 \text{ units}$$

The situation is now:

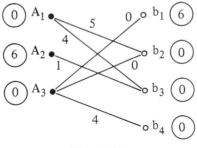

Fig. 12.13

We need to check if a different initial supply could increase the number of goods supplied. We do this by applying **Part 2** of the transportation algorithm.

Step 3 A_2 is the only vertex which can still supply goods. Label A_2 with (*)
Step 4 b_3 is connected to A_2. Label b_3 with (A_2)
Step 5 A_1 is actually supplying b_3 (A_2 has already been noted).
Step 4 b_2 is connected to A_1 (b_3 has already been noted).
Step 5 A_1 is actually supplying b_2.

Repeating steps 4 and 5 will not result in any new vertices being noted. Although A_3 is connected to b_2 we do not label it since A_3 is not supplying b_2 with goods yet. Breakthrough has not occurred since b_1 has not been reached. Thus the present supply of goods using the bipartite graph cannot be increased. Hence it is necessary to modify the cost matrix so that a new bipartite graph will be formed. The labelled bipartite graph is shown below:

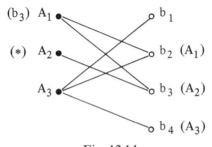

Fig. 12.14

Step 7   We modify the graph using **Part 3** of the algorithm. The supply vertices noted are A_1 and A_2. The demand vertices not noted are b_1 and b_4. Now A_2 is the only vertex with goods still available and b_1 is the only vertex which still requires goods. However, when reorganising the supply of goods, we need to consider A_1 and A_2, b_1 and b_4. This is because A_1 and A_2 are connected (via b_3), and b_1 and b_4 are connected (via A_3). When supplying goods from A_2 then this may indirectly involve A_1, and similarly when satisfying demand at b_1 we must also consider vertex b_4.

Step 8   Thus the costs of A_1b_1, A_1b_4, A_2b_1 and A_2b_4 are important.

$$A_1b_1 \quad \text{cost 3}$$
$$A_1b_4 \quad \text{cost 1}$$
$$A_2b_1 \quad \text{cost 6}$$
$$A_2b_4 \quad \text{cost 1}$$

The minimum cost here is 1. This minimum cost is subtracted from rows A_1 and A_2 to produce new zeros.

		⑥ b_1	⓪ b_2	⓪ b_3	⓪ b_4
⓪	A_1	2	-1	-1	0
⑥	A_2	5	2	-1	0
⓪	A_3	0	0	4	0

To rid the matrix of negative elements, 1 is added to columns b_2 and b_3, producing the revised cost matrix.

		⑥ b_1	⓪ b_2	⓪ b_3	⓪ b_4
⓪	A_1	2	0	0	0
⑥	A_2	5	3	0	0
⓪	A_3	0	1	5	0

The cost matrix has new zeros and the bipartite graph is:

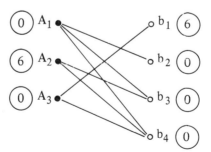

Fig. 12.15

Using the new bipartite graph we may be able to rearrange the supply and hence augment it. We use **Part 2** of the algorithm.

Step 3 A_2 is the supply vertex which can still supply goods.
Step 4 b_3 and b_4 are connected to A_2.
Step 5 A_1 and A_3 are the vertices actually supplying b_3 and b_4 (A_2 has already been noted).
Step 4 b_1 and b_2 are connected to A_1 and A_3 (b_3 and b_4 already noted).

Breakthrough has occurred since b_1 has been reached. Thus, it is possible, using the above bipartite graph, to increase the number of goods allocated. The labelled bipartite graph is

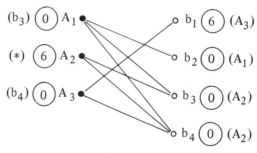

Fig. 12.16

Now we modify the flow pattern by applying **Part 4** of the algorithm. Starting with b_1 and working backwards through the graph produces the following route:

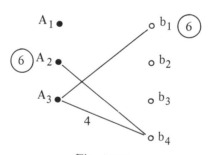

Fig. 12.17

A_2 can supply 6
b_1 requires 6

The flow along $A_3 b_4$ is 4.
   To increase the flow, the flow $A_3 b_4$ is reduced to 0, $A_3 b_1$ is increased to 4, .e. A_3 supplies 4 units to b_1 instead of b_4.

A_2 can now supply 4 units to b_4. The improved supply is thus:

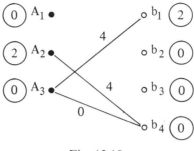

Fig. 12.18

An extra 4 units have been allocated. The full situation so far is:

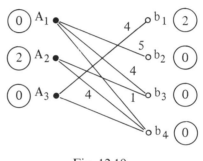

Fig. 12.19

It is again necessary to revise the cost matrix, obtain a new bipartite graph and try to allocate the final 2 units. We apply the algorithm again.

Part 2:   *Step 3* A_2 can still supply.
Step 4 b_3 and b_4 are connected to A_2.
Step 5 A_1 (and A_2) are actually supplying b_3 (and b_4).
Step 4 b_2 is connected to A_1 (b_3, b_4 have already noted).

Repeating steps 4 and 5 will not result in any more vertices being noted. Since b_1 has not been reached then breakthrough has not occurred.

Part 3:   *Step 7*   The supply vertices noted are A_1 and A_2. The demand vertex not noted is b_1.

Step 8   The costs of A_1b_1 and A_2b_1 are 2 and 5. Thus 2 is subtracted from row A_1 and row A_2. This produces:

		② b_1	⓪ b_2	⓪ b_3	⓪ b_4
⓪	A_1	0	-2	-2	-2
②	A_2	3	1	-2	-2
⓪	A_3	0	1	5	0

To avoid negative values, 2 is added to columns b_2, b_3 and b_4.

		② b_1	⓪ b_2	⓪ b_3	⓪ b_4
⓪	A_1	0	0	0	0
②	A_2	3	3	0	0
⓪	A_3	0	3	7	2

The bipartite graph is:

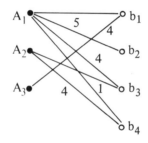

Fig. 12.20

We must try to increase the flow using this new bipartite graph. Applying the algorithm:

Part 2:   *Step 3* A_2 can still supply goods.
Step 4 b_3 and b_4 are connected to A_2.
Step 5 A_1 and A_2 actually supplying b_3 and b_4.
Step 4 b_1, b_2, b_3 and b_4 are all connected to A_1 and A_2.

Hence breakthrough has occurred since b_1 has been reached.

Part 4:   *Step 9*   Starting from b_1 and working backwards through the steps produces the route in Fig. 12.21.

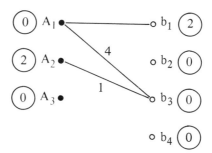

Fig. 12.21

A_2 can supply 2 units
b_1 requires 2 units
A_2b_3 has a flow of 1
A_1b_3 has a flow of 4

The flow can be augmented as follows.

Let A_1 supply 2 units to b_1, and reduce the A_1b_3 supply by 2 units. Increase the supply along A_2b_3 by 2. This gives:

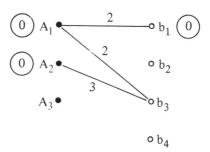

Fig. 12.22

The full solution is thus:

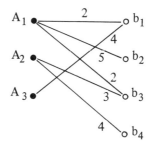

Fig. 12.23

The cost is

$$2(6) + 5(4) + 2(3) + 3(2) + 4(5) + 4(3)$$
$$= 12 + 20 + 6 + 6 + 20 + 12$$
$$= \underline{76}$$

Exercise 2.1   A printing firm has 4 retail outlets, b_1, b_2, b_3 and b_4. The firm buys paper from three wholesalers, A_1, A_2 and A_3. The demand, supply and unit charges are summarised below.

		Demand			
		⑥ b_1	⑤ b_2	③ b_3	④ b_4
Supply	⑥ A_1	6	7	5	8
	⑤ A_2	3	4	6	3
	⑦ A_3	7	4	5	5

How many units should each wholesaler supply to each retail outlet in order to minimise the total cost?

Exercise 2.2   Four garages, b_1, b_2, b_3 and b_4, have respective weekly petrol sales of 4000, 5000, 7000 and 2000 gallons. The transport firms A_1, A_2 and A_3 can supply 4000, 6000 and 8000 gallons per week respectively. The delivery charge, per 1000 gallons, is given in the table. Determine the best way of supplying the garages with petrol and calculate the weekly delivery charges.

		Demand			
		④ b_1	⑤ b_2	⑦ b_3	② b_4
Supply	④ A_1	4	3	9	5
	⑥ A_2	3	7	4	6
	⑧ A_3	6	5	6	7

Exercise 2.3   Three scrap-metal merchants, A_1, A_2, and A_3, sell their scrap to four processing plants, b_1, b_2, b_3 and b_4. The merchants supply 50, 80 and 50 tons of scrap per week. The processing plants require 40, 50, 60 and 30 tons per week. The amount paid for a ton of scrap metal is the same at each plant, but the costs of transporting the metal varies. The transport costs per 10 tons are given in the table.

| | | Demand | | | |
		④ b_1	⑤ b_2	⑥ b_3	③ b_4
⑤	A_1	4	4	3	6
⑧	A_2	2	3	5	2
⑤	A_3	6	7	4	5

How should the three merchants supply the metal in order to minimise the transport costs?

12.3 MISCELLANEOUS EXERCISES

M1 A firm has factories in Liverpool and Nottingham which supply goods to depots in Manchester, Birmingham, Leeds and Newcastle. The cost of transport per item, in £s, between the factories and the depots is shown in the table below.

	Manchester (b_1)	Birmingham (b_2)	Leeds (b_3)	Newcastle (b_4)
Liverpool (A_1)	5	12	8	20
Nottingham (A_2)	10	7	8	17

The Liverpool factory has an output of 15 000 items and the Nottingham factory an output of 10 000 items. The Manchester depot requires 6000 items, the Birmingham depot 7000 items, the Leeds depot 8000 items and the Newcastle depot 4000 items. How should the goods be transported to minimise the transport costs?

M2 The table gives the cost of transporting a lorry load of coal from mines A_1, A_2, A_3 to the power stations d_1, d_2, d_3, d_4 and d_5.

		⑩ d_1	⑮ d_2	⑳ d_3	⑩ d_4	⑮ d_5
⑳	A_1	24	16	8	10	14
㉚	A_2	21	15	7	12	16
⑳	A_3	23	14	7	14	12

The mines supply 20, 30 and 20 lorry loads per day; the power stations require 10, 15, 20, 10 and 15 loads per day. Determine a transport policy which minimizes the daily transport cost.

M3 Paper from three paper mills F_1, F_2 and F_3 has to be transported to printing works W_1, W_2, W_3 and W_4. The table gives the supply and demands (in tonnes), and the transport costs (in £s per tonne).

		⑦ W_1	⑤ W_2	⑥ W_3	⑫ W_4
⑧	F_1	5	4	7	5
⑫	F_2	6	5	8	8
⑩	F_3	7	5	6	7

How should the paper be supplied in order to minimise the total transport cost?

M4 Bricks have to be supplied from four builders' merchants, A_1, A_2, A_3 and A_4 to building sites b_1, b_2, b_3, b_4 and b_5. A_1 can supply 40 tonnes, A_2 can supply 10 tonnes, and so on. The building sites require 12, 15, 20, 15 and 18 tonnes respectively. The transport costs, in £s per tonne are given in the table.

		⑫ b_1	⑮ b_2	⑳ b_3	⑮ b_4	⑱ b_5
㊵	A_1	13	9	15	10	12
⑩	A_2	11	10	12	12	9
⑳	A_3	12	9	11	12	9
⑩	A_4	13	12	13	12	10

How should the bricks be supplied so that transport costs are minimised? What difference would it make if the transport cost from A_4 to b_3 was reduced to 11?

M5 Aggregate is supplied from quarries F_1, F_2 and F_3 to depots W_1, W_2, W_3 and W_4 to make ready-mix concrete. The supply and demand figures (in tonnes) are given in the table, with the transport costs (in £s per tonne). How can the cost be minimised?

		(5) W_1	(9) W_2	(15) W_3	(6) W_4
(12)	F_1	4	8	5	8
(18)	F_2	7	6	7	9
(10)	F_3	3	7	6	8

(*Note:* in this problem the supply and demand are not equal. To enable us to use the Hungarian algorithm we must introduce a dummy warehouse vertex (W_5). The demand of W_5 is equal to the excess supply (i.e. 5). The cost of supplying the dummy vertex is set at 0.)

13

Coding

13.1 INTRODUCTION

With the development of microprocessors and remote sensing apparatus have come tremendous advances in the theory of binary coding and its practical applications. Here we can attempt no more than an introduction to some of the main ideas. Coding of any kind is a part of the process of *communication*, which may be represented diagrammatically as shown in Fig. 13.1.

To take an example, in TV broadcasting the message for transmission is a picture in the studio. The camera converts this into a 625-row array of packages of information, each package denoting a particular colour. This array, in the form of an electrical signal, is broadcast via antennae and the atmosphere and is finally interpreted by the receiving set in the living room. The picture seen there differs somewhat from the original, errors having corrupted the information at various stages in the channel of communication. These errors may result in effects varying from subtle changes of colour tone to what looks like a violent snowstorm. Technically, the errors are all classified as 'noise'.

At this stage consider for yourself, or discuss with a friend, or in class, the various stages in communication:

  (i) In a telephone conversation.
 (ii) Between bees, about the location of a source of honey.
(iii) Of genetic information in cell division.

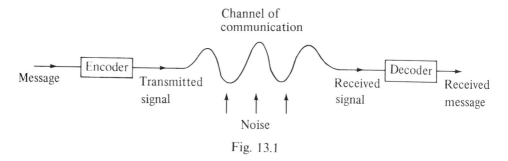

Fig. 13.1

In human communication a certain amount of noise may be tolerated. For example, we can often decipher the inscriptions on ancient tombstones, even though letters or even whole words are worn away, using our knowledge of the style of such inscriptions. When machines communicate with each other no such intuition is possible. For this reason it is important that machines should be able to detect errors. It is better still if the code is constructed in such a way that the unintelligent machine decoder not only finds errors but also corrects them. Methods of constructing *error-detecting* and *error-correcting* codes will be considered in this chapter.

In 1971 the Mariner-9 spacecraft, using a 20-watt transmitter, sent television pictures of the planet Mars over a distance of 84 million miles. The pictures finally shown on our screen were of very high quality despite the low power of the transmitter. This was partly the result of the sophisticated instrumentation but largely because of the error-correcting code used.

13.2 BINARY CODING

Take a look at the pack of eight cards shown in Fig. 13.2. Your friend chooses one of these and you must 'guess' which, by asking the minimum number of questions *to which your friend will answer only yes or no*. What is the least number of questions to be sure of finding the card? Try it.

You probably found that three questions suffice. The trick in the stategy is to halve the remaining possibilities at each stage, i.e. after the first question four of the cards should have been discarded, after the second question two of

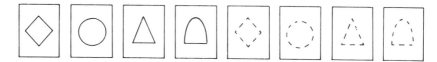

Fig. 13.2

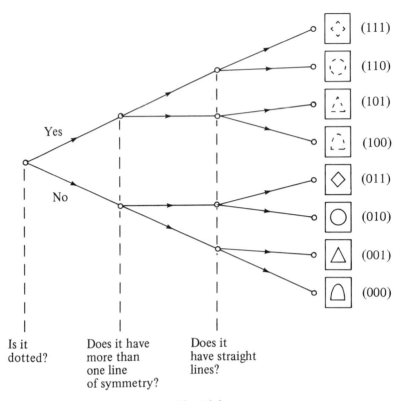

Fig. 13.3

the remaining four and after the third question one of the remaining two. One
possible way to achieve this is illustrated by the tree shown in Fig. 13.3. Such
a graph is called *a Decision Tree*.

Labels consisting of strings of 0's and 1's are given to the cards by assigning
1 for each 'Yes' answer and 0 for each 'No', giving the results shown in the
diagram. These labels are known in the theory as *codewords*. Each 0 or 1 in a
codeword is called a *bit* (*b*inary dig*it*), so the labels are all 3-bit codewords.

The set of all message objects (the cards in this example) is sometimes
called the *source*. To take another example, the source A, B, C, D could be
encoded using 2-bit codewords:

A	B	C	D
00	01	10	11

Exercise 2.1 How big is a source if its elements may be represented by
codewords with (i) 1 bit, (ii) 5 bits, (iii) 10 bits, (iv) n bits?

Exercise 2.2   The electronic sensing device on board the Mariner-9 space-craft could distinguish 512 shades of grey. How many message-bits would encode a particular shade?

Exercise 2.3   In the quiz game Twenty Questions contestants are allowed 20 'Yes-No' type questions to discover a 'mystery object'. If the game is fair how big should the universal set of 'mystery objects' be? How big would it be in the game of n questions?

Exercise 2.4   Design a decision tree to allocate binary codewords to the numbers 0, 1, 2, ..., 10.

In a game of finding which of the eleven numbers is being thought of by asking 'Yes-No' type questions what is the average number of questions needed per trial, over a large number of trials?

In a similar game of 'guessing which letter of the alphabet' find (i) the least number of questions to be sure of identifying the letter, (ii) the average number of questions over a large number of trials.

Exercise 2.5   Most microcomputers use the 8-bit ASCII code (see Appendix 1, p. 370). Why do you think the numerals $\emptyset$-9 have codewords which form the block of binary representations of the numbers 48 to 57? Why do the letters (upper and lowercase) form the blocks given by 65-90 and 97-122? How would you recognise instantly the codewords for graphics, programming instructions etc. coded by the block given by 128-255?

13.3   NOISE AND REDUNDANCY

If a channel of communication were noiseless then the barest signal would suffice. A 9-bit codeword from Mariner-9 could then have distinguished one of the 512 ($=2^9$) possible shades of grey, from white to black, or alternatively 512 different temperatures. As we have seen, though, channels are not normally noise-free. For instance, the sort of corruption which affects an electrical signal is shown in Fig. 13.4.

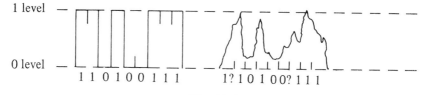

Fig. 13.4

To combat noise a binary signal normally has *check digits* in addition to the message digits in each codeword. To start with a simple example, each of the eight 3-bit codewords for our cards could have either 0 or 1 appended so that the number of 1's in the words is even in every case. (The number of 1's is sometimes called the *weight* of the word.) For instance

the message group 101 is of weight 2, and becomes 1010;

the message group 010 is of weight 1, and becomes 0101.

Now suppose we are to decode 1100. We note that the word is of weight 2 so we ignore the check digit and decode 110. On the other hand, if we received 1101, weight 3, we would know that the word contained one error (or three!). This *parity check* fails if there is more than one error. The code is a *single error detecting code* and it uses an *even parity check on 1's* (or an *even parity check on weight*). Of course, other kinds of checks are possible, for instance, even parity checks on 0's, odd parity checks on 1's and even parity checks on 0's. To avoid unnecessary complication all our parity checks will be even checks on 1's.

The ratio

$$\frac{\text{number of message bits}}{\text{total length of codeword}}$$

is called the *efficiency* (or *rate*) of the code, and we define the *redundancy* as

$$\text{redundancy} = 1 - \text{efficiency}.$$

So the efficiency and redundancy of the 4-bit code formed in the way just described are 3/4 and 1/4 respectively.

In electronic communication a good code introduces just the right amount of redundancy for the job. This may be quite a lot: the Mariner-9 codewords and the 'address' words used by British Telecom in their radio-paging scheme are both 32 bits long. Mere humans are only really happy when a great deal of extraneous redundancy is introduced. For example, we could perfectly well omit all th vwls n wrttn lngg (in fact, this is done in the case of the Hebrew language). Consider other cases of redundancy and their justification. Is the redundancy necessary or merely an embellishment? Think, for instance, of writing a cheque and of writing a novel.

Exercise 3.1   The message groups for part of a source are as shown

A	C	D	E	H	N	S	space
1011	1001	0111	0010	0101	1110	0000	1111

This source is used by a student in communicating with his parents. They receive this signal, which includes an even parity check on weight:

00000011011110101111111101001010111000001 1010

What do they make of it?

Exercise 3.2 In numerical work the *2-out-of-5 code* is sometimes used. In this code out of all possible words of length 5 only those with exactly two 1's are used. Thus

10100 is used but 11010 is not.

List all the words used and explain why the code is suitable for transmission of numerical data. Our definition of efficiency does not cover such a code. What do you think the efficiency should be?

Exercise 3.3 In radio telegraphy the *3-out-of-7 code* is used. How many codewords are there? What do you think is the efficiency of the code?

Exercise 3.4 Suppose that 5-bit messages are being transmitted with a parity check digit as 6-bit words. If the probability of error in transmitting each digit is 10^{-4} what is the probability of (at least one) error in any 6-bit word? How probable is failure of the parity check (i.e. not detecting an error)?

13.4 ERROR CORRECTION

There are two kinds of *error protection*. The *detection* of errors has already been mentioned and this form of protection may suffice if two-way communication is easy. However, as with Mariner-9, it is not always possible to send 'Repeat the message, please'. In such cases, a means must be found by which the uncorrupted message can be reconstituted; that is errors must not only be detected, but also located. This is error *correction*. It was shown by C. F. Shannon (*The Mathematical Theory of Communication*, 1948) that by using extra bits, data could be transmitted through a noisy channel subject to arbitrarily low error rates. One obvious procedure would be to repeat a signal many times, when the decoder would employ the common-sense method known technically as 'majority logic decoding'. ('What occurs most frequently is most likely to be right.') To get some idea of the sort of redundancy involved in this case, let us look at the repetition codes. They are

	Message	Codeword
R2 (twofold repetition code)	0	00
	1	11
R3 (threefold repetition code)	0	000
	1	111

and so on. Suppose we are using R2 and receive 01. Then an error is detected: the codewords are all pairs of identical digits. But we cannot locate the error and so correct the signal. On the other hand, if we are using R3 and receive 001 we use majority logic decoding to retrieve the signal 000 and the message 0. With R3 we can *detect and correct one error*. You should now be able to show that with R4 we can detect two errors and correct one error.

R3, containing 2 check bits for each message bit, is a (3, 1) code (codewords of length 3 with 1 message digit) and so has efficiency 1/3.

Exercise 4.1 Continue this table for the repetition codes R_n ($n = 2, 3, \ldots$)

	No. of errors	
n	detected	corrected
2	1	0
3	1	1
4		
5		
6		

How many errors may be detected and corrected by the code R_n?

Exercise 4.2
(i) Write out the complete (4, 4) code. What is its efficiency?
(ii) How many elements has the complete (n, n) code?

Exercise 4.3 What is the efficiency of an (n, k) code?

Exercise 4.4 The *even-weight code of length 4* has codewords

        0000, 0011, 0101, 0110, 1001, 1010, 1100, 1111

What error protection does it give?

Exercise 4.5 Write out the codewords of the even-weight code of length 5. What error protection does it give?

13.5 HAMMING DISTANCE

The definition and systematic use of the idea of the distance between two codewords in error correction was introduced by R. W. Hamming in 1950. Consider the 2-bit codewords 01, 00, 10, 11. The pair 01 and 00 have the same first digit but different second digits. Now the pair 01 and 10 have different first *and* second digits. We can see that this pair have most differences in first and second digits. Similarly the pair 00 and 11 have different first and second digits.

If we wanted a 2-bit code to distinguish between two messages we should use one of these pairs, each of which is a single error detecting code. (The second pair is familiar to us as R2.)

Geometrically these pairs of two-bit codewords represent points diagonally opposed in the unit square (Fig. 13.5). We can carry on the geometrical idea a further stage, using the unit cube (Fig. 13.6). You will see that there are four pairs of 3-bit words which differ in every position. One pair is 000 and

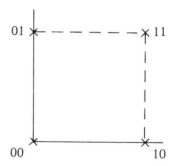

Fig. 13.5

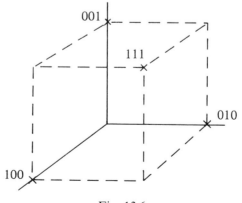

Fig. 13.6

111 (already met in R3). Another is 101 and 010. You can find the others; they all represent the ends of diagonals of the cube. Besides these pairs we can find two quadruples of words differing from one another in two positions. One of these quadruples is marked in the diagram. To represent a four-dimensional hypercube in two dimensions is not so easy. One attempt is shown in Fig. 13.7. It is left as an exercise to pick out the pairs of diagonals of the hypercube (giving differences in all four bits), the quadruples of diagonals of its cubes (giving differences in three positions) and the octuples of diagonals of its squares (differences in two positions).

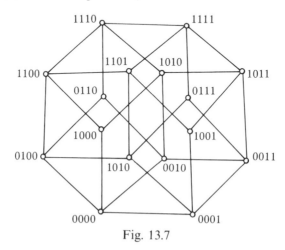

Fig. 13.7

Now for the formal definition. The *Hamming distance* $d(x, y)$ between two binary codewords x and y of the same length is the number of places in which their bits differ, for example the Hamming distance between 0101 and 1010 is 4. The distance between 10000 and 00101 is 3.

You will recall that a code with words of length n having k message bits is called an (n, k) code. If the minimum Hamming distance for the words of such a code is m then the code may be called an (n, k, m) code. Hamming's procedure for constructing a $(6, 3, 3)$ code was as follows. Let

$$x = x_1 x_2 x_3 x_4 x_5 x_6$$

be a codeword. Let x_1, x_2 and x_3 be the message digits and x_4, x_5 and x_6 be check digits. We arrange that the sums

$$x_2 + x_3 + x_4$$
$$x_1 \quad\;\; + x_3 \quad\quad + x_5$$
$$x_1 + x_2 \quad\quad\quad\quad\quad + x_6$$

are all even. Note that the *first* check-digit checks all the message digits *except the first*, an so on. For example, if 011 is our message group then $x_1 = 0$,

$x_2 = x_3 = 1$. To find x_4, x_5 and x_6 we must make all of the following sums even.

$$1 + 1 + x_4$$
$$0 \quad\;\; + 1 \qquad\;\; + x_5$$
$$0 + 1 \qquad\qquad\qquad + x_6$$

So $x_4 = 0$, $x_5 = x_6 = 1$ and the codeword obtained is

$$011011$$

Try (before reading further) to find the remaining 7 codewords of the full $(6, 3, 3)$ code. You should find that the code is

000000, 001110, 010101, 011011, 100011, 101101, 110110, 111000

Using Hamming's procedure where the first check digit checks all the message digits except the first, and so on, we may construct $(2k, k, k)$ codes for all positive integer values of k. The $(10, 5, 5)$ code has been used by the Marconi Company under the name AUTOSPEC (automatic single path error correction) for transmission of messages using the International Telegraph Alphabet with single error correction along a single path (no return transmission).

Exercise 5.1   What is the efficiency of the $(2k, k, k)$ codes?

Exercise 5.2   Use Hamming's procedure to find the codes (i) $(4, 2, 2)$, (ii) $(8, 4, 4)$.

Exercise 5.3   In AUTOSPEC, append check groups to the message groups (i) 00100, (ii) 11000.

Exercise 5.4   The receiver of an AUTOSPEC signal forms a 5-bit error word as follows. If the first check digit works, note 1 in the first position of the error word, if not, note 0. If the second check digit works, note 1 in the second position of the error word; if not, note 0. And so on, for example

Signal	Error word
11111 10101	01010
11101 10101	01111

(i)   Write out the error word for the signals
      (a) 01101 11010, (b) 00101 10010
(ii) Explain the error words you obtain
(iii) Describe how a computer should process AUTOSPEC signals.

(A flow diagram for example, would be an appropriate description.)

Exercise 5.5   With a partner, practise sending and receiving signals using the International Telegraph Alphabet (see Appendix 2, p. 372) and AUTOSPEC, and incorporating occasional single errors in the codewords.

Exercise 5.6   Show that the Hamming distance is a *metric* on the codewords of any code whose words all have the same length. (A metric d on any set must satisfy the conditions that for any three members of the set, x, y and z.

$$d(x, x) = 0 \text{ (reflexivity)}$$
$$d(x, y) = d(y, x) \text{ (symmetry)}$$
$$d(x, y) \leqslant d(x, z) + d(z, y) \text{ (the 'triangle inequality')}$$

Exercise 5.7   (Investigation). Devise a (5, 3, 2) code using Hamming's procedure but with only two parity checks instead of three. Compare the error protection given by the (4, 3, 1), the (5, 3, 2) and the (6, 3, 3) codes. Extend your investigation to other codes designed in a similar way, with the aim of making a general statement about the error protection given by (n, k, m) codes.

13.6   THE MARINER-9 CODE

In transmissions from Mariner-9 the message, in 9-bit strings was repackaged into 6-bit groups and each 6-bit group was sent with 26 bits of protection as a 32-bit codeword. This seems a staggering amount of redundancy but when we recall that the transmitter had a power of only 20 watts it seems a near miracle that the feeble signal could be picked out of the continuous radio-noise of space and interpreted, no matter how much protection was given. Compare, for instance, a transmitter like that at Crystal Palace, which has a power of 40 000 watts and a range of only 60 miles.

   Before describing how the 32-bit Mariner-9 code is constructed the idea of *addition of codewords* should be introduced. Two words of the same length may be added by adding corresponding bits modulo 2 (i.e. $0 + 0 = 0$, $0 + 1 = 1 + 0 = 1$, $1 + 1 = 0$).

   For instance
$$\begin{array}{r} 1100 \\ +0110 \\ \hline =1010 \end{array}$$

Using this sort of bit-wise addition we can generate new codewords from a given set of words. For instance, let

$$x = 0110, \quad y = 1001, \quad z = 1000$$

Then

$$y + z = 0001, \quad x + z = 1110, \quad x + y = 1111, \quad x + y + z = 0111$$

We now have the complete set of *linear combinations* of x, y and z of the form $ax + by + cz$ where a, b and c are all either 0 or 1, with the exception of the result 0000 obtained when $a = b = c = 0$, i.e. the set

$$\{ax + by + cz : a, b, c \in \{0, 1\}\}$$
$$= \{0000, 0110, 1001, 1111, 1000, 1110, 0001, 0111\}$$

We are now ready to tackle the Mariner-9 code, whose name is H_5. The code belongs to a sequence H_1, H_2, $H_3 \ldots$ which are all formed using the same system. It will be easier to look first at the simpler example H_2. We start with the codewords

$$s_1 = 0101,$$
$$s_2 = 0011,$$
$$s_3 = 1111$$

(the reason for this choice is made clearer in Exercise 6.4) and then list all linear combinations of them. Let us start with all linear combinations of s_1

$$0s_1 = 0000$$
$$1s_1 = 0101$$

We repeat this list and extend it by adding s_2 to each in turn.

$$0s_1 + 0s_2 = 0000$$
$$1s_1 + 0s_2 = 0101$$
$$0s_1 + 1s_2 = 0011$$
$$1s_1 + 1s_2 = 0110$$

Finally we add s_3 in turn to each of the members of this extended list to obtain the complete code H_2.

$$
\begin{aligned}
0 &= 0000 \\
s_1 &= 0101 \\
s_2 &= 0011 \\
s_1 + s_2 &= 0110 \\
s_3 &= 1111 \\
s_1 \quad + s_3 &= 1010 \\
s_2 + s_3 &= 1100 \\
s_1 + s_2 + s_3 &= 1001
\end{aligned}
$$

In fact, you may recognise H_2 as the even weight code of length 4, met in Exercise 4.4. It gives only single-error detection.

To find the next code in the sequence $\{H_n\}$, i.e. H_3, we use the same system as before to form all linear combinations of the words.

$$t_1 = 01010101,$$
$$t_2 = 00110011,$$
$$t_3 = 00001111,$$
$$t_4 = 11111111.$$

(At this stage it would be helpful to compare the s-words with the t-words so as to appreciate how the system works.) Before reading further, see if you can construct H_3. You should find that H_3 has these members.

$$
\begin{array}{rl}
0 & = 00000000 \\
t_1 & = 01010101 \\
t_2 & = 00110011 \\
t_1 + t_2 & = 01100110 \\
t_3 & = 00001111 \\
t_1 \quad\;\; + t_3 & = 01011010 \\
t_2 + t_3 & = 00111100 \\
t_1 + t_2 + t_3 & = 01101001 \\
t_4 & = 11111111 \\
t_1 \qquad\qquad + t_4 & = 10101010 \\
t_2 \quad + t_4 & = 11001100 \\
t_1 + t_2 \quad\; + t_4 & = 10011001 \\
t_3 + t_4 & = 11110000 \\
t_1 \quad + t_3 + t_4 & = 10100101 \\
t_2 + t_3 + t_4 & = 11000011 \\
t_1 + t_2 + t_3 + t_4 & = 10010110
\end{array}
$$

Check that H_3 is an $(8, 4, 4)$ code, the first four bits being the message group. If we take any word in H_3 and change up to three of its bits then the result is not in H_3, so H_3 is a 3-error detecting code. If we change just one bit then majority logic decoding allows us to correct that bit; on the other hand, changes in two bits result in a word which cannot be corrected. So H_3 is a single-error correcting code.

Exercise 6.1
(i) Show that the linear combinations of the codewords

$$011, 110 \text{ and } 100$$

give all possible 3-bit words (which we will call the code C_3).
(ii) In such a case we say that the given words *span* C_3. Find another set of 3 words which span C_3.
(iii) Under what circumstances will a chosen set of 3 words *not* span C_3?

Exercise 6.2   Show that the complete n-bit code C_n cannot be spanned by fewer than n of its codewords. (*Hint*: consider the number of linear combinations of k words.)
   Under what circumstances will n n-bit words *not* span C_n?

Exercise 6.3
(i) Construct the code H_1.
(ii) Find the error protection given by the codes H_n for $n = 1, 2, 3, 4$ and 5.

Exercise 6.4

(i) Verify that the code C_3 is embedded in H_2 *systematically* in that the 1st, 2nd and 4th digits of the words in H_2 form all the members of C_3.

(ii) What system embeds C_4 in H_3? (i.e. which digits of the words in H_3 form the words in C_4?)

(iii) Generalise on the results in (i) and (ii) and explain how the message bits are embedded in the Mariner-9 code.

13.7 UNEQUAL FREQUENCIES

The elements of many sources occur with very different frequencies. A well known example is the English alphabet, as used in ordinary prose. For instance, the letter E occurs much more often than the letter Z. Where the memory of a processor is limited and error protection is not needed it could be useful for the more frequent message elements to have short codewords and the rarer ones to have long words.

Suppose (in a carefully rigged example, to illustrate the idea) that a typical sample of output from a source is

ABAACBAEBAADACAB

A count shows that the probabilities of the various letters are given by this table.

Letter	A	B	C	D	E
Probability	1/2	1/4	1/8	1/16	1/16

Following the strategy described in section 13.2 of 'halving possibilities at each stage', a good decision tree for 'guessing what letter comes next' would be:

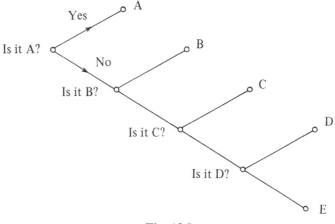

Fig. 13.8

Using the scheme given by this tree you might have to ask as many as four questions but in half the cases one question only would suffice. The average number of questions would be

$$\frac{(8 \times 1) + (4 \times 2) + (2 \times 3) + (4 \times 1) + (1 \times 4)}{16} = 1\tfrac{7}{8}.$$

The code derived from the tree is

Letter	A	B	C	D	E
Codeword	1	01	001	0001	0000

When this code is used the average length of codewords is $1\tfrac{7}{8}$ bits, whereas if a *block code* (codewords all of the same length) were used for the same source then 3-bit words would be needed. Even so, our code would be worthless if it did not have the important property that strings of digits can be decoded without ambiguity. For example, try decoding

001000001101001.

You should have

CEBABC.

When a code works without ambiguity in this way it is said to be *instantaneous*.

For an instantaneous code the encoding is most efficient when the average length of codewords is least.

Exercise 7.1   A code is given by this tree.

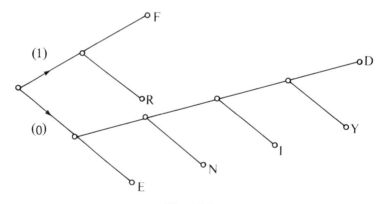

Fig. 13.9

(i) Decode these bit strings
    (a) 1100010, (b) 011111001110, (c) 110110100001111
(ii) Encode these messages
    (a) FIN, (b) REEF, (c) DENY

Exercise 7.2

(i) Describe a simple test to check that a code is instantaneous.
(ii) Show that all binary tree codes are instantaneous. (*Hint*: it may be best to prove the equivalent result that codes which are not instantaneous cannot be binary tree codes.)

Exercise 7.3   Devise a decision tree for the source:

Letter	A	B	C	D	E
Probability	1/4	1/4	1/4	1/8	1/8

Hence encode the source and find the average word length.

Exercise 7.4   Show that for a source having members with probabilities p_1, $p_2, \ldots, p_n$ having codewords with lengths $l_1, l_2, \ldots, l_n$ respectively the average word length is

$$\sum_{i=1}^{n} p_i l_i$$

Exercise 7.5   Suppose that for the decision tree in Fig. 13.10 the remaining probabilities are *exactly* halved at each branching. What must be the probabilities of the members A, B, C, D and E of the source? What do you notice about these probabilities? In general, if probabilities are halved exactly at each stage of the construction of a tree what can be said about the probability distribution for the source?

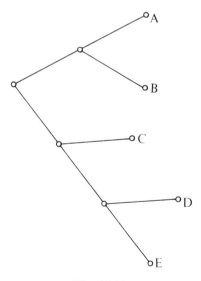

Fig. 13.10

Using this result, or otherwise, find all the non-isomorphic binary decision trees for sources with (i) 5 members, (ii) 6 members.

Exercise 7.6   Find the most efficient instantaneous codes for these sources:

(i) Letter	A	B	C	D	E	
Probability	0.3	0.3	0.2	0.1	0.1	
(ii) Letter	A	B	C	D	E	F
Probability	0.06	0.23	0.11	0.26	0.15	0.19

13.8   HUFFMAN CODES

The most efficient instantaneous code for any given source is sometimes called the Huffman code. Huffman devised a procedure for obtaining such codes which is compact to set out but rather awkward to explain. Essentially the same result is obtained by our decision tree method. For instance, take the source

Letter	A	B	C	D	E	F	G	H
Probability	0.12	0.21	0.08	0.10	0.04	0.15	0.25	0.05

Rearrange in descending order of probability

Letter	G	B	F	A	D	C	H	E
Probability (%)	25	21	15	12	10	8	5	4

Form a decision tree, or nearly as possible *halving the remaining total probability* at each stage. (See Figure 13.11.)

Note that letters must not be taken out of their order in the list. For example, in starting the tree you might be tempted to ask the question 'Is it G, B or E?', since the combined probabilities of these three letters total exactly 0.50. But this would result in the rare letter E and the common letter B having the same length codeword, with a consequent increase in average word length. Try the effect of such attempts to improve on the tree given.

The codewords obtained are

A	B	C	D	E	F	G	H
010	10	0001	001	00000	011	11	00001

Use the procedure just described to encode the sources in the following exercises.

Exercise 8.1

Letter	A	B	C	D	E
Probability	0.23	0.11	0.19	0.25	0.22

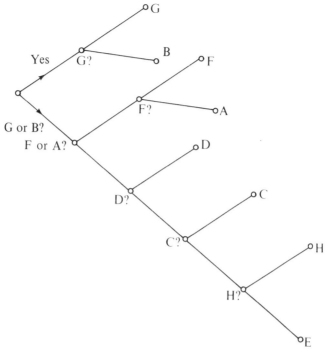

Fig. 13.11

Exercise 8.2

Letter	A	B	C	D	E	F
Probability	0.31	0.08	0.12	0.05	0.39	0.05

Exercise 8.3

Letter	A	B	C	D	E	F	G	H
Probability (%)	7.5	20.0	2.5	27.5	5.0	10.0	2.5	25.0

Exercise 8.4   For the English alphabet (see Appendix 3, p. 372), show that the average length of your codewords is less than that needed in a block code.

13.9 MISCELLANEOUS EXERCISES

M1 The diagram shows part of the display board of the operator of a large shunting yard.

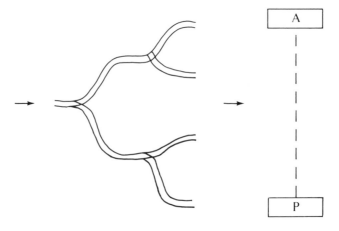

Fig. 13.12

Sixteen bays, labelled A–P, are the ultimate destinations of wagons which enter the system with enough speed to reach their bays. The operator sets the route for each wagon electronically by keying in a codeword switching the points at each stage in sequence up (1) or down (0).
(a) Find the codeword for a wagon to go to bay F.
(b) To which bay would a wagon be directed by the codeword 0100?

M2 Design a knockout singles tennis tournament table for 20 players so that in each round the maximum number of matches is played, any player not having an opponent being given a bye into the next round.
(a) How many rounds are there?
(b) How many matches are played?
(c) How many byes?

M3 Answer question M2 parts (a) and (b) in the case when there are n players in the tournament. (c) How many byes are there in a tournament with (i) $(2^k - 1)$, (ii) $(2^k + 1)$ players?

M4 MAR MAT RIM DRIP RANT PAINT DRAIN PART
TRAM MINT PIN PART TRIP
The above message may be taken as typical of those using an 8-letter source (A, D, I, M, N, P, R, T), in that the letters in the message occur with the correct frequencies for the source. (The spaces between the words in the message should be ignored.)
(a) Encode the source using three-bit code names. What is the total number of bits required to encode the whole message?

(b) Now find the frequency with which each letter occurs and hence devise a Huffman code for the source. What is the total number of bits needed to encode the whole message?

M5 What error protection is given by the even-weight code of length 6? What is its efficiency?

M6 (a) Of the four members of C_2, the complete code of length 2, two are selected at random. Show that the probability of their spanning C_2 is $\frac{1}{2}$.

(b) Now suppose that of the eight members of C_3 we select three randomly. Show that the probability of their spanning C_3 is again $\frac{1}{2}$.

M7 Suppose we call a code which is formed from a binary decision tree a *tree code*. How many tree codes are possible for a source with (i) 4, (ii) 5 members.

M8 (a) Encode a source with 9 members using 2-digit *ternary* code names (each digit may be 0, 1 or 2). Illustate your encoding using a *ternary decision tree*.

(b) Four coins are identical in appearance but one is slightly heavier or lighter than the other three, which are equal in weight. A scale balance is available but no other apparatus. Devise a decision tree to find the odd coin and to decide whether it is heavy or light, in three weighings. Explain why two weighings will not suffice.

(c) Of eight coins of identical appearance one has a different weight from the rest. Again find which and whether it is heavier or lighter, in three weighings using a scale balance.

(d) As (c) but replace 'eight' by 'twelve'.

Character set and codes

Code	Character	Code	Char.	Code	Char.
0	⎫	51	3	102	f
1		52	4	103	g
2	not used	53	5	104	h
3		54	5	105	i
4		55	7	106	j
5	⎭	56	8	107	k
6	**PRINT** comma	57	9	108	l
7	**EDIT**	58	:	109	m
8	cursor left	59	;	110	n
9	cursor right	60	<	111	o
10	cursor down	61	=	112	p
11	cursor up	62	>	113	q
12	**DELETE**	63	?	114	r
13	**ENTER**	64	@	115	s
14	number	65	A	116	t
15	not used	66	B	117	u
16	**INK** control	67	C	118	v
17	**PAPER** control	68	D	119	w
18	**FLASH** control	69	E	120	x
19	**BRIGHT** control	70	F	121	y
20	**INVERSE** control	71	G	122	z
21	**OVER** control	72	H	123	{
22	**AT** control	73	I	124		
23	**TAB** control	74	J	125	}
24	⎫	75	K	126	~
25		76	L	127	©
26		77	M		
27	not used	78	N	128	
28		79	O	129	
29		80	P		
30		81	Q	130	
31	⎭	82	R	131	
32	space	83	S		
33	!	84	T	132	
34	"	85	U	133	
35	#	86	V		
36	$	87	W	134	
37	%	88	X	135	
38	&	89	Y		
39	'	90	Z	136	
40	(	91	[	137	
41	)	92	/		
42	*	93	]	138	
43	+	94	↑	139	
44	,	95	—		
45	− (minus sign)	96	£	140	
46	.	97	a	141	
47	/	98	b		
48	0	99	c	142	
49	1	100	d	143	
50	2	101	e		

144	(a) ┐	200	> =
145	(b)	201	< >
146	(c)	202	LINE
147	(d)	203	THEN
148	(e)	204	TO
149	(f)	205	STEP
150	(g)	206	DEF FN
151	(h)	207	CAT
152	(i)	208	FORMAT
153	(j)	209	MOVE
154	(k) ├─ user graphics	210	ERASE
155	(l)	211	OPEN #
156	(m)	212	CLOSE #
157	(n)	213	MERGE
158	(o)	214	VERIFY
159	(p)	215	BEEP
160	(q)	216	CIRCLE
161	(r)	217	INK
162	(s)	218	PAPER
163	(t)	219	FLASH
164	(u) ┘	220	BRIGHT
165	RND	221	INVERSE
166	INKEY$	222	OVER
167	PI	223	OUT
168	FN	224	LPRINT
169	POINT	225	LLIST
170	SCREEN$	226	STOP
171	ATTR	227	READ
172	AT	228	DATA
173	TAB	229	RESTORE
174	VAL$	230	NEW
175	CODE	231	BORDER
176	VAL	232	CONTINUE
177	LEN	233	DIM
178	SIN	234	REM
179	COS	235	FOR
180	TAN	236	GO TO
181	ASN	237	GO SUB
182	ACS	238	INPUT
183	ATN	239	LOAD
184	LN	240	LIST
185	EXP	241	LET
186	INT	242	PAUSE
187	SQR	243	NEXT
188	SGN	244	POKE
189	ABS	245	PRINT
190	PEEK	246	PLOT
191	IN	247	RUN
192	USR	248	SAVE
193	STR$	249	RANDOMIZE
194	CHR$	250	IF
195	NOT	251	CLS
196	BIN	252	DRAW
197	OR	253	CLEAR
198	AND	254	RETURN
199	< =	255	COPY

APPENDIX 2 INTERNATIONAL TELEGRAPH ALPHABET

Letter	Figure	Code group	Letter	Figure	Code group
A	–	00111	Q	1	00010
B	?	01100	R	4	10101
C	:	10001	S	!	01011
D	Who are you?	01101	T	5	11110
E	3	01111	U	7	00011
F	%	01001	V	=	10000
G	@	10100	W	2	00110
H	£	11010	X	/	01000
I	8	10011	Y	6	01010
J	BELL	00101	Z	+	01110
K	(	00001	Carriage return		11101
L	)	10110	Line feed		10111
M	.	11000	Letter shift		00000
N	,	11001	Figure shift		00100
O	9	11100	Space		11011
P	0	10010			

APPENDIX 3 PROBABILITIES OF SYMBOLS IN ENGLISH (Reza: *Introduction to Information Theory*, McGraw-Hill, 1961)

Symbol	Probability	Symbol	Probability
Space	0.1859	N	0.0574
A	0.0642	O	0.0632
B	0.0127	P	0.0152
C	0.0218	Q	0.0008
D	0.0317	R	0.0484
E	0.1031	S	0.0514
F	0.0208	T	0.0796
G	0.0152	U	0.0228
H	0.0467	V	0.0083
I	0.0575	W	0.0175
J	0.0008	X	0.0013
K	0.0049	Y	0.0164
L	0.0321	Z	0.0005
M	0.0198		

14

Critical Path Analysis

14.1 INTRODUCTION

The technique of critical path analysis has widespread applications in industry and commerce, in situations where it is important to optimise resources. One early use was by the US Navy to plan the Polaris missile project. In an industrial environment it is essential that neither manpower nor machinery is left idle unnecessarily. Critical path analysis entails deciding on the order in which these activities have to take place and indicates where it is critical that one activity starts as soon as the preceding activity has finished.

A simple situation which illustrates the technique would be decorating a room, including putting in new self-assembly units. It is necessary first to list the jobs involved together with the time each takes.

Table 14.1

	Activity description	Preceding activities	Activity duration (in hours)
A	Paint woodwork		8
B	Allow paint to dry	A	4
C	Assemble units		4
D	Fit units	A, B, C, E, F,	2
E	Fit carpet	A, B, F,	5
F	Hang wallpaper	A, B,	12
G	Hang curtains	A, B, F,	2

Note that the units of time must all be the same, i.e. all hours or all day or all weeks etc. This information can then be arranged in a **precedence network** indicating the order and relationship between activities as shown in Fig. 14.1.

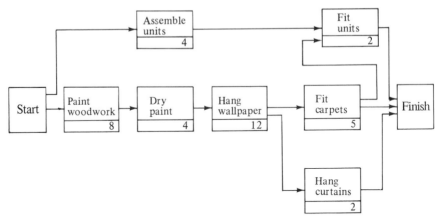

Fig. 14.1

It is clear from this network that hanging the wallpaper cannot be started until painting the woodwork is finished. However, assembling the units can take place while these activities are proceeding. In this simple case it can be seen by inspection that the critical activities are painting the woodwork, hanging the wallpaper, fitting the carpets and fitting the units. Thus if the scheduling ensures that each of these activities starts immediately the preceding one is finished the whole operation will be completed in the shortest possible time, i.e. 31 hours.

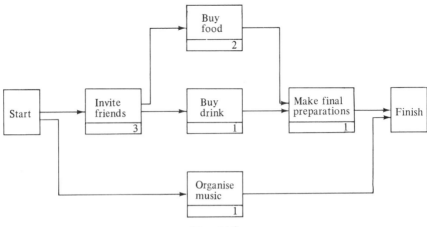

Fig. 14.2

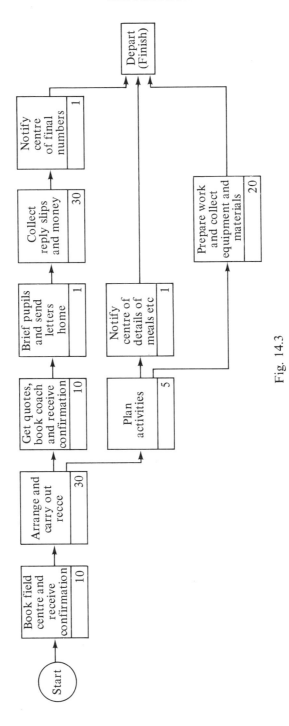

Fig. 14.3

Exercise 1.1   Figure 14.2 shows the activities for organising a party (times given in days). What is the shortest time needed to prepare for this party? Which are the critical activities?

Exercise 1.2   A teacher is planning a field study trip to take place during the first week in July. Figure 14.3 shows the major activities required and the times (in days) that must be allowed for their completion. What is the latest date at which the planning process can start?

Exercise 1.3   In the network shown in Fig. 14.4 times are given in minutes. What is the minimum completion time? What is the critical path, the sequence of activities whose timing is critical?

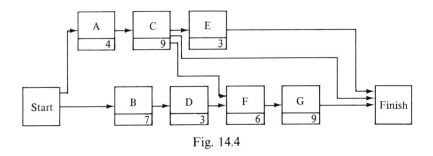

Fig. 14.4

14.2 CONSTRUCTING PRECEDENCE NETWORKS

Obviously real situations will result in far more complicated networks and algorithms will be needed for the different stages of the operation of finding the critical path.

Some situations in precedence networks are referred to by specific names. **Activity** is used to describe any operation which has to be planned and which has a duration. In some cases, as in drying the paint in the first example, no manpower or materials are required. However, a period of time must elapse before a following activity can take place and therefore this activity must be included in the plan.

A **burst** is any activity which has two or more activities dependent upon it. Hanging the wallpaper and fitting the carpets are bursts. (Fig. 14.5)

A **merge** is any activity which depends upon two or more preceding activities. (Fig. 14.6)

In practice it is not always necessary for one activity to finish before another can start. Figure 14.7 illustrates a **simple overlap** where activity B can

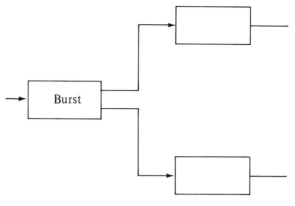

Fig. 14.5

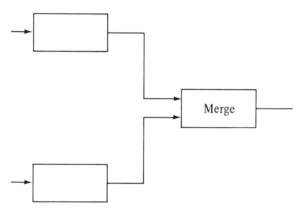

Fig. 14.6

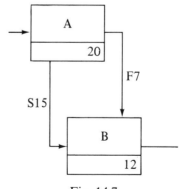

Fig. 14.7

start 15 hours after activity A has started. Activity B cannot finish until at least 7 hours after activity A has finished, i.e.

Start to start relationship A to B of 15 hours
Finish to finish relationship A to B of 7 hours.

Below are two examples of a more **complex overlap**.

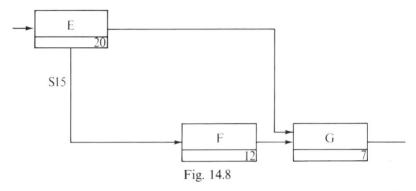

Fig. 14.8

In Fig. 14.8 F can start when E is part way through so that both can continue independently. Both E and F, however, must be complete *before* G can start. In Fig. 14.9 K can start 15 hours after J has started, but J must finish at least 7 hours before K finishes. Once J is complete L can start but M cannot start until both L and K are complete.

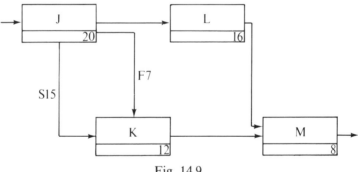

Fig. 14.9

The **lag value** is the expression used for the time delay when one activity overlaps another. In Fig. 14.10 wallpapering can start when some of the paintwork is dry but must finish at least 4 hours (the drying time) after the painting is finished. The lag value of the start to start relationship is 5 hours. The lag value of the finish to finish relationship is 4 hours. Sometimes it is necessary to have an interval of time, or lag value, between the finish of one activity and the start of the next. This delay would be indicated as shown in Fig. 14.11 Q cannot start until 6 time units after P is finished.

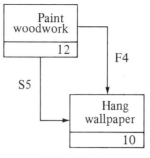

Fig. 14.10

Fig. 14.11

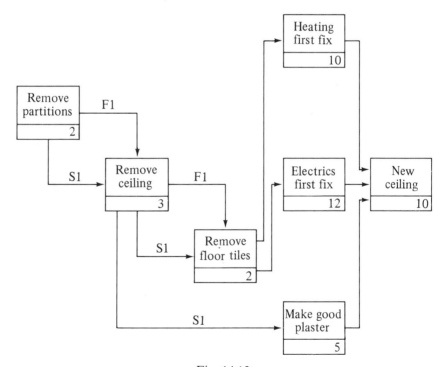

Fig. 14.12

We have reached a stage where we have a precedence network with all the durations and lags shown on it. The network shown in Fig. 14.12 is for the replacement of a ceiling.

Now what we want to do is to work out the overall duration of this network, that is the minimum time required to complete all the activities and finish the job. This is done by calculating the **earliest** times that each activity can start and finish. Earliest start times are shown at the top left-hand corner of the box and since the earliest start time of the first activity is nought then this is shown top left as in Fig. 14.13. Where there is no finishing lag between activities the earliest finish is arrived at by adding the duration of the activity to its earliest start time. In the case of remove partitions the duration is 2, therefore the earliest finish is 0 plus 2 = 2 and is shown at the top right-hand corner of the box. Where there is a start to start relationship between activities the earliest start time for the second activity is arrived at by adding the start lag time to the earliest start time of the first activity as in Fig. 14.14.

Remove partitions starts Day 0—remove ceiling starts at Day 0 plus 1 (from S1) which is Day 1. So remove ceiling can start 1 day after remove partitions has started.

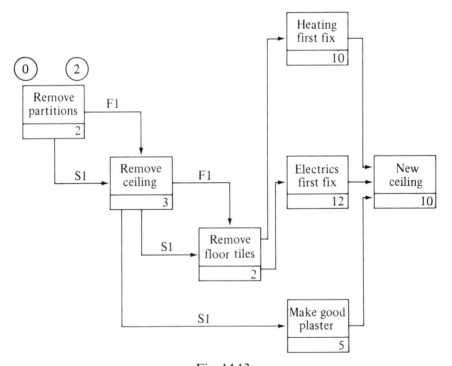

Fig. 14.13

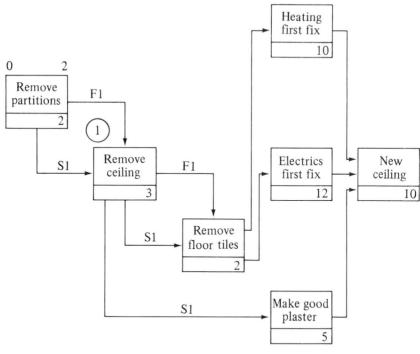

Fig. 14.14

Where there is a finish to finish relationship the earliest finishing time is arrived at by adding the finishing lag time to the earliest finishing time of the previous activity. Here we have to make a check because we have two possible times.

(i) Earliest finish date of remove partitions = end of Day 2 plus finish lag of 1 Day = end Day 3
(ii) Earliest start date of remove ceiling (calculated above) = end of Day 1 plus duration of 3 Days = end of Day 4.

It is obvious that the earliest time remove ceiling can be finished is Day 4 and not Day 3. Moving along the network remove floor tiles and make good plaster can be calculated in the same way. Earliest start time for remove floor tiles is 1 plus S1 which is Day 2. Earliest finish is 4 plus F1 which is Day 5. Earliest start time for make good plaster is 1 plus S1—which is Day 2. Earliest finish is Day 7 (2 plus duration of 5). Where there is no lag time the earliest start time is the same as the earliest finish time of the previous activity. Heating first fix can start immediately after remove floor tiles, i.e. Day 5, and finish 10 days later on Day 15. Electrics first fix starts Day 5 and finishes Day 17.

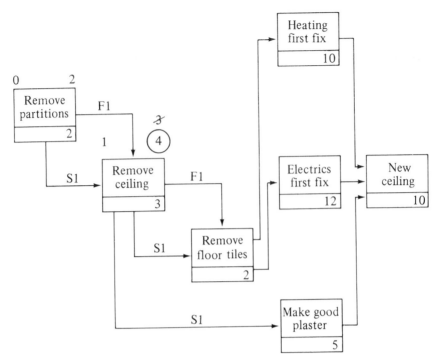

Fig. 14.15

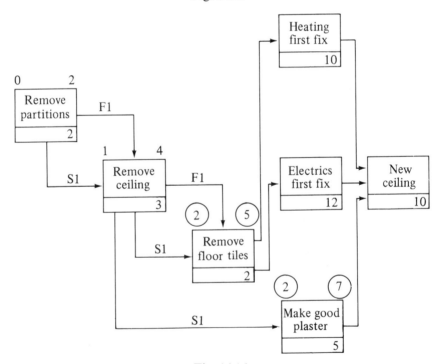

Fig. 14.16

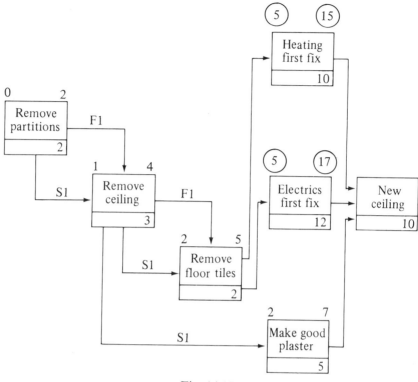

Fig. 14.17

Now we come to a merge. New ceiling has three other activities linked to it and the earliest time at which it can start will be related to the latest time at which any one of the three previous activities finish. In this case although make good plaster could finish on Day 7 and heating first fix on Day 15, electrics first fix is not complete until Day 17 so new ceiling cannot start until Day 17 and it will be completed by Day 27.

The rule is that *all* routes into a merge activity must be calculated and considered before calculating the merge activities' earliest finish date.

So we see that the whole network takes 27 days. If this was just a section of a larger network or consisted of one line on a chart labelled 'alterations to existing building' then you would have to check that 27 days fitted in with the remainder of the programme before going any further.

We have now completed a *forward pass*. The critical activities (i.e. those activities which are vital to completion on time) must be found. This is how we do it using a network, by working backwards from the finish time. New ceiling has a finish time of 27 days from previous figure. Deduct the duration of 10 days gives us 17 days. So that is the latest time that new ceiling can start.

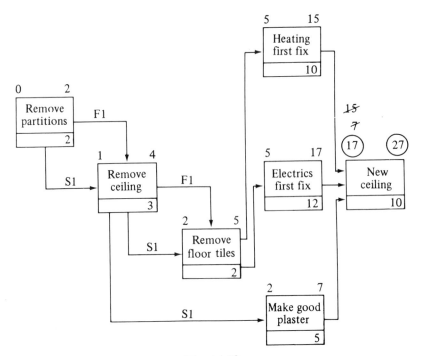

Fig. 14.18

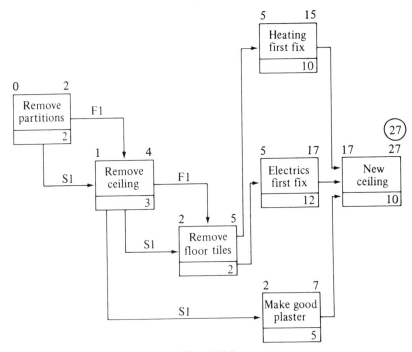

Fig. 14.19

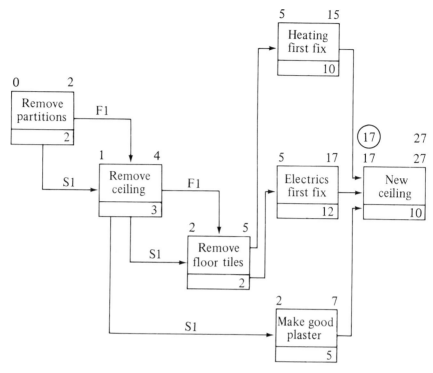

Fig. 14.20

Since Day 17 is the latest time at which new ceiling can start, the three activities before it need not be finished before Day 17.

Deduct their individual durations and we get this result (Fig. 14.21). The latest time at which heating must start is Day 7, electrics Day 5 and make good plaster Day 12. Where there is a 'burst' then the **smallest** latest start time is transferred. Remove floor tiles has a choice of two times — 7 and 5. It is fairly obvious by inspection that remove floor tiles must be finished before Day 5 rather than Day 7. This means that the latest time at which remove floor tiles can begin is 5 minus a duration of 2 days, i.e. Day 3. Now we have a finish to finish relationship and we take the latest finish and deduct the lag time. In this case the latest finish for remove floor tiles is Day 5 so the latest finish for remove ceiling is Day 5 minus a lag of 1 day which gives Day 4. Following the same principle the latest time for finishing remove ceiling is Day 4 less a one day lag, which means that the latest time at which remove partitions can finish is 4 minus 1 — Day 3.

Where there is a start to start relationship, as in Fig. 14.23, we deduct duration from the latest start times of the activities it leads into it and then

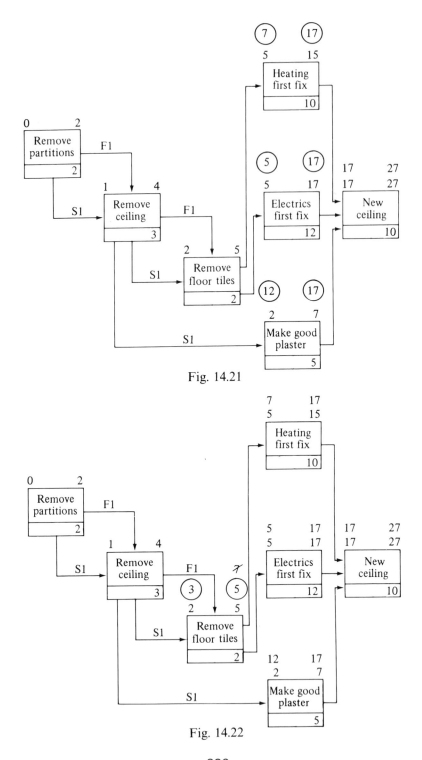

Fig. 14.21

Fig. 14.22

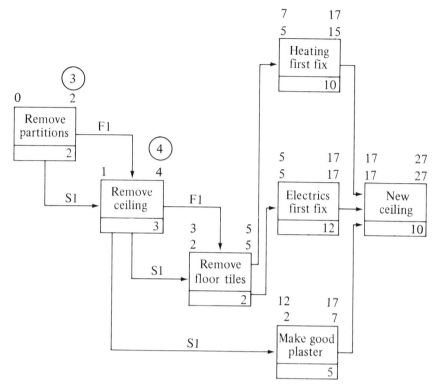

Fig. 14.23

select the **smallest** figure. The latest time at which make good plaster can start is Day 12 less a lag of 1 day, which means that remove ceiling could be held back until Day 11. However, the latest start time of remove floor tiles is Day 3, and if we deduct a lag of 1 day, then the latest time at which remove ceiling can start is Day 2. But the latest finish time for remove ceiling is Day 4 and it has a duration of 3 days, so the latest start date is Day 1. Likewise the latest time at which remove partitions can start has to be Day 0, and we are back to zero. If it was anything else then the arithmetic would be wrong.

The next step is to identify the critical items. Critical activities, as we saw earlier, are those activities where there is no spare time, i.e. the earliest and latest start and finish times are the same. For example, remove ceiling, electrics and new ceiling have the earliest and latest start times shown above the box (left) the same, and the earliest and latest finish times shown above the box (right) are the same. These activities have no spare time or float. Where there are two adjacent critical activities with direct start and finish

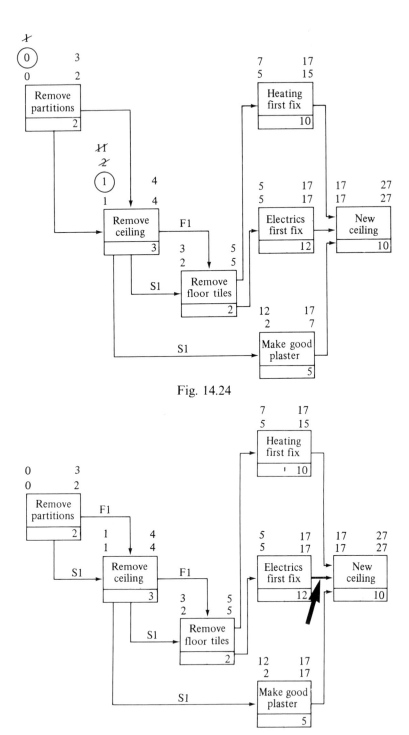

Fig. 14.24

Fig. 14.25

388

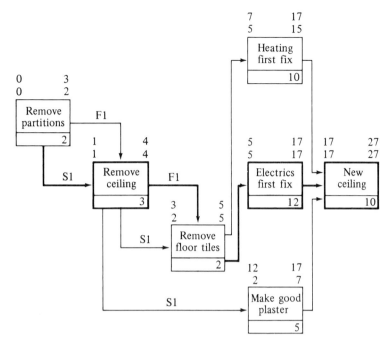

Fig. 14.26

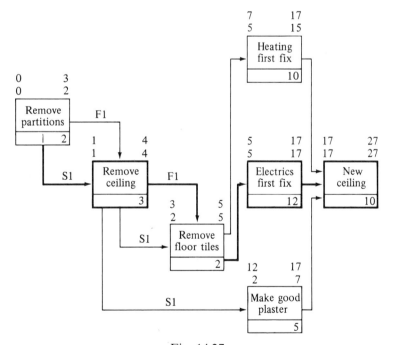

Fig. 14.27

relationships, the arrow linking them should be marked to indicate that it is critical.

A rule for all networks is that there must be at least one path of critical activities from the start to the finish of the network.

Heating and make good plaster are not critical because they both contain spare time or float as you can see by comparing figures above the boxes. However, some of the consecutive activities do not have identical start and finish dates, but if you deduct the lag time from the difference between these times the answer is zero, which indicates that some of the activity is critical—in this case the latter part of remove floor tiles. By doing this we find that the critical 'path' follows the lines shown on the diagram in Fig. 14.26. Study it for a moment and make sure you understand the general principles. So you can see here the critical path. The first day of remove partitions. All of remove ceiling. The last day of remove floor tiles. All of electrics first fix and all of new ceiling. And that briefly is how to check a network and how to work out the critical path. (Fig. 14.27)

Exercise 2.1 Use the algorithms developed in section 14.2 to answer the questions given in Exercises 1.1, 1.2 and 1.3.

Exercise 2.2 Use the given algorithms to find the minimum time (in minutes) needed to complete the project shown in Fig. 14.28. What is the critical path? (Fig. 14.28)

Exercise 2.3 What is the minimum time in which the project shown in Fig. 14.29 can be completed? (times given in hours). Describe the critical path. (Fig. 14.29)

Exercise 2.4 The list below gives the activities involved in assembling a bicycle, together with a procedure table. Draw a network to illustrate this and work out the critical path.

	Activity	Time in minutes
A	Frame preparation	9
B	Fixing front wheel	7
C	Fixing back wheel	7
D	Attaching gear change to frame	2
E	Install gears	3
F	Attach chain wheel to crank	2
G	Attach crank to frame	1
H	Mount left pedal	8
I	Mount right pedal	8
J	Final attachments and adjustments	21

Activity	Preceding activities
J	B, C, H, I
C	D, E
E	D
F	D
H	E, G
I	E, G
G	F
B	A
D	A

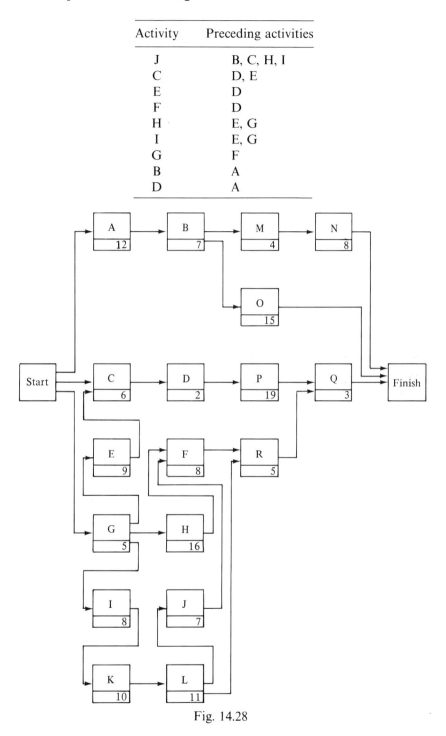

Fig. 14.28

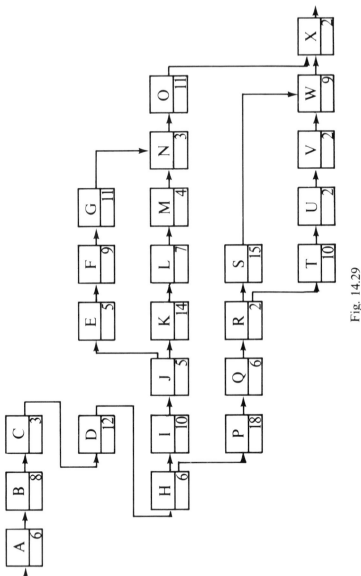

Fig. 14.29

14.3 PROCEDURE FOR NUMBERING ACTIVITIES

In order to ensure that activities appear in a logical manner when we are dealing with manual cascade charts there is a special order for numbering activities on a network. This can be arrived at by using the following algorithm illustrated by the activities involved in alterations to a building.

Activity	Preceding activity
A	C
B	A
C	
D	B
E	B
F	C
G	D, E, F

Step 1 Draw a bipartite graph showing the relation 'is followed by' where previous activities map onto those which must follow them.

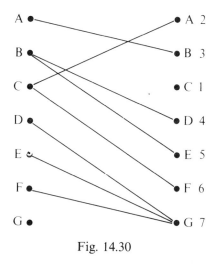

Fig. 14.30

Step 2 Number as 1 the first vertex on the right-hand side which is not joined to a vertex on the left-hand side (Vertex C in this case).

Step 3 Starting at this vertex on the left-hand side (C) number any vertex it maps onto (e.g. A) unless it is a merge (A is not). Continue numbering from this activity (A) until reaching the end of the chain or in this case a merge (G), for example (A → B → D → G). Do not number the merge at this stage, as there are still unnumbered activities mapping onto it.

Step 4 Follow the chain backwards until you reach a vertex where you had a choice (B) and continue numbering along the new chain (B → E → G). G is a merge so follow the whole procedure backwards again until you reach another situation with a choice, in this case right back to C. This gives C → F then F → G can be completed as all those activities depending on G are now numbered.

Step 5 Return to the next vertex on the right-hand side which is not mapped onto and start again. (In this particular example this is not necessary.) Having the vertices numbered and being aware of bursts and merges enables the network to be drawn more easily. However, if the network is already drawn the same algorithm can be used to number the vertices. The number is usually placed in the bottom left-hand corner.

If A, B, C, D, E, F and G are the activities shown below

A	Remove ceiling
B	Remove floor tiles
C	Remove partitions
D	Heating first fit
E	Electrics first fit
F	Make good plaster
G	New ceiling

then we see that the network is the same one as in section 14.2.

Exercise 3.1 For each of the following groups of activities (i) number the activities (ii) draw a precedence network.

(a) Making a car door

	Activity	Immediately preceding activities
A	Press outer metal door	—
B	Press inner metal door	—
C	Spot weld metal door	A, B
D	Fit handles and trimmings	G
E	Fit window	H
F	Prepare inner lining	—
G	Attach inner lining to metal door	E, F
H	Paint metal door	C

(b) Planning a field study trip

		Duration	Preceding activities
A	Book centre and receive confirmation	10	—
B	Get quotes for coaches and confirm	10	C
C	Arrange and carry out reconnoitre	30	A
D	Plan activities	5	C
E	Prepare work and collect materials	20	D
F	Notify centre of details of meals etc.	1	D
G	Brief pupils	1	B
H	Collect money	30	G
I	Notify centre of final numbers	1	H
J	Departure	0	All

14.4   THE CASCADE CHART

A cascade chart shows the same information as a precedence network, but in the form of bars drawn against a time-scale to show when activities will take place.

Figure 14.31 shows how the information is transferred to a cascade chart.

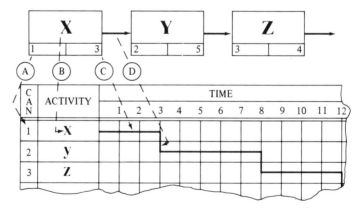

A   The CAN number (Cascade Activity Number)

B   Transfer the ACTIVITY into this column in order
     of Cascade Activity Number

C   Draw a bar line representing the number of time units

D   Indicate the relationship of one activity to another
     by a vertical line (replacing the arrow)

Fig. 14.31

So these activities

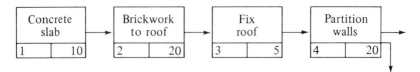

Fig. 14.32

would be recorded like this:

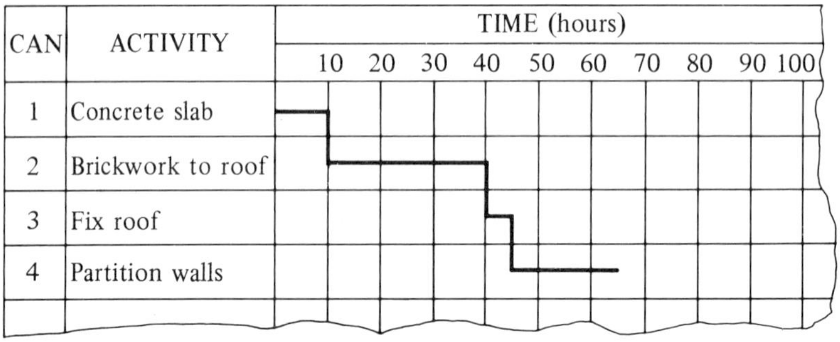

CAN	ACTIVITY	TIME (hours)									
		10	20	30	40	50	60	70	80	90	100
1	Concrete slab										
2	Brickwork to roof										
3	Fix roof										
4	Partition walls										

Fig. 14.33

So far we have progressed in simple steps, but we have now reached a **burst** in activity 4.

The 'path' to follow from this **burst** is fixed by the CAN number so we can carry on plotting.

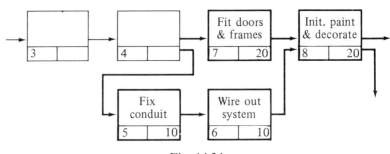

Fig. 14.34

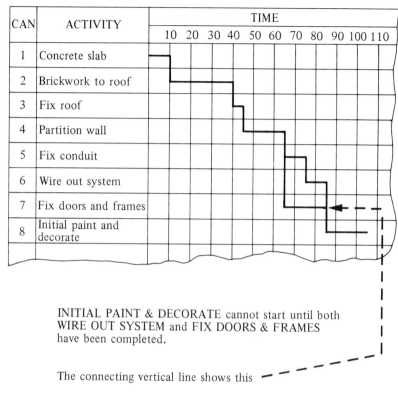

CAN	ACTIVITY	TIME										
		10	20	30	40	50	60	70	80	90	100	110
1	Concrete slab											
2	Brickwork to roof											
3	Fix roof											
4	Partition wall											
5	Fix conduit											
6	Wire out system											
7	Fix doors and frames											
8	Initial paint and decorate											

INITIAL PAINT & DECORATE cannot start until both
WIRE OUT SYSTEM and FIX DOORS & FRAMES
have been completed.

The connecting vertical line shows this

Fig. 14.35

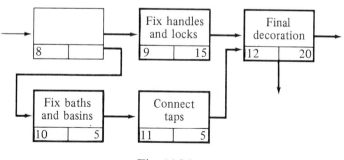

Fig. 14.36

Figure 14.37 shows what the chart would now look like.

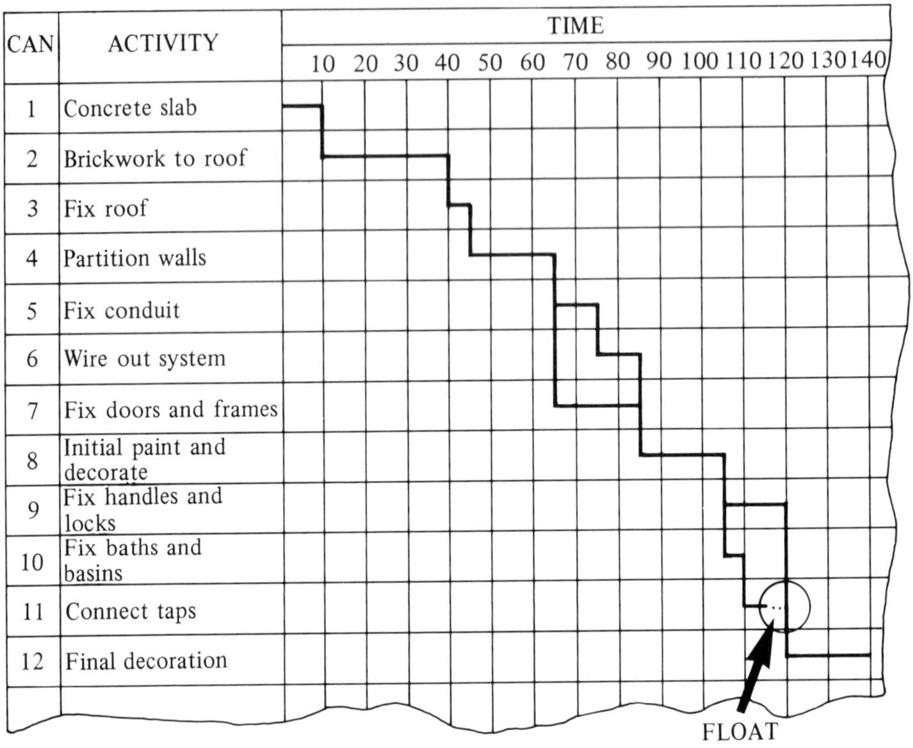

CAN	ACTIVITY	TIME													
		10	20	30	40	50	60	70	80	90	100	110	120	130	140
1	Concrete slab														
2	Brickwork to roof														
3	Fix roof														
4	Partition walls														
5	Fix conduit														
6	Wire out system														
7	Fix doors and frames														
8	Initial paint and decorate														
9	Fix handles and locks														
10	Fix baths and basins														
11	Connect taps														
12	Final decoration														

FLOAT

Fig. 14.37

Very often the separate 'paths' leading from a **burst** to a **merge** do not take the same time. This is what has happened to the chart in Fig. 14.37 for activities 9, 10 and 11. The combined time for fixed bath and basins and connect taps is shorter than the time it takes to fix handles and locks.

Since final decoration cannot start until handles and locks are fixed we have some spare time after connect taps. *Spare time* like this is always shown on the chart as a *dotted line* and is called **float**.

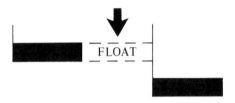

FLOAT

Fig. 14.38

Activities on a path which includes **float** are called:

Non-critical activities

and between them they can use up the float in that path, but when they have done so they too become critical. For example:

If a path has a float of 3 days and the first activity on that path takes 3 days longer than planned—then the remaining activities on that path become **critical activities**.

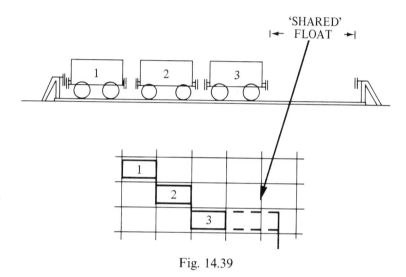

Fig. 14.39

Consider now the following situation.

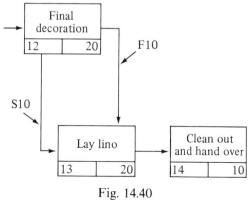

Fig. 14.40

You will see that lay lino can start before final decoration is complete but clean out and hand over cannot start until lay lino is finished. For overlapping activities like this, a bar is drawn for the duration of each activity and vertical lines used to illustrate the relationships. (Fig. 14.41)

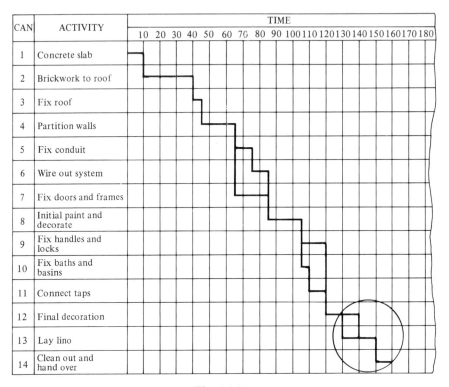

Fig. 14.41

In this case the first vertical line indicates that lay lino can start 10 hours after the start of final decoration. The second vertical line indicates that there is still 10 hours work to do on laying lino after final decoration has finished.

There is another point to consider in constructing a cascade chart. (Fig. 14.42). This, however, gives the impression that a relationship exists between activities 4 and 5 which is not so as the network shows. When this happens we avoid the **crossover** of vertical lines by using a reference number as shown in Fig. 14.43. This indicates that **activities** 3 and 5 are connected, i.e. **activity 5** can start 5 days after the start of **activity 3**.

Exercise 4.1 Draw a cascade chart for planning a field trip (see Exercise 3.1(b)). Make a list of those groups of activities which have shared float, stating how much float they share.

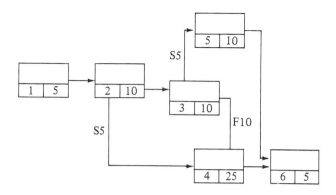

If this is transferred to a Cascade Chart it will look like this —

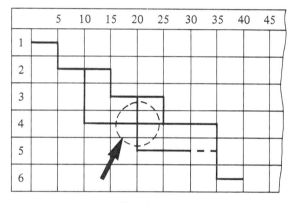

Fig. 14.42

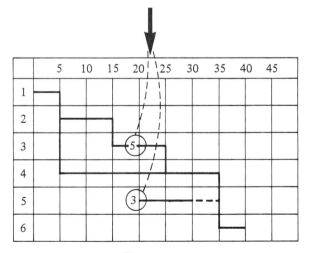

Fig. 14.43

401

Exercise 4.2   Transfer to a cascade chart the information in the network for the new ceiling project used to describe the method for determining the critical path section 14.2 (p. 376).

14.5 BUILDING A SPORTS PAVILION: A CASE STUDY

In this section we consider as a case study the operation of the planning required to build the sports pavilion shown in Fig. 14.44. The activities

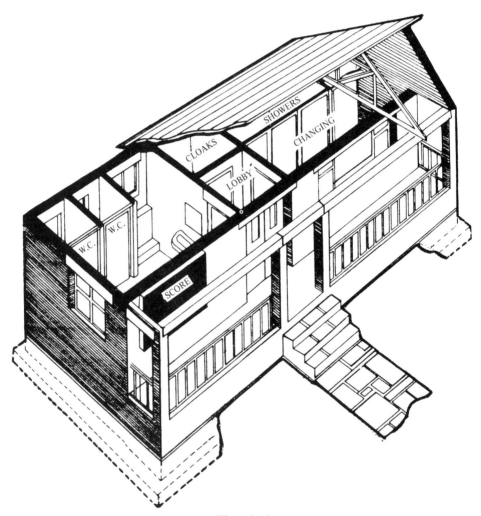

Fig. 14.44

needed in the construction are given in the table together with the times
needed for each activity and the activities which immediately precede it.

Activity (duration in days)		Immediately preceding Activity
A	Strip turf (1)	—
B	Excavate foundations (2)	A
C	Lay drains (2)	E
D	Back fill drains (1)	C
E	Excavate drains	A
F	Concrete foundations (2)	B
G	Brickwork to ground floor level (2)	F
H	Rubble fill (1)	G
I	Concrete slab (2)	D, H
J	Brickwork to roof level (4)	I
K	Roof carpenter (2)	J
L	Glazier (1)	M
M	Windows and external doors (2)	J
N	Balustrading (1)	J
O	Tile roof (2)	K
P	Partitions (4)	O
O	Painter external (4)	L, R, N
R	Rainwater goods (1)	O
S	Plumber first fix (2)	P
T	Plumber pipe work (2)	S
U	Internal doors and frames (2)	R
V	Initial paint and decorate (4)	T, U, X
W	Electrical conduit (2)	P
X	Electrical wiring (1)	W
Y	Joiner fixings (1)	V
Z	Electrical fixing (1)	V
AA	Plumber second fix (1)	V
BB	Lay lino (1)	V
CC	Final paint and decorate (1)	Q, Y, Z, AA, BB
DD	Entrance steps (1)	O
EE	Paving to path (1)	DD
FF	Replace turf (1)	EE
GG	Clean and hand over (1)	CC, FF

Note: The electrical wiring may be started one day after the start of
the electrical conduit but cannot finish before the electrical conduit
is finished.

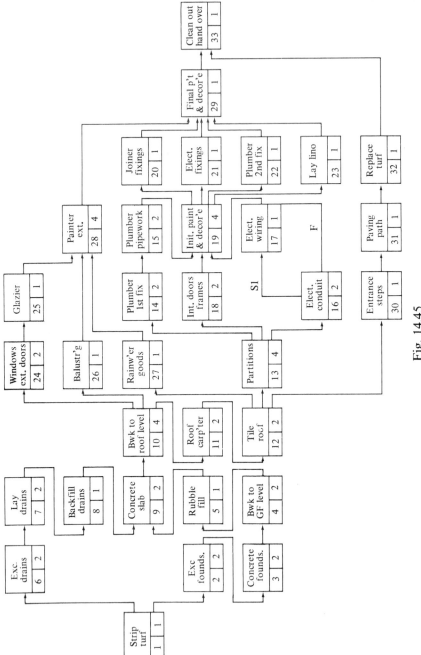

Fig. 14.45

Exercise 5.1
 (i) Use the algorithm to allocate CANs to these activities.
 (ii) Use the CANs to construct a network to represent the whole operation. When you have completed this exercise compare your answer with the one given in Fig. 14.45 opposite.

Exercise 5.2   Using your own network or a copy of Fig. 14.45 find the critical path.

Exercise 5.3
 (i) Draw up a cascade chart from the precedence network for the pavilion.

CAN	Activity description	Dur-ation (Days)		1	2	3	4	5	6	7	8	9	10	11	12	13	14	15	16	17	18	19	20	21	22	23	24	25	26	27	28	29	30	31	32	33
1	Strip turf	1	6																																	
2	Excavate founds.	2	12																																	
3	Concrete founds.	2	8																																	
4	Bwk to G F level	2	6																																	
5	Rubble fill	1	6																																	
6	Excavate drains	2	8																																	
7	Lay drains	2	4																																	
8	Backfill drains	1	4																																	
9	Concrete slab	2	6																																	
10	Bwk to roof level	4	24																																	
11	Roof carpenter	2	6																																	
12	Tile roof	2	8																																	
13	Partitions	4	12																																	
14	Plumber 1st fix	2	8																																	
15	Plumber pipework	2	8																																	
16	Electrical conduit	2	4																																	
17	Electrical wiring	1	2																																	
18	Internal doors & frames	2	8																																	
19	Init paint & decorate	4	12																																	
20	Joiner fixings	1	2																																	
21	Electrical fixings	1	2																																	
22	Plumber 2nd fix	1	4																																	
23	Lay lino	1	4																																	
24	Windows & external d'rs	2	8																																	
25	Glazier	1	4																																	
26	Balustrading	1	4																																	
27	Rainwater goods	1	4																																	
28	Painter external	4	8																																	
29	Final paint & decorate	1	2																																	
30	Entrance steps	1	3																																	
31	Paving to path	1	1																																	
32	Replace turf	1	4																																	
33	Clean out & hand over	1	6																																	

Man–day content

Fig. 14.46

(ii) List the CAN numbers of those activities on the critical path.
(iii) Which of the following activities are **non-critical**? 3, 6, 8, 13, 16, 21, 25, 29, 30, 32, 33.
(iv) Work on the pavilion is planned to take 33 days.

What would be the effect of each of the following alterations—and why? (consider each alteration on its own)

a	PLUMBER 1st FIX and PLUMBER PIPEWORK will each take one day instead of two
b	OMIT - LAY LINO
c	The start of GLAZIER will be delayed by TWO DAYS
d	EXCAVATE DRAINS and LAY DRAINS will each take THREE DAYS
e	JOINER FIXING will take TWO DAYS instead of ONE

Fig. 14.47

14.6 RESOURCE LEVELLING

Before calculating the duration of an activity the first step should be: *to decide what resources are needed to carry it out.*

Since the **cascade chart** shows activities taking place at the **earliest time** it is likely there will be variations in the demand for resources. In other words the chart may show up resource demands which have 'peaks' and 'troughs'.

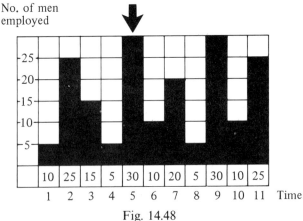

Fig. 14.48

Resource levelling helps to ensure there is a reasonable **balance** between

The amount of work to be done
and
The resources available

There are **three** methods of resource levelling. Two of these methods make use of **float**, the third alters the **duration** of activities and the **logic** of the **network**.

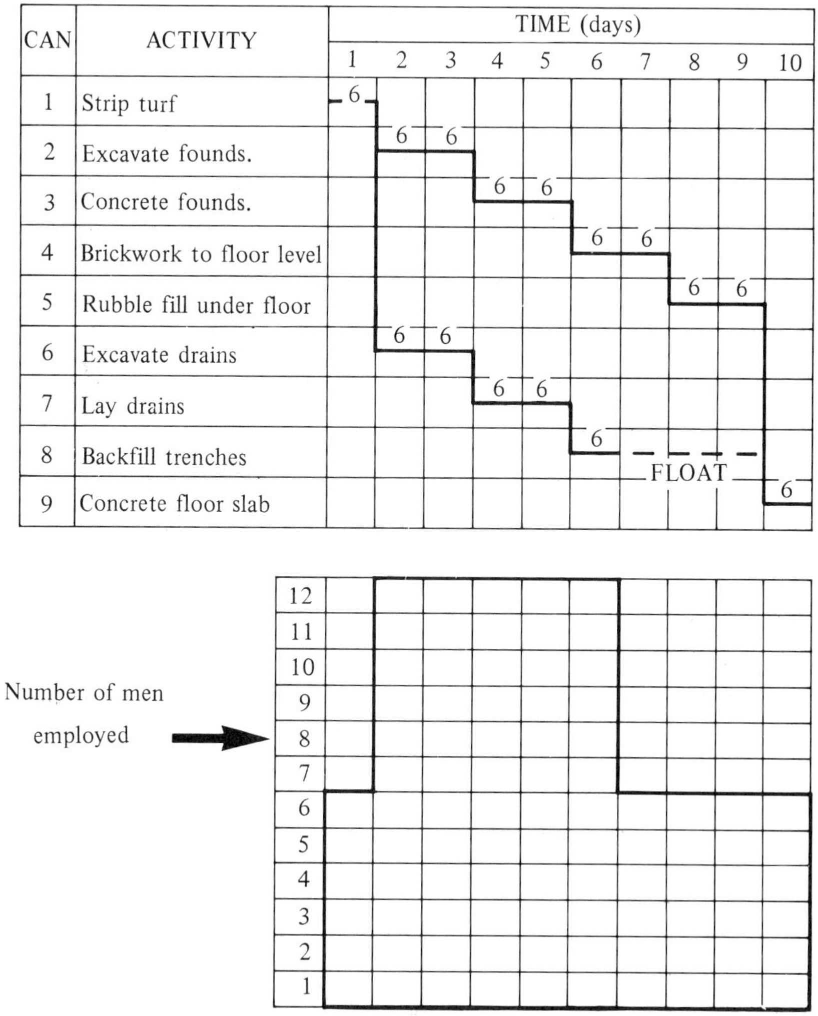

CAN	ACTIVITY	TIME (days)									
		1	2	3	4	5	6	7	8	9	10
1	Strip turf	6									
2	Excavate founds.		6	6							
3	Concrete founds.				6	6					
4	Brickwork to floor level						6	6			
5	Rubble fill under floor								6	6	
6	Excavate drains		6	6							
7	Lay drains				6	6					
8	Backfill trenches						6	FLOAT			
9	Concrete floor slab										6

Number of men employed →	12										
	11										
	10										
	9										
	8										
	7										
	6										
	5										
	4										
	3										
	2										
	1										

RESOURCE HISTOGRAM

Fig. 14.49

First we must calculate the resource demands to highlight any significant variations. To do this we must allocate the resources to each bar-line and then produce a **histogram** (or block diagram) at the bottom of the chart to depict the demand.

The first method of resource levelling extends the work to fill the available time, by using up the float.

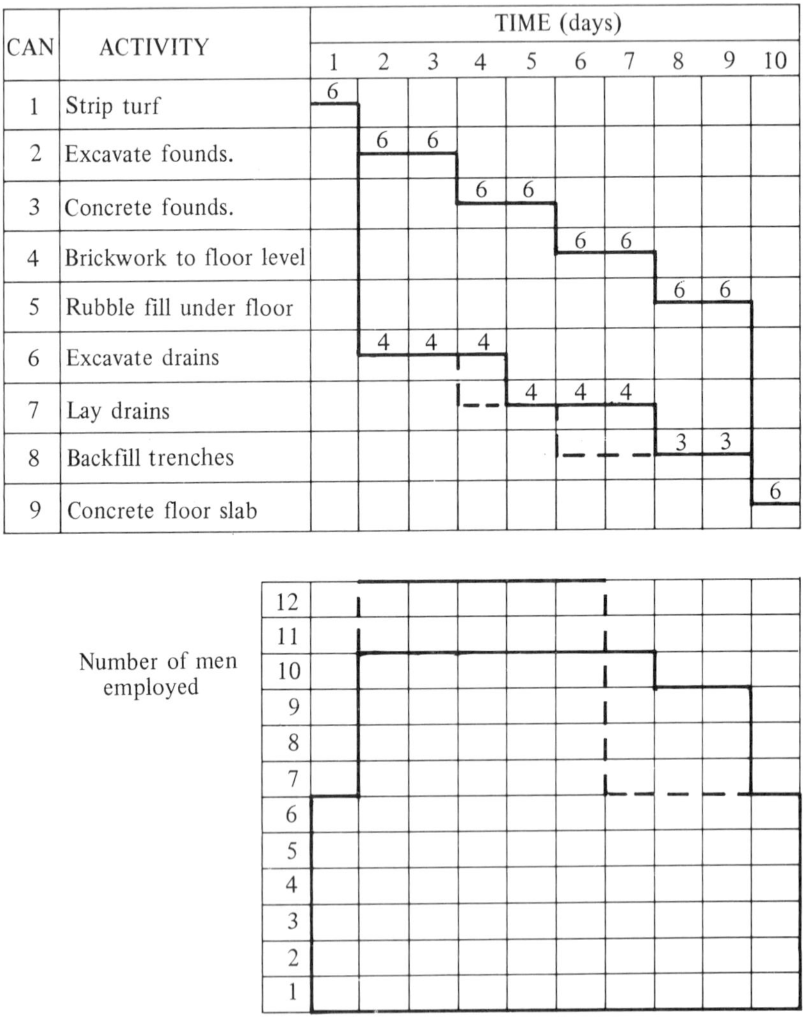

CAN	ACTIVITY	TIME (days)									
		1	2	3	4	5	6	7	8	9	10
1	Strip turf	6									
2	Excavate founds.		6	6							
3	Concrete founds.				6	6					
4	Brickwork to floor level						6	6			
5	Rubble fill under floor								6	6	
6	Excavate drains		4	4	4						
7	Lay drains					4	4	4			
8	Backfill trenches								3	3	
9	Concrete floor slab										6

Number of men employed

	1	2	3	4	5	6	7	8	9	10
12										
11										
10										
9										
8										
7										
6										
5										
4										
3										
2										
1										

There can be variations on this answer, the key question is — does it give the most balanced answer?

Fig. 14.50

In Fig. 14.49 one of the paths has *three days' float*. Therefore in order to
to balance out the number of men more realistically we can extend the work
of any activity on that path. For example:

4 men for 3 days instead of
6 men for 2 days

or

2 men for 3 days instead of
6 men for 1 day

So, by using only 4 men to exavate and lay the drains and 3 to backfill the
trenches, we get the revised charts shown in Fig. 14.50.

The second method used for resource levelling uses **float—by altering the start
times** of *non-critical* activities. (*Note*: 'do' is an abbreviation for ditto.) This
cascade chart (Fig. 14.51) shows two paths with float. By delaying the start of

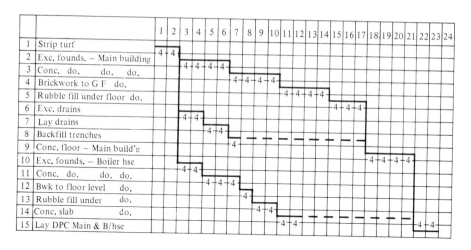

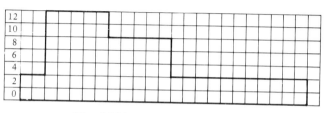

Fig. 14.51

work on the boiler-house until after the drains are completed, we can level off the number of men required.

The third method of levelling which can be used **alters duration and changes logic**. Look at the chart in Fig. 14.52. By **halving** the duration and **doubling** the number of men working on strip turf, concrete floor main building and d.p.c. the labour requirement can be kept quite level and this section of the plan can be shortened. There are, however, some activities for which common sense

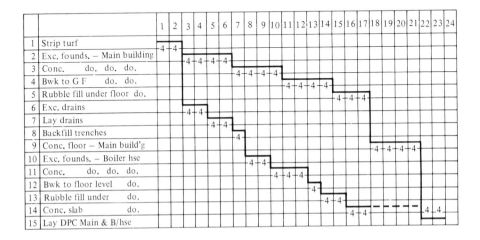

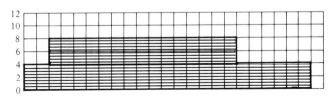

Fig. 14.52

will tell us that this is not feasible, often because of the limited availability of specialist workers or equipment. (Naturally the levelling of different trades must be carried out separately. For example, the work of general operatives, carpenters and bricklayers would need to be balanced for each trade to avoid peaks and troughs. The general principles, however, apply throughout.)

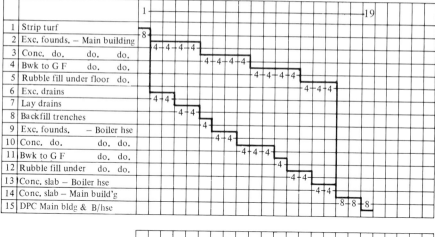

Fig. 14.53

Concrete floor main building is now CAN 14 and **no float** is left on the path for **drains** and **boiler-house**.

The third method of resource levelling is also used when there is **no float** available or if, after using up the float, the work-force is still **variable**. When this happens examine the whole problem to see if it can be solved by doing the work in a longer time with fewer men. This generally means reducing or eliminating overlapping activities. For example:

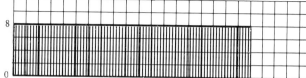

Fig. 14.54

From this you will see that by adding an extra day, a labour force of six men can be used throughout.

When a situation is arrived at where there is **no float**, it will be necessary to decide between

The cost of greater resources to enable the job to finish on time

and

The cost of allowing the job to overrun its completion date.

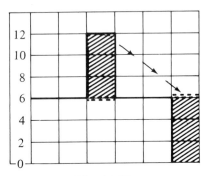

Fig. 14.55

Exercise 6.1   Examine the last four activities in this cascade chart, each of which is carried out by 4 erectors. Level the manpower needed for these four activities. (Fig. 14.56)

Exercise 6.2   Consider the pavilion case study in section 14.5. The table in Fig. 14.57 shows the minimum duration and number of man-days required for each of the activities. You have six men available to do the job, although extra casual labour could be hired if necessary. It is not feasible to employ more than 3 casual workers on any day.

Cost data
1. Overheads—£150 per day of project duration
2. Labour
      permanent—£50 per day of project duration
      casual—£80 per day of employment
(i) Using your cascade chart from section 14.4, Exercise 4.2 draw a histogram showing labour requirements for each day of the project. Calculate the total cost of labour and overheads.
(ii) Use the three techniques for smoothing resources to even out the labour requirements for this project. You may extend the duration of the project if you wish, but you should aim to minimise the total labour and overhead costs. The activities which may be shortened by deploying more labour on them are: B, C, E, F, I, Q, V.

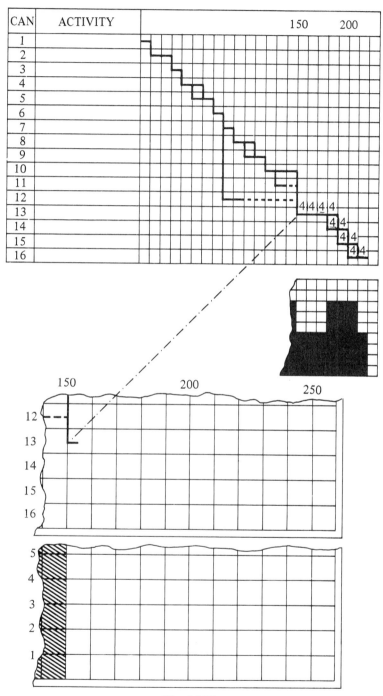

Fig. 14.56

CAN	Activity description	Duration (days) −minimum	Man-day content
1	Strip turf	1	6
2	Excavate foundations	2	12
3	Concrete foundations	2	8
4	Bwk to G F level	2	6
5	Rubble fill	1	6
6	Excavate drains	2	8
7	Lay drains	2	4
8	Backfill drains	1	4
9	Concrete slab	2	6
10	Bwk to roof level	4	24
11	Roof carpenter	2	6
12	Tile roof	2	8
13	Partitions	4	12
14	Plumber 1st fix	2	8
15	Plumber pipework	2	8
16	Electrical conduit	2	4
17	Electrical wiring	1	2
18	Internal doors and frames	2	8
19	Initial paint and decorate	4	12
20	Joiner fixings	1	2
21	Electrical fixings	1	2
22	Plumber 2nd fix	1	4
23	Lay lino	1	4
24	Windows and external doors	2	8
25	Glazier	1	4
26	Balustrading	1	4
27	Rainwater goods	1	4
28	Painter external	4	8
29	Final paint and decorate	1	2
30	Entrance steps	1	3
31	Paving to path	1	1
32	Replace turf	1	4
33	Clean out and hand over	1	6
		Total	208

Fig. 14.57

Draw a revised chart, level the resources using a histogram and calculate the revised total cost.

Exercise 6.3   Refer back to Exercise 5.3 (iv). Answer the same question for your revised project plan.

14.7 MISCELLANEOUS EXERCISES

M1 The activities needed to replace a broken window pane are given in the table below.

	Activity	Duration in mins	Preceding activity
A	Order glass	10	—
B	Collect glass	30	A
C	Remove broken pane	15	B, D
D	Buy putty	20	—
E	Put putty in frame	3	C
F	Put in new pane of glass	2	E
G	Putty outside and smooth	10	F
H	Sweep up broken glass	5	C
I	Clean up	5	All

   (i) Draw a network to show these activities.
   (ii) What is the critical path?
   (iii) What is the minimum time needed to complete the replacement?

M2 The precedence network in Fig. 14.58 shows the main activities in the organisation of GCE examinations and the relationships between them. By completing a forward and reverse pass, the earliest and latest starting and finishing times have been calculated and most of them are shown in the network in the usual fashion. It can be seen that the time required for the whole operation is 41 weeks.

   (i) Explain the relationship between activity 9 ('Candidates sit exams') and activity 11 ('Papers marked') which is indicated by the two arrows marked 'S1' and 'F1' joining them.
   (ii) Complete a forward pass through the network to show that the minimum completion time is 40 weeks.
   (iii) Use a reverse pass through the network to find those activities which are on the critical path.
   (iv) List the non-critical activities and the amount of float associated with each.

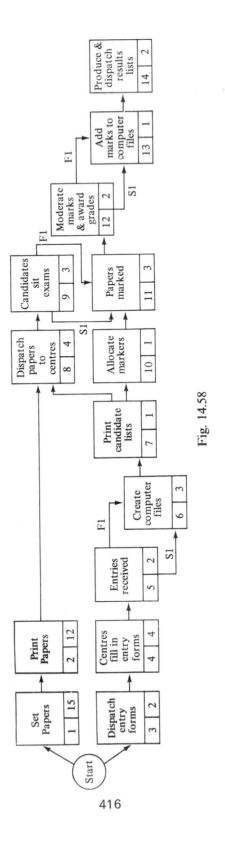

Fig. 14.58

(v) Draw a cascade chart for this project.

(vi) (a) What would be the effect of a delay of 2 weeks in activity 2 ('Print papers')?

(b) What could the examinations board do to ensure that candidates could still sit their examinations from the start of week 31?

(vii) If the candidates are due to start sitting their examinations in the first week of June:

(a) when must the whole process start?

(b) when will the results be published to candidates?

M3 Use the technique of critical path analysis to plan one of the following projects and find the minimum time needed for completion. You may prefer to use the technique on an alternative project of your own. First you will need to:

Decide on the activities involved.

Estimate the time needed for each activity.

Draw up a precedence table.

Draw the network.

Then find the critical path.

(i) Organising a group outing.

(ii) Putting on a school production.

(iii) Making a birthday cake.

(iv) Building a doll's house.

(v) Moving house.

(vi) Making and putting up curtains and curtain rail.

(vii) Opening a sports shop.

(viii) Organising a craft market to raise funds for charity.

(ix) Resurfacing a road.

(x) Developing and launching a new brand of washing-up liquid.

(xi) Starting up a mini-enterprise.

(xii) Setting up a school crèche.

15

Algorithms

15.1 DEFINITIONS

Throughout this text we have been meeting examples of algorithms, for example, the shortest path technique, dynamic programming, or maximum flow through a network. These techniques or algorithms are characterised by the fact that they are precise *procedures* that if you follow correctly will lead you to the solution. Once you have understood how to use the algorithm, it is just a matter of following the procedures correctly.

So we can define an **algorithm** as a finite set of instructions which have all the following properties:

1. **Precision**   Each step is precisely defined
2. **Uniqueness**   All intermediate results of each step are uniquely defined and depend only on the input and the results of preceding steps
3. **Finiteness**   The algorithm will stop after a finite number of steps
4. **Input**   The algorithm receives input
5. **Output**   The algorithm produces output
6. **Generality**   The algorithm can be applied to any set of inputs

As an example consider the algorithm below which searches a sequence of numbers, say

$$S(1), S(2), \ldots, S(N)$$

in order to find the largest value.

419

Algorithm
1. Set I = 1 and LARGE = S(1)   (Initialisation)
2. If S(I) > LARGE, then LARGE = S(I)   (find a larger value?)
3. If I = N, then stop   (terminate)
4. I = I + 1 and Go to Step 2   (continue search)

Note that the largest value is returned as LARGE.

We can see how the algorithm works when finding the largest value in the sequence

$$S(1) = 2.3, \quad S(2) = 4.1, \quad S(3) = 3.2$$

Step	Action	Comment
1	I = 1, LARGE = 2.3	
2	—	Statement 2.3 > 2.3 is false so we move to Step 3
3	—	Here $N = 3$, and I = 1, so false
4	I = 2	
2	LARGE = 4.1	4.1 > 2.3, so we redefine LARGE
3	—	False
4	I = 4	
2	—	Statement 3.2 > 4.1 is false, so we continue to Step 3
3	STOP	Since I = 3

Another way of seeing whether a technique is an algorithm is to convert it to a computer program. If the technique can be converted into a set of instructions so that a machine can carry out the procedure, we have an algorithm. For example, we can write the algorithm above as a BASIC program. (Warning to programming purists: the following program is purely for illustration, and is neither pretty nor well structured. However, it will run on most versions of BASIC!)

```
10   REM Program to find the largest value in a sequence of numbers
20   PRINT 'Please input the number of terms in your sequence'
30   INPUT N
40   DIM S(N)
50   FOR I = 1 TO N
60   PRINT 'Please input a term in the sequence'
70   INPUT S(I)
80   NEXT I
90   I = 1
```

```
100   LARGE = S(1)
110   IF S(I) > LARGE THEN LARGE = S(I)
120   IF I = N THEN PRINT 'Largest term is'; LARGE: END
130   I = I + 1
140   GOTO 110
```

The following exercises ask for various algorithms to be constructed. Computer programs are not wanted at this stage.

Exercise 1.1   Write an algorithm which finds the INDEX, J, of the *first* occurrence of the largest element in a sequence of numbers

$$S(1), \ldots, S(N)$$

(e.g. for the sequence

$$7, 9, 3, 8, 9, -1, 9$$

the algorithm must return the value 2)

Exercise 1.2   Write an algorithm to find the smallest prime number greater than the positive integer N.

Exercise 1.3   Convert the formula for solving quadratic equations of the form $ax^2 + bx + c = 0$ into an algorithm.

Exercise 1.4   Write an algorithm which reverses the sequence

$$S(1), \ldots, S(N)$$

15.2   COMPLEXITY OF ALGORITHMS

There are many questions which we can ask about an algorithm

  (i) Is it correct (i.e. does it do what it is meant to do)?
 (ii) How long does it take to complete the task?
(iii) How much storage space is needed when using the algorithm on a computer?

We will concentrate on the second question. The time taken by an algorithm will certainly depend on the size of the input. (For the algorithm in section 15.1, the size would be N, the number of terms in the sequence.) We define the **time complexity function**, $f(n)$, as the longest time taken to solve any input of size n. So $f(n)$ is an *upper bound* for the time taken to solve the problem.

So far, we have not been precise by what is meant by the time taken—we essentially mean the time taken by a computer to execute the algorithm. This will depend on the number of iterations made and so an estimate of the time needed is given by the number of instructions executed, or the number of times each loop is executed, or the number of comparisons made. We are, though, usually only interested in a general estimate of the time taken to execute the algorithm so that we can make a comparison between different algorithms—for example, does the time depend on n, or n^2 or 2^n? So if $f(n)$ behaves like, for example, the function n, then we say that the **order** of the algorithm is n. As an example, consider the algorithm introduced in section 15.1 which found the largest value in a sequence of n numbers. For *any* sequence of n numbers, the loop will be executed n times, and so the order of this algorithm is n.

Different algorithms can have different orders. As another example, consider the problem of determining the number of n tuples of the form

$$(x_1, x_2, \ldots, x_n)$$

where $x_i = 0$ or 1, which have more than m zeros. For $n = 3$, and $m = 1$, we have $2^3 = 8$ 3-tuples, namely

$$(0,0,0)$$
$$(0,0,1)$$
$$(0,1,0)$$
$$(1,0,0)$$
$$(1,1,0)$$
$$(1,0,1)$$
$$(0,1,1)$$
$$(1,1,1)$$

and 4 of these have more than one zero. One method of determining the answers for given values of n and m is to consider every n-tuple and count the number of zeros in each. Since each element can be 0 or 1, there are 2^n possibilities to look at. So the order of this type of algorithm would be 2^n. Now the function n and 2^n behave very differently as n gets larger. Although they both tend to infinity, 2^n increases at a faster rate. This is illustrated in the table below, where we take the time to execute 1 step as 1 microsecond (i.e. 10^{-6} seconds).

Order of algorithm	Time to execute if $n =$					
	1	10	50	100	1000	10^6
n	10^{-6} s	10^{-5} s	5×10^{-5} s	10^{-4} s	10^{-3} s	1 s
n^2	10^{-6} s	10^{-4} s	2.5×10^{-3} s	10^{-2} s	1 s	12 days
n^3	10^{-6} s	10^{-3} s	1.25×10^{-1} s	1 s	16.7 min.	31 710 years
2^n	2×10^{-6} s	10^{-3} s	36 years	4×10^{16} years	3×10^{287} years	3×10^{301016} years

The crucial distinction here between time complexity functions is whether the function is *polynomial* in n (e.g. n, n^2, n^3) or *exponential* in n (e.g. 2^n, 3^n, e^n). We can see from the table above why we make this distinction. Algorithms which have exponential time functions take an extremely long time, even for moderate size problems, whereas polynomial time functions are not so intractable. The table below shows the order of some of the algorithms that we have met in this text.

Algorithm	Time complexity function
Shortest path algorithm	n^2
Minimum connection	n^2
Planar graph	n^3
Chinese postman	n^3

Exercise 2.1 Draw up a table of times to execute algorithms for $n = 10$, 20, 30, 40, 50 and for time complexity functions $\ln n$, n, n^2, n^3, 2^n and 3^n.

Exercise 2.2 The algorithm below searches through an unordered sequence of numbers,
$$S(1), S(2), \ldots, S(N)$$
in order to find the first location of the value KEY. The algorithm returns the index of its first location in I, and the value 0 in I if KEY is not found.

1. $I = 1$
2. If $I > N$, then set $I = 0$ and stop
3. If $KEY = S(I)$, then stop
4. $I = I + 1$ and goto step 2

Show how this algorithm searches for the value 5 in the sequence
$$10, 6, 8, 3, 5, 7, 2, 5, 1$$
What is the order of this algorithm?

Exercise 2.3 Determine the order of one of the algorithms for finding the shortest path through a network.

15.3 USING RECURRENCE RELATIONS
TO FIND ORDERS OF ALGORITHMS

Although it is sometimes quite straightforward to find the order of an algorithm, in most cases it is far from obvious. For the following algorithm, we will see how solving recurrence relations will help. First though the algorithm, which is a **binary search**, to find the given KEY in an increasing ordered sequence

$$S(1), S(2), \ldots, S(N)$$

We will need the notation

$\lfloor x \rfloor$, which is the greatest *integer* less than or equal to x

$\lceil x \rceil$, which is the least integer greater than or equal to x

(e.g. $\lfloor 8.7 \rfloor = 8, \lfloor 9 \rfloor = 9, \lfloor -7.3 \rfloor = -8$

$\lceil 8.7 \rceil = 9, \lceil 9 \rceil = 9, \lceil -7.3 \rceil = -7$)

Now to the algorithm, which returns the position of KEY in M if found; otherwise it returns the value 0 in M.

1. $I = 1, J = N$	(I, J mark the boundaries of the sequence being searched)
2. If $I > J$, then set $M = 0$ and stop	(KEY not found)
3. $M = \lfloor (I + J)/2 \rfloor$	(Subdivide)
4. If KEY $= S(M)$, then stop	(KEY found)
5. If KEY $< S(M)$, then $J = M - 1$; otherwise Set $I = M + 1$	(Reset boundaries)
6. Goto step 2	(Loop)

We will illustrate how the algorithm works when KEY = 'S' and the sequence is

$$S(1) = \text{'B'}, S(2) = \text{'D'}, S(3) = \text{'F'}, S(4) = \text{'S'}$$

Step	Action	Comment
1	$I = 1, J = 4$	
2	—	Statement $1 > 4$ false, so move to Step 3
3	$M = \lfloor 5/2 \rfloor = 2$	
4	—	Statement 'S' = 'D' false, so move to Step 5
5	$I = 3$	'S' $\geqslant$ 'D', so we set $I = 3$
6	—	Move to Step 2
2	—	Statement $3 > 4$ false, so move to Step 3
3	$M = \lfloor 7/2 \rfloor = 3$	
4	—	Statement 'S' = 'F' false, so move to Step 5
5	$I = 4$	'S' $\geqslant$ 'F', so we set $I = 4$
6	—	Move to Step 2
2	—	Statement $4 > 4$ false, so move to Step 3
3	$M = \lfloor 4 \rfloor = 4$	
4	STOP	Since KEY = $S(4)$

We have used a letter sequence to illustrate the algorithm, so that 'S' ≥ 'D' means that 'S' comes after 'D' in the alphabet. We could, of course, use a numerical sequence (see Exercise 3.1).

We want to examine the worst case time for the execution of this algorithm. We will measure the time by the number of iterations of the loop 2–3–4–5–6–2. For the above example, when $N = 4$, it was 2.

So let

a_N = number of iterations of the loop in the worst-case for an input of size N

Suppose that $N > 1$. Initially $I = 1$ and $J = N$, and at step 3, we set $M = \lfloor (I + J)/2 \rfloor = \lfloor (1 + N)/2 \rfloor$. In the worst case, $KEY \neq S(M)$ and at step 5, if $KEY < S(M)$, we execute the loop again with the sequence

$$S(1), S(2), \ldots, S(M - 1) \tag{1}$$

Whereas if $KEY > S(M)$, we execute the loop again with

$$S(M + 1), \ldots, S(N) \tag{2}$$

We now need to find the maximum size of either of the above arrays which will give us the worst possible case. We must consider the two cases, N even or N odd, separately.

When N is even, $1 + N$ will be odd, and so

$$M = \left\lfloor \frac{1 + N}{2} \right\rfloor = \frac{N}{2}$$

The size of array (1) is

$$M - 1 = \frac{N}{2} - 1,$$

and array (2) is

$$N - (M + 1) + 1 = \frac{N}{2}$$

So for N even the worst case is an array of length $N/2$. Now if N is odd, $1 + N$ is even and

$$M = \left\lfloor \frac{1 + N}{2} \right\rfloor = \frac{1 + N}{2}$$

The size of array (1) is

$$M - 1 = \frac{1 + N}{2} - 1 = \frac{N - 1}{2}$$

and array (2) is

$$N - (M + 1) = N - \frac{(1 + N)}{2} = \frac{N - 1}{2}$$

In this case both arrays are of size $(N - 1)/2$.

To summarise, we can see that in both cases, the array will be at most of length $\lfloor N/2 \rfloor$.

$$\left(\text{for } N \text{ even} \left\lfloor \frac{N}{2} \right\rfloor = \frac{N}{2}, \text{where for } N \text{ odd} \left\lfloor \frac{N}{2} \right\rfloor = \frac{N - 1}{2} \right)$$

So we have reduced the problem from a sequence of length N to one of at most length $\lfloor N/2 \rfloor$.

Hence

$$a_N = 1 + a_{\lfloor N/2 \rfloor}$$

with initial condition $a_1 = 1$.

So we need to solve a recurrence relation, but unfortunately, not quite of the usual type. We can make progress by considering the special case when N is a power of 2, that is when $N = 2^k$. Then we have

$$a_{2^k} = 1 + a_{2^{k-1}}$$

and, writing $b_k = a_{2^k}$, we have

$$b_k = 1 + b_{k-1} \quad \text{and} \quad b_0 = a_1 = 1$$

We can solve this equation, and from the techniques of Chapter 7, we know that its solution is given by

$$b_k = 1 + k \text{ (see Exercise 3.2)}$$

Thus, when $N = 2^k$,

$$a_N = a_{2^k} = b_k = 1 + k = 1 + \log_2 N$$

i.e.,

$$a_N = 1 + \frac{\ln N}{\ln 2}$$

Although we have taken a special case, namely $N = 2^k$, it can be shown that the solution of

$$a_N = 1 + a_{\lfloor N/2 \rfloor}$$

is given by

$$a_N = 1 + \left\lfloor \left(\frac{\ln N}{\ln 2} \right) \right\rfloor$$

In Exercise 3.1 we noted the behaviour of $\ln N$ for large N.

An algorithm of order ln N, which this is, will be far more efficient than an algorithm of order N. So we conclude that a binary search is a much more efficient method for searching than a complete search, as given in the algorithm in Exercise 6.

Exercise 3.1   Show how the binary search algorithm of this section searches for the value $KEY = 7$ in the sequence

$$-5, -4, 2, 5, 7, 9, 10$$

Exercise 3.2   Solve the recurrence relation

$$b_k - b_{k-1} = 1$$

and find the complete solution for $b_0 = 1$.

Further Reading

Over the past decade there have been many books written on the various topics in this text. Unfortunately most of them have been written at a higher level than our text, usually for courses in operational research at undergraduate or postgraduate level. The books in the list below which are starred indicate that some of the material is at an appropriate level.

Basic Linear Programming, B. Bunday (Arnold, 1984).

Basic Optimization Methods, B. Bunday (Arnold, 1984).

Introductory Finite Mathematics with Computing, W. Dorn and D. McCracken (Wiley, 1976).

Elementary Mathematics from an Algorithm Standpoint, A. Engel (Keele University, 1984).

Graph Algorithms, S. Even (Computer Science Press, 1979).

Sequencing and Scheduling, S. French (Arnold, 1984).

Decision Making, Models and Algorithms, S. Gass (Wiley, 1985).

Dynamic Programming with Management Applications, N. Hastings (Butterworth, 1973).

Combinatorial Algorithms, T. Hu (Addison-Wesley, 1981).

Discrete Mathematics, R. Johnsonbaugh (Macmillan, 1984).

Game Theory, A. Jones (Ellis Horwood, 1980).

Introduction to Mathematical Programming, B. Lev and H. Weiss (Arnold, 1982).

Graphs, Networks and Design, Open University, Course TM 361 (Open University Press, 1981).

Network Optimization Practice, D. Smith (Ellis Horwood, 1982).

Model Building in Mathematical Programming, H. Williams (Wiley, 1978).

Principles of Operations Research, H. Wagner (Prentice-Hall, 1975).

Introduction to Graph Theory, R. Wilson (Longman, 1975).

Answers to Exercises

1 SORTING

Exercise 3.1 No. of comparisons = 45, no. of exchanges = 8.

Exercise 3.2 (i) Comparisons = 15, exchanges = 5.
(ii) Comparisons = 66, exchanges = 8.
(iii) Comparisons = 36, exchanges = 7.

Exercise 4.2 Intelligent bubble sort: comparisons = 42, exchanges = 22.

Exercise 4.3

	Bubble sort					
	Primitive		Simple		Intelligent	
Data set	C	E	C	E	C	E
(i)	81	0	45	0	9	0
(ii)	81	45	45	45	45	45
(iii)	81	17	45	17	45	17

Exercise 4.6

Data set	Pair of sorts	C	E	E/C
Standard	Primitive and intelligent	0.00308	0.00913	2.96
2	Primitive and any other	0.00278	0.00878	3.16
3	Primitive and any other	0.00333	0.00941	2.83

Exercise 4.7

	C	E	T (s)
Primitive	9801	2343	45.72
Simple	4950	2343	31.90
Intelligent	4884	2343	31.66

Exercise 5.1

Data set	Simple shuttle sort			Intelligent shuttle sort			Shell sort		
	C	E	T	C	E	T	C	E	T
(i)	45	0	45	9	0	9	22	0	22
(ii)	45	45	180	45	45	180	27	13	66
(iii)	45	17	96	24	17	75	27	9	54

Exercise 5.4   Simple shuttle sort: C = 4950, E = 2343, T = 11 979.
Intelligent shuttle sort: C = 2439, E = 2343, T = 9468.
Shell sort: C = 836, E = 381, T = 1979.

Miscellaneous Exercises

M2   (i) Shell sort: C = 21, E = 7, T = 42.
        Quicksort: C = 35, E = 6, T = 53.
    (ii) Shell sort: C = 28, E = 14, T = 70.
        Quicksort: C = 44, E = 6, T = 62.

2 PACKING

Exercise 1.1

Workers	1	2	3	4	5
Activity	A, B	D, E	F, I	G, H, C	J, K

Exercise 1.2 Yes.

Exercise 1.3 No.

Exercise 2.1 5 workers.

Exercise 2.2 4 workers.

Exercise 3.1 First-fit method — 5 lengths.

Exercise 3.2

Worker	1	2	3	4	5
Activity	A, B, G	C, H	D	E	F

Exercise 3.3

Disc	1	2	3	4
Programme	B, C, D, G	A, E, F, P, Q	H, J, K, L	I, M, N, O, R

Exercise 4.1 Bin 1—D, E   2—F, H   3—B, C, A   4—G. Not optimal

Exercise 4.2 Disc 1—G, L, A   2—J, F, C, D   3—R, O, N, P, I
4—Q, K, M, H, B, E

Exercise 4.3 Lane 1—Lorry, car and tent   Lane 2—Car and caravan, lorry
Lane 3—van, camper, car (i.e. one car will not fit on).

Miscellaneous Exercises

M1 (i) Rack 1—A, B   2—D, E   3—C, G, F.
(ii) Rack 1—D, G   2—F, B   3—E, A   4—C.
(iii) Rack 1—C, G   2 — D, E   3—B, F, A.

M2 No.

M3 Minimum number is 4.

M4 Yes.

M5 (i) £10.   (ii) £11.20.   (iii) Yes, cost can be reduced to £9.60.

M6 (i) Minimum number is 3.
(ii) Disc 1—A, E   2—D, B   3—C, F, G, H

3 LINEAR PROGRAMMING

Exercise 1.1 Maximise $z = 8x + 5y$ subject to

$$x \leqslant 3$$
$$3x + y \leqslant 12$$
$$x + y \leqslant 7$$
$$x, y \geqslant 0$$

where x = no. of bicycles, y = no. of trucks to be built in one day.

Exercise 1.2 Minimise $z = 0.12x + 0.08y$ subject to

$$0.32x + 0.12y \geqslant 24$$
$$0.2x + 0.24y \geqslant 30$$
$$0.08x + 0.36y \geqslant 18$$
$$x, y \geqslant 0.$$

Exercise 2.1 2 high-back chairs and 3 rockers per day.

Exercise 2.2 $x = 5/2$, $y = 9/2$ and maximum value of $z = 42\frac{1}{2}$.
$x = 41$, $y = 91$ and minimum value of $z = 12.2$.

Exercise 2.3 $x = 3/2$, $y = 3$ and $P = 9/2$.

Exercise 3.1 $z = 8860$

Exercise 3.2 $z = 274$ and $x = 28/5$, $y = 1$.

Exercise 3.3 $z = 188/19$ at $x = 30/19$, $y = 32/19$.

Exercise 3.4 $z = 43/11$ at $x = 28/11$, $y = 15/11$.

Exercise 3.5 $z = 56$ at $x = 2$, $y = 12/5$.

Exercise 4.2 $P = 72$ at $x = 3$, $y = 6$.

Exercise 4.3 $P = 96/13$ at $x = 33/13$, $y = 30/13$.

Exercise 4.4 $P = 100/11$ at $x = 36/11$, $y = 32/11$.

Exercise 5.1 $P = 21$ at $x = 0$, $y = 7/2$.

Exercise 5.2 $P = 206/19$ at $x = 50/19$, $y = 28/19$.

Exercise 5.3 $P = 45$ at $x = 0$, $y = 5/2$, $z = 15/8$.

Exercise 5.4 $P = 8$ at $x = 0$, $y = 1$, $z = 0$.

Exercise 5.5 $P = 140$ at $x_1 = 0$, $x_2 = 45/2$, $x_3 = 5$.

Exercise 5.6 $P = 12/5$ at $x = 2/5$, $y = 1/5$, $z = 0$.

Exercise 6.1   £$55\frac{1}{8}$ with $13\frac{1}{8}$ units of A, $2\frac{5}{8}$ units of B, 0 units of C.

Exercise 6.2   Profit = £720 when no. of $\frac{1}{2}$ litre bottles = 72 000/7
no. of 1 litre bottles = 21 600/7.

Exercise 6.3   Profit = £3875 when no. of type A = 400, no. of type B = 0, type C = 150 and type D = 0.

Exercise 6.4   Profit = £10 350 when 2000 type A and 7000 type B are produced.

Exercise 6.5   Profit = £3 400 000 when spending £200 000 on television
£100 000 on radio
£100 000 on newspapers
£100 000 on posters.

Miscellaneous Exercises

M1   Produce $\dfrac{4000}{3}$ type A and $\dfrac{4000}{3}$ type B.

M2   Produce 920 units of A.

M3   8 of model A and 3 of model B.

M4 $x_1 = x_2 = 0$ and $x_3 = 1$.

M5   300 A cabinets and 200 B cabinets.

M6 $\dfrac{6000}{13}$ Caprice cars and $\dfrac{5800}{13}$ Fiasco cars.

M7   36/7 hours on upper seam and 5/7 hours on lower seam.

4   GAME THEORY

Exercise 1.1   A—play row 2   B—play column 2.

Exercise 1.2   A—play row 4   B—play column 1   Yes

Exercise 2.1   (i) Yes.   (ii) No.   (iii) No.

Exercise 2.2   For 1.1, A plus 3, B minus 3.
For 1.2, A plus 4, B minus 2.

Exercise 2.3   (i) Yes.   (ii) No.   (iii) Yes.

Exercise 2.4

		Player B		
		Paper	Scissors	Stones
	Paper	0	-1	1
Player A	Scissors	1	0	-1
	Stones	-1	1	0

Exercise 3.1 (i), (iii), (iv) and (v)—stable.   (ii)—not stable.

Exercise 3.2 No stable solution.

Exercise 4.1 (i) Not stable.   (ii) Stable, value = 3.
(iii) Not stable.   (iv) Stable, value = 2.
(v) Not stable.

Exercise 4.2 No stable solution.

Exercise 4.3 Points are $(1, 3), (1, 5), (4, 3), (4, 5)$. Solution = 3.

Exercise 5.1 (i) $3/2, -3/2$.   (ii) $3/2, -3/2$.
A—play row 1 with probability 3/5 and expected gains 7/5
B—play column 1 with probability 4/5 and expected gains $-7/5$.

Exercise 5.2   (i) A—row 1 with $p = 5/8$;   B—column 1 with $p = 1/8$.
(ii) A—row 1 with $p = 2/3$;   B—column 1 with $p = 1/6$.
(iii) A—row 1 and B column 1.
(iv) A—row 1 with $p = 3/5$;   B—column 1 with $p = 3/5$.

Exercise 5.3 Row 1 with $p = 2/3$ and row 2 with $p = 1/3$.

Exercise 5.4 A—row 1 with $p = 0$ B—column 1 with $p = 1/2$
row 2 with $p = 1/2$ column 2 with $p = 1/2$
row 3 with $p = 1/2$

Exercise 6.1 Row 1 with $p = 3/5$, Row 2 with $p = 2/5$

Exercise 6.2 Column 1 with $p = 3/7$, Column 2 with $p = 4/7$

Exercise 6.3 Row 1 with $p = 2/7$, Row 2 with $p = 5/7$

Exercise 6.4 Row 1 with $p = 3/5$, Row 2 with $p = 2/5$, Row 3 with $p = 0$.

Exercise 7.1 Government should inoculate 2/3 of population with vaccine 1, and 1/3 population with vaccine 2.

Exercise 7.2   Network A—programme 2
                  Network B—programme 1

Exercise 7.3   Probability $= 1/2$.

Miscellaneous Exercises

M1   (a) (i) A plays row 2, B plays column 2.
            (ii) A plays row 2, B plays column 2.
            (iii) A plays row 2, B plays column 3.
            (iv) A plays row 2, B plays column 1.

        (b) (i) Yes.   (ii) No.   (iii) No.

M2   (i) $\mu = 2, v = -5$—no stable solution.
        (ii) $\mu = -3, v = -2$—no stable solution.
        (iii) $\mu = -2, v = -2$—stable solution.
        (iv) $\mu = 1, v = -1$—stable solution.

M3   (i) A plays row 1 with $p = 2/3$, B plays column 1 with $p = 4/9$.
        (ii) A plays row 1 with $p = 3/7$, B plays column 1 with $p = 9/14$.
        (iii) A plays row 2, B plays column 2.
        (iv) A plays row 2, B plays column 2.

M4   (ii) Stable solution—A plays row 2, B plays column 3.
        (iv) Stable solution—A plays row 2, B plays column 1.
        (vi) Stable solution—A plays row 2, B plays column 1.

M5   For M4 (i) A's optimum strategy is play row 1 with $p = 0$, row 2 with
                $p = 4/5$, and row 3 with $p = 1/5$.

        For M4 (ii) A's optimum strategy is play row 1 with $p = 1/2$, row 2
                with $p = 1/2$.

5 PLANAR GRAPHS

Exercise 1.1   No route crosses each bridge.

Exercise 1.2   Several routes.

Exercise 1.3   Several routes.

Exercise 1.5 K_2 has 1 arc. K_3 has 3 arcs. K_9 has 36 arcs. K_n has $\dfrac{n}{2}(n-1)$ arcs.

Exercise 1.8 K_1, K_2, K_3 and K_4 are planar. K_5 is non-planar.

Exercise 2.2 $\dfrac{2n \times n}{n} = n^2$ arcs.

Exercise 2.3 The graph is $K_{3,3}$ which is non-planar.

Exercise 4.1 (a) (ii);   (b) (i);   (c) (iv);   (d) (iii).

Exercise 4.2 (a) (i) 4 faces.   (ii) $f_1 = 4, f_2 = 3, f_3 = 3, f_4 = 4$.
             (iii) A = 2, B = 2, C = 4, D = 2, E = 4.

         (b) (i) 5 faces.   (ii) $f_1 = 3, f_2 = 4, f_3 = 3, f_4 = 5, f_5 = 9$.
             (iii) A = 2, B = 4, C = 1, D = 4, E = 3, F = 3, G = 3,
             H = 2, I = 2.

Exercise 4.3 Graph has 6 faces. Sum of the degrees of the faces is 20.

Exercise 4.4 There are 21 spanning trees.

Exercise 4.5 $v - e + f = 9 - 13 + 6 = 2$ as required by Euler's formula.

Exercise 5.1 (a) $v - e + f = 6 - 10 + 6 = 2$.
         (b) $v - e + f = 5 - 7 + 4 = 2$.
         (c) $v - e + f = 5 - 8 + 5 = 2$.

Exercise 5.2 Tetrahedron: $v - e + f = 4 - 6 + 4 = 2$.
         Cube: $v - e + f = 8 - 12 + 6 = 2$.
         Octahedron: $v - e + f = 6 - 12 + 8 = 2$.

Exercise 5.3 $v - e + f = 6 - 8 + 4 = 2$.

Exercise 5.4 $v - e + f = 5 - 6 + 3 = 2$, verifying Euler's formula for $K_{3,2}$.

Exercise 6.1 (i) $\displaystyle\sum_{i=1}^{3} \deg f_i = 4 + 3 + 5 = 12 = 2e$.

         (ii) $\displaystyle\sum_{i=1}^{4} \deg f_i = 4 + 3 + 3 + 8 = 18 = 2e$.

         (iii) $\displaystyle\sum_{i=1}^{4} \deg f_i = 3 + 3 + 4 + 4 = 14 = 2e$.

Exercise 6.2 (i) $\sum_{i=1}^{5} \deg f_i = 5 \times 4 = 20 = 2e.$

(ii) $v - e + f = 7 - 10 + 5 = 2$, verifying Euler's formula

for $K_{5,2}$. $\sum_{i=1}^{n} \deg f_i = 4n = 2e.$

Exercise 6.3 (i) $\sum_{i=1}^{5} \deg v_i = (3 \times 2) + (2 \times 3) = 12 = 2e.$

(ii) $\sum_{i=1}^{7} \deg v_i = (3 \times 2) + (2 \times 4) + 3 + 1 = 18 = 2e.$

(iii) $\sum_{i=1}^{5} \deg v_i = (3 \times 3) + 2 + 3 = 14 = 2e.$

Exercise 7.1 (i) $\sum_{i=1}^{3} \deg f_i = 3 + 3 + 4 = 10 = 2e$

(handshaking theorem holds true)
$v - e + f = 4 - 5 + 3 = 2$ (Euler's formula holds true).

(ii) $\sum_{i=1}^{3} \deg f_i = 3 + 4 + 5 = 12 = 2e$

(handshaking theorem holds true)
$v - e + f = 5 - 6 + 3 = 2$ (Euler's formula holds true).

(iii) $\sum_{i=1}^{4} \deg f_i = 4 \times 4 = 16 = 2e$

(handshaking theorem holds true)
$v - e + f = 6 - 8 + 4 = 2$ (Euler's formula holds true).

Exercise 7.2 $K_{3,3}$ is non-planar.

Exercise 7.3 G is non-planar.

Exercise 7.4 Subgraphs of G are non-planar, hence G is non-planar (see Solution).

Exercise 7.5 $e \leqslant 3v - 6.$

Exercise 7.6 $e \leqslant \dfrac{n(v - 2)}{n - 2}$

Exercise 7.7 The inequalities in Exercises 7.5 and 7.6 become equalities when $2e = nf$.

Exercise 8.1   (a) Graph is non-planar.   (b) Graph is non-planar.
(c) Graph is non-planar.

Exercise 8.2   The graph of $K_{3,3}$ is non-planar.

Exercise 8.3   The Petersen graph is non-planar.

Exercise 8.4   The graph is non-planar.

Exercise 8.5 $K_{r,r}$ is non-planar for $r \geqslant 3$.

Exercise 9.1   Only (i) is a subdivision of $K_{3,2}$.

Exercise 9.2   (i) contains a subgraph $= K_5$, graph $=$ subdivision of K_5.
(ii) contains *no* subgraph $= K_5$, *no* subgraph of K_5.
(iii) contains a graph $=$ subdivision of K_5.
(iv) contains *no* subgraph $= K_5$, *no* subgraph of K_5.

Exercise 9.3   (a) Subdivision of $K_{3,3}$.   (b) Subdivision of K_5.
(c) Subdivision of K_5.   (d) Subdivision of $K_{3,3}$.
(e) Subdivision of $K_{3,3}$.

Exercise 9.4   Graph K_n $(n > 5)$ containing K_5 as a subgraph is non-planar.

Exercise 9.5 $K_{r,s}$ is non-planar for $r, s = 3$.

Exercise 9.6 P_7 is non-planar.

Exercise 10.3   (a) 4   (b) 1   (c) -2 (d) 1.

Exercise 10.4   Sum of two parts, i and f, $= i$ if $f = 0$, and $= i + 1$ if
$0 < f < 1$.

Exercise 10.5 $\left\{\dfrac{a}{a+1}\right\} = \left[\dfrac{2a}{a+1}\right]$

Exercise 10.6   (i) $t(G) \geqslant 1$.

Exercise 10.6   (ii) $t(G) = 2$. The graph is non-planar.

Exercise 10.7 $t(K_6) = 2$, $t(K_{20}) = 4$, $t(K_{30,30}) = 6$.

Exercise 10.8   Smallest value of n is 3.

Exercise 10.9 $t(s) = 1$, meeting the requirements of $t(S) \geqslant 1$.

Miscellaneous Exercises

M1

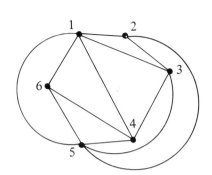

M2

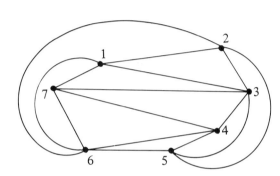

M4 (a)

 (b)

(c) 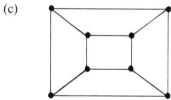 (d)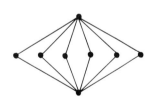

M5 (a) True (b) True (c) False (d) True (e) True (f) False
(g) False (h) False.

M6 (a) Non-planar (b) Planar (c) Non-planar (d) Planar
(e) Non-planar.

M7 $r \leqslant 2$ and for all s such that $r \leqslant s$.

M8

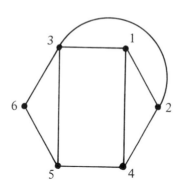

M10

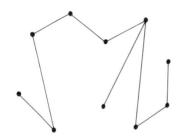   and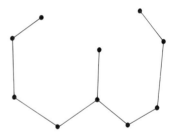

M11

M12   Regular graphs

M13   (c) 4   (b) $n-1$ (c) r.

M14 $e \leqslant \dfrac{d(f-2)}{d-2}$

M16

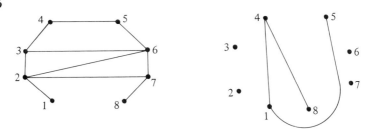

M18

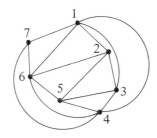

M20 (a) 1 (b) 1 (c) 16.

M21 $cr(G) = \sum_{r=1}^{n-2} r$, $t(G) \geqslant 1$.

M23 (a) No (b) Yes.

M24 (a) Yes (b) No.

6 NETWORKS

Exercise 1.1 Total length = 61 miles.

Exercise 1.2 Best answer uses 821 km of cable.

Exercise 1.3 Derby–Nottingham–Grantham (40 miles).

Exercise 1.4 Total number of miles = 110.

Exercise 2.1 S–C–D–E–T (length 4), S–B–D–T
                                       S–A–E–F–T (length 17).
                                  S–C–F–T

Exercise 2.2

	L	M	N	P	Q
L	—	70	70	50	20
M	70	—	40	60	50
N	70	40	—	20	50
P	50	60	20	—	70
Q	20	50	50	70	—

Exercise 3.1 S–B–D–T (length 12), S–C–E–D–T (length 20).

Exercise 3.2 Shortest path is S–B–E–T or S–B–C–E–T (length 8).
Longest path is S–A–E–D–T (length 17).

Exercise 3.3 Best path is S–B–C–T with 17 specimens.

Exercise 3.4 S–C–F–T (length 21).

Exercise 4.1 Total length of cable = 141 miles.

Exercise 4.2 Total length of cable = 529 miles.

Exercise 5.1 Linkages AD, DE, EC, EB—total length = 25 miles.

Exercise 5.2 Linkages AG, GL, AS, AD, DW—total length = 365 miles.

Exercise 5.3 Linkages GZ, ZS, ZM, MP, MV—total length = 1640 km.

Exercise 6.1 A–W–D–R–Cha–S–Che–A (77 miles).

Exercise 6.2 Lu–Le–A–M–B–Lu (75 miles).

Exercise 6.3 (iii) 1194 km is the shortest length.

Exercise 7.1 (i) Greatest lower bound 92 miles (by removing Grantham or Melton Mowbray).
(ii) Upper bound 128 miles.

Exercise 7.2

Deleted	Lower bound
Wigston	14
Countesthorpe	14
Blaby	13
Cosby	13
Croft	13
Oadby	14

Best lower bound is 14 miles.

Exercise 7.3 Best lower bound is 40 miles. Upper bound of 42 miles can be found.

Exercise 8.1 Arcs must be repeated in (i) and (iii).

Exercise 8.2   (i) Possible route S–A–B–C–D–A–C–B–A–D–S.
             (ii) Possible route S–A–C–F–E–C–D–B–C–S.
          (iii) Possible route S–E–B–C–E–D–C–B–A–S–B–D–E–S.

Miscellaneous Exercises

M1   17.

M2

	To				
From	London	Birmingham	Cambridge	Oxford	Exeter
London	—	£10	£6	£6	£15
Birmingham	£10	—	£10	£7	£24
Cambridge	£6	£10	—	£7	£21
Oxford	£6	£7	£7	—	£17
Exeter	£15	£24	£21	£17	—

M3   Two routes give £320 commission, L–G–B–S–N–E or
                                   L–G–B–S–M–C–E.

M4   A–D–C–B–E–F–H–I–Z yields 82 units.

M5   Links AB, BC, CE, ED—total length = 47.

M6   Links RU, VU, US, ST—total length = 20.

M7   Possible upper bound = 43 miles.
          Possible lower bound = 35 miles.

M8   Best route is U–X–Z–Y–V–W–X–U = 37 miles.

M9   Possible upper bound = 46 miles. Greatest lower bound = 46 miles.

M10   Possible route is Depot–A–C–D–E–Depot–A–B–D–Depot–B–C–E–
           Depot = 93 km.

M11   Possible route is A–B–C–E–F–G–F–D–B–A–E–A of length 1410 m.

7   RECURRENCE RELATIONS—1

Exercise 1.1   585 billion years.

Exercise 2.1   £1362.20.

Exercise 2.2   (i) 18 706 491 mice.   (ii) 175 mice per month should be sold.

Exercise 3.1   (i) $U_n = 3^{n-1}U_1$.

(ii) $U_n = 2^{n-1}U_1 + 2^{n-1} - 1$.

(iii) $U_n = (-2)^{n-1}U_1 + \frac{4}{3}((-2)^{n-1} - 1)$.

(iv) $U_n = U_1 + 2n - 2$.

(v) $U_n = 2^{n-1}U_1 + 3(2^{n-1} - 1)$.

(vi) $t_n = \left(-\frac{2}{3}\right)^{n-1} t_1 - \frac{4}{5}\left(\left(-\frac{2}{3}\right)^{n-1} - 1\right)$.

(vii) $b_n = b_1 + n - 1$.   (viii) $a_n = a_1 - n + 1$.

Exercise 3.2 $U_{2n} = 2^{n-1}U_2$. Sequence is U_1, 1, U_3, 2, U_5, 4, ...

Exercise 3.3 $U_n = U_{n-2} - 1$, n odd. Sequence is 1, U_2, 0, U_4, -1, U_6 ...

Exercise 3.4   £110.62.

Exercise 3.5   Flat Rate—£124.93. Compound interest—£124.58.

Exercise 3.6   After 10 years, £25 839 still has to be paid back.

Exercise 3.7   (i) P_n large $= 0.8$.   (ii) $p_n = 0.2$.   (iii) $p_n = 0.5$.
(iv) $p_n = 1$.   (v) $p_n = 0$.

Exercise 4.1   She will be overdrawn before the end of the 14th year.

Exercise 4.2   (i) $U_3 = 7$, $U_4 = 11$.   (ii) $U_n = U_{n-1} + n$.
(iii) Minimum number required is 10.

(iv) $U_{20} = 211$, because $U_n = 1 + \frac{1}{2}n(n+1)$.

Miscellaneous Exercises

M1   (i) $U_n = \left(\frac{1}{5}\right)^{n-1} U_1$.   (ii) $U_n = 5^{n-1}U_1 + 2(5^{n-1} - 1)$.

(iii) $U_n = U_1 + 4 - n$.   (iv) $U_n = \left(\frac{2}{3}\right)^{n-1} U_1$.

(v) $U_n = \left(-\frac{1}{2}\right)^{n-1} U_1 - \frac{2}{3}\left(\left(-\frac{1}{2}\right)^{n-1} - 1\right)$.

(vi) $U_n = (-1)^{n-1}U_1 - \frac{1}{8}((-1)^{n-1} - 1)$.

(vii) $U_n = U_1 + \frac{1}{4}(n-1)$.   (viii) $U_n = \left(\frac{4}{5}\right)^{n-1} U_1$.

(ix) $U_n = \left(\frac{1}{3}\right)^{n-1} U_1 - 3\left[\left(\frac{1}{3}\right)^{n-1} - 1\right]$.   (x) $U_n = U_1 + \frac{1}{3}(n-1)$.

M2 $U_n = 3n + 2$, $U_{20} = 62$.

M3 (i) $U_n = 50\left(\dfrac{3}{10}\right)^{n-1}$. (ii) $U_n = 2.2 + (-1)^{n-1}2^n$.

   (iii) $U_n = \dfrac{3}{2^{n-1}} + \dfrac{5}{2}$ (iv) $U_n = n - 2$.

M4 (i) $U_{10} = 196\,828$. (ii) $U_{12} = -2048\frac{1}{6}$.

M5 (i) $U_1 = 2$. (ii) $U_1 = 5$.

M6 $k = 10$.

M7 $p = 6$.

M8 (i) £1999. (ii) £2106.85. (iii) £2164.74.

M9 Spode Building Society is better investment by £34.32.

M10 (i) £190.72. (ii) £19.373. (iii) 18 years.

M11 (i) $U_6 \approx 15259$. (ii) 1991. (iii) 44\,621. (iv) 5301. (v) 2500.

M12 1802.

M13 (i) £370. (ii) £1045. (iii) £1585.65.

8 RECURRENCE RELATIONS—2

Exercise 1.1 Estimated 14th year cost = £104.06.
Estimated 15th year cost = £103.98.
Estimated 18th year cost = £104.

Exercise 1.2 In 3rd year, operator charges £210 and hopes to let 260 chalets.

Exercise 2.1 (i) $U_n = A3^n + B2^n$.
  (ii) $U_n = (A + Bn)2^n$.
  (iii) $U_n = A3^n + B(-1)^n$.
  (iv) $U_n = \dfrac{A(-1 + \sqrt{3}i)^n}{2^n} + \dfrac{B(-1 - \sqrt{3}i)^n}{2^n}$.
  (v) $U_n = (A + Bn)\left(\dfrac{5}{2}\right)^n$.
  (vi) $U_n = A(4i)^n + B(-4i)^n$.

Exercise 2.2   (i) $U_n = \frac{1}{2}(5^n + 3(-1)^n)$

(ii) $U_n = \dfrac{96 - 32n}{4^n}$

(iii) $U_n = 4n - 1.$

(iv) $U_n = (1 + \sqrt{2})^n.$

Exercise 2.3   (i) $U_n = -\frac{1}{2}(3 + (-1)^n)(5i)^n$ or $U_n = -\frac{1}{2}5^n i^{n+1}(3 + (-1)^n).$

(ii) $U_n = \frac{1}{2}[(i - 2)(-5i)^n - (2 + i)(5i)^n].$

Exercise 2.4 $U_n = 5 + 2(-1)^n.$ $U_{37} = 3,$ $U_{38} = 7.$

Exercise 2.5 $U_n = 2(1 + \sqrt{2i})^n + B(1 - \sqrt{2i})^n.$

Exercise 3.1   (i) $U_{10} = 89.$ (ii) $U_{10} = 89.$ (iii) $U_{10} = 89.$

Exercise 3.2 There will be 10 946 pairs of rabbits.

Exercise 3.3 At the end of 1 year there will be 2 731 pairs of gerbils.

Exercise 3.4 After 5 months he will have 164 pairs.

Exercise 3.5   (i) The economy is stable.

(ii) The economy is unstable.

Miscellaneous Exercises

M1   (i) $U_n = A2^n + B(-3)^n.$

(ii) $U_n = (A + B_n)5^n.$

(iii) $U_n = (A + (-1)^n B)2^n.$

(iv) $U_n = (A + (-1)^n B)(3i)^n.$

(v) $U_n = A(1 + \sqrt{2})^n + B(1 - \sqrt{2})^n.$

(vi) $U_n = A(2 + i\sqrt{5})^n + B(2 - i\sqrt{5})^n.$

M2 General solution $U_n = A4^n + B(-1)^n.$

(i) $U_n = 3(4)^n + (-1)^{n+1}.$

(ii) $U_n = 4^n.$

(iii) $U_n = (-1)^n.$

M3 General solution $U_n = A(-1 + \sqrt{3})^n + B(-1 - \sqrt{3})^n.$

(i) $U_n = \frac{1}{2}(\sqrt{3} - 1)^n.$

(ii) $U_n = (-1 + \sqrt{3})^n + (-1 - \sqrt{3})^n.$

(iii) $U_n = 2(-1 + \sqrt{3})^n - 2(-1 - \sqrt{3})^n.$

M4 (i) $U_n = A(2 + i)^n + B(2 - i)^n$.

(ii) $U_n = i(2 + i)^n - i(2 - i)^n$; $U_3 = -22$, $U_4 = -48$.

(iii) $U_n = (2 + i)^{n+1} + (2 - i)^{n+1}$; $U_5 = -234$.

M5 $U_n = 2(3)^n - 3(2)^n$; $U_{10} = 37830$.

M6 $U_n = 2(1 + \sqrt{2})^n + 2(1 - \sqrt{2})^n$; $U_6 = 396$.

M7 $p = q = 1$; $U_n = \dfrac{(1 + \sqrt{5})^n}{2} + \dfrac{(1 - \sqrt{5})^n}{2}$.

M8 $U_r = 0.8U_{r-1} + 2.4U_{r-2}$; $r \geqslant 2$.

$U_r = A.2^r + B(-1.2)^r$; $U_r = 25 \times 2^r + 15 \times (-1.2)^r$, 6464 plants.

M9 (i) (b) $U_r = A(2)^r + B(-1)^r$ (c) $U_r = \frac{20}{3} \times 2^r + \frac{10}{3} \times (-1)^r$.

(d) Continued rapid growth.

(ii) (a) $U_{r+1} = 0.7U_r + 1.2U_{r-1}$ (b) $U_r = A(1.5)^r + B(-0.8)^r$.

(c) $U_r = \frac{180}{23} \times (1.5)^r + \frac{50}{23} \times (-0.8)^r$.

(d) Grows but not as rapidly as in (i).

9 DYNAMIC PROGRAMMING

Exercise 1.1 (i) 12(S–B–D–T) (ii) 7 (various routes).

Exercise 1.2 S–B–D–T.

Exercise 1.3 Yes, S–B–F–K–T.

Exercise 2.1 (i) S–B–D–T (value 12). (ii) S–A–G–F–E–T or

S–A–G–F–H–T or

S–A–G–F–H–K–T or

S–A–G–F–H–E–T (value 7).

(iii) S–B–F–K–T (value 18).

Exercise 3.1 (i) Optimal value is 18.

(ii) 47 computations (28 additions and 19 comparisons).

Exercise 3.2 (i) $(nrk^{n-2} - 1)$ computations.

(ii) $r(2k - 1)(n - 2) + 2r - 1$ computations.

Exercise 3.3 (i) Shortest path is S–A–C–E–T (17).
                        Longest path is S–B–C–F–T (20).
            (ii) Shortest path is S–A–F–T (13).
                        Longest path is S–C–E–I–T (20).

Exercise 3.4 Value is 26 with three possible optimas.

Exercise 3.5 Buy and sell in every year, except the third, when stock is held in store. Value is £300.

Exercise 3.6 Optimal route is S–C–E–H–I–T with value £776.

Exercise 4.1 (i) maxmin optimal plan is S–A–E–T with value 6.
                        minmax optimal plan is S–B–D–T with value 4.
            (ii) minmax–S–B–C–F–T, value 4.
                        maxmin–S–A–D–G–T, value 4.

Exercise 4.2 (i) S–A–F–G–T, value 800.
            (ii) S–A–G–T, value 1800.

Exercise 4.3 B–C–A

Exercise 4.4 Solution is B, C, A   Both value 3
                   or C, B, A

Exercise 5.1 1 ton each of types 1 and 3, 2 tons of type 2—return £3500.

Exercise 5.2 4 days preparation, 4 days erection, 12 days finishing—total cost £38 000.

Exercise 5.3 (i) 4 cars in March, 6 in April, May, June and July.
            (ii) Schedule unchanged.

Exercise 5.4 (i) He should carry one of each model. Profit £54.
            (ii) Plan unchanged.

Exercise 5.5 Optimal plan is to feed pigs up as quickly as possible to 60 kg. Profit = £256 per pig.

Exercise 5.6 Expand at the end of first year, and optional at end of second.

Exercise 5.7 C–A–B.

Exercise 5.8 (i) Plan: delay offering Italy for further year; do not offer Austria.
            (ii) Plan: offer Italy immediately; do not offer Austria.

Miscellaneous Exercises

M1 (a) least S–A–D–T (20).
      (b) greatest: S–B–D–G–T (26) or S–B–D–H–T (26).
      (c) minmax: S–B–E–H–T (6).
      (d) maxmin: S–B–D–T (5).

M2   (a) A–C–F–I–T (32 squares).
       (b) By one square.
       (c) A–C–G–I–T (8 hazard squares)

M3   (a)

Month	Feb.	March	April	May	June
Boats built with cost of £1490	2	2	4	4	3

       (b)

Month	Feb.	March	April	May	June
Boats built with costs of £1580	2	4	4		

M4   (a) Expand as quickly as possible to 3 shops.
       (b) (i) No.
           (ii) No change in strategy.

10 NETWORK FLOWS

Exercise 1.1   (i) 500 cars.   (ii) 800 cars.

Exercise 1.2   (i) 18 000 tons per week.   (ii) 19 000 tons per week.

Exercise 1.3   (i) 31 000 passengers.

Exercise 2.1   (i) 36.   (ii) 23.   (iii) 21.

Exercise 2.2   (i) 7.   (ii) 5.   (iii) 8.   (iv) 19.

Exercise 2.3   (i) 26.   (ii) 16.

Exercise 2.4   (i) 9.   (ii) This is maximum flow.

Exercise 2.5   Maximum flow is 9.

Exercise 2.6   (i) Maximum flow is 6.   (ii) Maximum flow is 140.

Exercise 2.7   Maximum flow is 17.

Exercise 3.1   (i) Maximum flow is 7.   (ii) Maximum flow is 5.
               (iii) Maximum flow is 8.   (iv) Maximum flow is 19.
               (i) Maximum flow is 26.   (ii) Maximum flow is 16.

Exercise 3.2   (i) Maximum flow is 12.   (ii) Maximum flow is 6.
               (iii) Maximum flow is 8.

Exercise 3.3   Maximum flow is 50.

Exercise 4.1   (i) Maximum flow is 17.   (ii) 33.

Exercise 4.2   24.

Exercise 4.3   (i) 3.   (ii) 4.   (iii) 5.

Exercise 5.1   (i) 11.   (ii) 14.   (iii) 17.

Exercise 5.2   (i) 13.   (ii) 6.   (iii) 20.

Exercise 6.1   (i) Network is feasible.
                    (ii) Network is feasible.
                    (iii) Network is feasible.

Exercise 6.2   (i) Maximum flow is 7.   (ii) Maximum flow is 9.
                    (iii) Maximum flow is 8.   (iv) Maximum flow is 10.

Exercise 6.3   (i) Maximum flow is 14.   (ii) Maximum flow is 17.
                    (iii) Maximum flow is 16.

Exercise 6.4   (a) Maximum flow is 15.
                    (ii) (a) Network is feasible.   (ii) (b) Network is not feasible.

Exercise 6.6   (i) 14.   (ii) 11.

Exercise 6.7   (i) Network feasible when $a = 2$, $b = 6$.
                 (ii) Network not feasible when $a = 2$, $b = 8$.

Miscellaneous Exercises

M1   1500 calls.

M2   (i) 6.   (ii) 18.   (iii) 10.   (iv) 6.

M5   Maximum flow is 9.

M7   Minimum cuts are AT, BT, CT and SA, BC, CT.

M8   Maximum flow is 17.   (ii) Maximum flow is 136.

M9   Network is not feasible.

M10   Maximum flow is 13.

M11   Maximum flow is 12.

11   ASSIGNMENT

Exercise 1.1   Two possible arrangements: June—Home Office or Foreign
                 Office, Kay—Foreign Sec. or Treasury; Sir Len—Treasury or
                 D.E.S.; Michael—D.E.S. or Home Office.

Exercise 1.2 Fred—joiner/fitter; George—driver; Harry—glazier;
Ian—machine operator.

Exercise 1.3 All 4 applications cannot be satisfied unless the 4-berth yacht
is replaced by a 6-berth yacht.

Exercise 1.4 3 solutions: 1 B, B, B
                           2 C, A, E
                           3 D, D, D
                           4 E, C, C
                           5 A, E, A.

Exercise 2.1

Ann	Clean rooms	Wash up
Barbara	Wash up	Clean rooms
Chris	Serve	Serve
Diana	Receptionist	Receptionist
Sally	Prepare meals	Prepare meals

Exercise 2.2 A—N, B—D, C—Te, D—Ty, E—Ny.

Exercise 2.3

Godson	FL	or	CDT
Johnson	CDT	or	FL
Pegg	CDT	or	M
Watson	E	or	E
Royston	S	or	S
Coulston	Ma	or	Ma

Exercise 2.4 A—1500 m, B—Long jump, C—100 m, D—High jump,
E—400 m, F—Javelin.

Exercise 2.5 No breakthrough. Maximum matching has 5 arcs.

Exercise 2.6 No breakthrough. Two schools will be disappointed.

Exercise 3.1 Road Rollers—Exford; Safe Goods—Dorton;
Tidy Move—Fording.

Exercise 3.2 Ann—800 m; Barbara—400 m; Carolyn—100 m;
Donna—1500 m.

Exercise 3.3 Maximum profit of £125 000 obtained by:
High Farm—Bungalow; George Farm—Semi-detached;
Tidy Farm—Detached; or High Farm—Semi-detached;
George Farm—Detached; Tidy Farm—Bungalow.

Exercise 3.4   George—Turning; Harry—Cutting; Ian—Milling; John—Welding.

Exercise 4.1   Keith—path D; Lorraine—path A; Mary—path C; Nigel—path B.

Exercise 4.2   The Echo—D; The Advertiser—A; Freesheet—B; Central News—C.

Exercise 4.3   Servicing—A; Exhaust—B; Tyre replacement—D; Renewal of brake shoes—E; Sign writing—C.

Miscellaneous Exercises

M1   Complete Solutions

Mr P	Inv.	Work
Miss W	M.Tech	Inv.
Mrs B	Work	M.Tech
Mr A	P.S.	P.S.

M2   Possible Solutions

Mr W	Prod.	Prod.	Prod.
Miss F.	Per.	Sales	Per.
Mrs S.	Acc.	Per.	Sales
Mr F.	Sales	Acc.	Acc.

M3
ACRID
ANVIL
BEGIN
BOXED
BROIL
1
2
3
4
5

M4   Possible maximum matchings are

Eric	A	A
Fleur	C	D
Grace	B	B
Harry	D	C

(Total distance of 253 miles in each case).

M5   Possible solutions

Home Improvement	Electrics	Decorating
Little & Son	Plumbing	Plumbing
House Repairs	Decorating	Electrics
Cowboy & Son	Plastering	Plastering

Each has a total cost £2900.

M6   Possible solutions

P	Plant C	Plant E
Q	Plant D	Plant D
R	Plant B	Plant B
S	Plant E	Plant C
T	Plant A	Plant A

producing 185 units of electricity.

12   TRANSPORTATION

Exercise 1.1   190 (minimum cost solution).

Exercise 2.1   78.

Exercise 2.2   81.

Exercise 2.3   56.

Miscellaneous Exercises

M1   £214 000.

M2   860.

M3   171.

M4   821, a reduction of 8 units.

M5   199.

13   CODING

Exercise 2.1   (i) 2.   (ii) $2^5 = 32$.   (iii) $2^{10} = 1024$.   (iv) 2^n.

Exercise 2.2   9.

Exercise 2.3 2^{20}; 'mystery objects', which is just over a million. 2^n.

Exercise 2.4   (i) 5.   (ii) 5.

Exercise 2.5   Numerals start with 0011000; upper case letters start with 01000001; lower case letters start with 01100001; graphics etc. start with 10000000.

Exercise 3.1   SEND CASH (with two errors E and H).

Exercise 3.2   11000, 10100, 10010, 10001, 01100, 01010, 01001, 00110, 00101, 00011.

Exercise 3.3   35 codewords.

Exercise 4.1   Errors detected $= \frac{1}{2}n$ if n is even, $\frac{1}{2}(n-1)$ if n is odd.
Errors corrected $= \frac{1}{2}(n-2)$ if n is even, $\frac{1}{2}(n-1)$ if n is odd.

Exercise 4.2   (i) Efficiency is 1.   (ii) 2^n.

Exercise 4.3 $\frac{k}{n}$.

Exercise 4.4   Single error detection, no correction.

Exercise 4.5   Single error detection, no correction.

Exercise 5.1   0.5.

Exercise 5.2   (i) 1111, 1001, 0110, 0000.
                 ((ii) no answer given)

Exercise 5.3   (i) 00100   11011.
                 (ii) 11000   11000.

Exercise 5.4   (i) (a) 10111   (b) 01000.
                 (ii) error in second check bit of (i) (a)
                      error in second message bit of (i) (b).

Exercise 6.1   (ii) Possible set 100, 010, 001.
                 (iii) When one of the words is a linear combination of the other two.

Exercise 6.3   (i) 00, 01, 11, 10.

Exercise 6.4   (ii) 1st, 2nd, 4th and 8th.
                 (iii) 1st, 2nd, 4th, 8th, 16th and 32nd digits.

Exercise 7.1   (i) (a) FEN   (b) DRY   (c) FIRED.
                 (ii) (a) 110110010   (b) 10000011   (c) 011110001001110.

Exercise 7.2 (i) No codeword must be the start of another codeword.

Exercise 7.3 Average word length = 2.25.

Exercise 7.5 Probability distribution

A	B	C	D	E
$\frac{1}{4}$	$\frac{1}{4}$	$\frac{1}{4}$	$\frac{1}{8}$	$\frac{1}{8}$

(i) 3 non-isomorphic trees   (ii) 6 non-isomorphic trees.

Exercise 7.6 (i)

Letter	A	B	C	D	E
Codeword	11	10	01	001	000

(ii)

Letter	A	B	C	D	E	F
(possible Codeword	0000	10	0001	11	001	01
solutions) or	001	11	011	10 · 010	000	

Exercise 8.1

Letter	A	B	C	D	E
Codeword	10	000	001	11	01

Exercise 8.2

Letter	A	B	C	D	E	F
Codeword	01	0001	001	00001	1	00000

Exercise 8.3

Letter	A	B	C	D	E	F	G	H
Codeword	0010	01	00001	11	0001	0011	00000	10
or	0001	01	000001	11	00001	001	000000	10

Exercise 8.4 Average word length = 4.13 bits, whereas block coding would need 5 bits per word.

Miscellaneous Exercises

M1 (a) 1010 (b) L.

M2 (a) 5 (b) 19 (c) 2.

M3 (a) $\log_2 n$ if n is a power of 2, otherwise $[\log_2 n] + 1$.
(b) $(n - 1)$.
(c) (i) 1 (ii) k.

M4 (a) 3-bit code C_3; 150 bits needed.
(b) 148.

M5 Single error detection only; efficiency = 5/6.

M7 (i) 3.   (ii) 6.

14 CRITICAL PATH ANALYSIS

Exercise 1.1   6 days.

Exercise 1.2   Mid-April.

Exercise 1.3   28 minutes.

Exercise 2.1   (i) 82 days.

Exercise 2.2   Minimum time is 57 minutes. Critical path is G, I, K, L, J, F, R, Q.

Exercise 2.3   Minimum time is 91 hours. Critical path A, B, C, D, H, I, J, E, F, G, N, O, X.

Exercise 2.4   Critical paths are A, D, E, H, J and A, D, F, G, I, J and the shortest time is 43 minutes.

Exercise 4.1   Activities 7, 8 and 9 share 17 days float. 'Notify...' has additional 19 days float.

Exercise 5.3   (i) Activities on critical path—1, 2, 3, 4, 5, 9, 10, 11, 12, 13, 14, 15, 19, 20, 21, 22, 23, 29, 33.

(ii) Non-critical activities—6, 8, 16, 25, 30, 32.
(iii) (a) 2 days.   (b) No effect.
(c) Painter external delayed by 1 day but remains non-critical.

(d) No delay.   (e) Whole job delayed by 1 day.

Exercise 6.2   (i) £18 050.   (ii) £15 740.

Exercise 6.3   (a) Saving—£610.   (b) Saving—£450.
(c) Glazier could be delayed 4 days without requiring extra labour.

(d) Drains—1 extra day costs £320. Number of extra labour too high. Whole project—1 extra day costs £450.
(e) Float available but means additional cost of £160.

Miscellaneous Exercises

M1   (i) A–B–C–E–F–G–I.
(ii) 75 minutes.

M2 (i) 'Papers marked'—must start 1 week after start of 'Candidates sit exams', and must finish 1 week after 'Candidates sit exams' finishes.

(ii) and (iii) Critical path is 1, 2, 8, 9, 11, 12, 13, 14.

(iv) Activity 3   4   6   7   10
     Float   16 16 16 16 20

(vi) (a) Delay—2 weeks. (b) Employ additional staff.

(vii) (a) Beginning of December in previous year.
      (b) Second week in August.

15 ALGORITHMS

Exercise 2.1 Taking each execution time as 10^{-6} seconds, we have

Time complexity function	10	20	Time if $n = 30$	40	50
$\ln n$	2.3×10^{-6} s	3×10^{-6} s	3.4×10^{-6} s	3.7×10^{-6} s	3.9×10^{-6} s
n	10^{-5} s	2×10^{-5} s	3×10^{-5} s	4×10^{-5} s	5×10^{-5} s
n^2	10^{-4} s	4×10^{-4} s	9×10^{-4} s	1.6×10^{-3} s	2.5×10^{-3} s
n^3	10^{-3} s	8×10^{-3} s	2.7×10^{-2} s	6.4×10^{-2} s	1.3×10^{-1} s
2^n	10^{-3} s	1 s	18 min	305 hr	36 yr
3^n	6×10^{-2} s	1 hr	6.5 yr	4×10^5 yr	2×10^{10} yr

Exercise 2.2 Order is N.

Exercise 3.2 $b_k = 1 + k$.

Index